MATHEMATICAL TEXTS FOR SCHOOLS

Edited by PERCEY F. SMITH, PH.D.

Professor of Mathematics in the Sheffield Scientific School
of Yale University

First Course in Algebra

Second Course in Algebra

Complete School Algebra

> By H. E. HAWKES, PH.D., W. A. LUBY, A.B.,
> and F. C. TOUTON, PH.B.

Plane Geometry

> By WILLIAM BETZ, M.A., and H. E. WEBB, A.B.

Advanced Algebra

> By H. E. HAWKES, PH.D.

Plane and Spherical Trigonometry and Four-Place
Tables of Logarithms

Plane and Spherical Trigonometry

Plane Trigonometry and Four-Place Tables of
Logarithms

Four-Place Tables of Logarithms

> By W. A. GRANVILLE, PH.D.

FIRST COURSE IN ALGEBRA

BY

HERBERT E. HAWKES, Ph.D.

PROFESSOR OF MATHEMATICS IN COLUMBIA UNIVERSITY

AND

WILLIAM A. LUBY, A.B.

HEAD OF THE DEPARTMENT OF MATHEMATICS, CENTRAL HIGH SCHOOL
KANSAS CITY, MISSOURI

AND

FRANK C. TOUTON, Ph.B.

PRINCIPAL OF CENTRAL HIGH SCHOOL, ST. JOSEPH, MISSOURI

GINN AND COMPANY

BOSTON · NEW YORK · CHICAGO · LONDON

The Athenæum Press
GINN AND COMPANY · PRO-
PRIETORS · BOSTON · U.S.A.

PREFACE

This book, intended for beginners in algebra, contains ample material for the introductory course in that subject. In its preparation a serious effort has been made to utilize the valuable suggestions in which the widespread discussion of the teaching of algebra for the last ten years has been fruitful. The aim throughout has been to build up a textbook thoroughly modern, scientifically exact, teachable, and suited to the needs and to the ability of the boy and the girl of fourteen.

The choice of topics and their treatment have been determined by the fact that many students now enter geometry and physics after one year's work in algebra. In the arrangement of topics it has seemed wise to adhere closely to the traditional order. The material itself has been selected with the intention of affording the student ample drill in the elementary technic of algebra and a commensurate development of his reasoning power.

Constant reference has been made to arithmetic in explaining the various algebraic processes. Each process has been exemplified in one or more typical solutions, and wherever practicable these solutions have been accompanied by a suitable method of checking.

The material intended to develop purely technical skill has been graded carefully, no extremely difficult exercises being included. Especial care has been used in the selection of the exercises in equations, the object being to have as great a variety as possible and yet to give only equations whose roots can be verified with a reasonable amount of labor. Usually the verification is far more brief and less difficult than the solution.

In factoring only the simpler types have been considered. Many examples give the student timely assistance with the numerous difficulties which necessarily arise. From the frequent lists of review exercises in factoring he should acquire in the shortest possible time a secure grasp of forms and methods.

Algebra teachers know that the progress of many students in problem-solving is slow and difficult. Yet progress is always possible if the student is first taught to express himself in the language of algebra, if the problems are based on familiar ideas, if the number of new ideas is increased slowly, if the problems are well graded, and if the problem work is wisely distributed throughout the course. With these ideas in mind a large number of problems has been given and the lists occur at frequent intervals throughout the book. The many changes from technical work to problem work afford variety, and avoid the spending of long periods of time on mere technic. At first the problems are based on number relations or other familiar ideas. A large number of "motion" problems are given which, with many problems based on physical ideas and physical formulas, should give much desirable correlation with the subject of physics. A very large number of problems are based on geometrical ideas, and as the needs of geometry largely decided the choice of the exercises in radicals, it is hoped that a close correlation of algebra with geometry has been secured.

Some "informational" problems have been included, but wholly with the intention of stimulating interest and not with the idea that such problems are practical, or that they arise in everyday life, or that it is the function of algebra to teach history, geography, or other subjects.

In choosing the problems the ability of the average student was borne in mind, but in nearly every list, usually near the end, a few difficult problems have been inserted for the stronger students. On account of the careful grading of both the exercises and problems, omissions, where necessary, should preferably be made from the ends of the various lists.

Free use has been made of graphs. These in every case precede or are embodied in the treatment of the topics they are intended to illustrate.

In giving the portraits of the mathematicians who have contributed most to the development of elementary algebra, a new feature in algebra texts has been introduced. The accompanying biographical material is designed to awaken the student's interest, and the historical notes on the development of algebra are intended to give a human touch which is so often lacking in mathematical study.

The English of this text has received painstaking consideration. An earnest effort has been made to give the definitions accurately, to state the problems clearly, and to formulate the rules with simplicity and precision.

In conclusion we wish to express our appreciation of the suggestions and criticisms received from many teachers. We must, however, mention particularly Mr. E. H. Barker of Los Angeles, California; Mr. E. M. Bainter of Kansas City, Missouri; Mr. E. L. Brown of Denver, Colorado; Mr. L. Jay Caldwell of Orange, New Jersey; Miss Esther Crowe of Kansas City, Missouri; and Mr. A. H. Huntington of St. Louis, Missouri, who have read the manuscript critically; and also Dr. J. M. Greenwood of Kansas City, Missouri, who has read the entire proof. In addition, we are under great obligation to Professor David Eugene Smith of Columbia University for putting at our disposal his matchless collection of portraits of mathematicians.

CONTENTS

ILLUSTRATIONS

FIRST COURSE IN ALGEBRA

CHAPTER I

INTRODUCTION TO ALGEBRA

1. Algebra deals with many topics which are new to the student, yet he will find the subject a continuation of his previous work in arithmetic.

2. Symbols. Symbols are employed far more extensively in algebra than in arithmetic, and many new ideas arise in connection with their meaning and use. Some symbols represent numbers, others indicate operations upon them, and others represent relations between numbers. Arabic numerals, and letters are used to represent numbers. The following symbols of operation, $+$, $-$, $\times$, and $\div$, have the same meaning as in arithmetic. The sign $+$ is read *plus;* $-$, *minus;* $\times$, *multiplied by;* and $\div$, *divided by.* The sign of multiplication is usually replaced by a dot or omitted. For example, $3 \times a$ is written $3 \cdot a$, or $3\,a$, and $2 \times a \times b$ is written $2\,ab$. Also $a \div b$ is often written $\dfrac{a}{b}$. The sign $=$ is read *equals,* or *is equal to.*

EXERCISES

1. Express $4\,h + 3\,m$ in seconds, if h and m stand for the number of seconds in an hour and in a minute respectively.

2. Express $5\,y + 4\,f$ in inches, if y and f stand for the number of inches in a yard and in a foot respectively.

3. If q and d represent the number of cents in a quarter and in a dime respectively, find the value in cents of $4\,q + 6\,d$.

4. If t and h represent the number of pounds in one ton and in one hundredweight respectively, express $4t + 6h$ in pounds.

5. $3x + 5x =$ how many x?

6. $4x + 5x = (?) x$.

7. $2x + 3x + 6x = ?$

8. $2x + 2 + 3x + 4 = (?) x + ?$

9. $x + x + 2 + x + x + 2 = ?$ **11.** $5a + 18 - 3a - 7 = ?$

10. $n + n + 1 + n + 2 = ?$ **12.** $8x - 3 + 18 - 5x = ?$

13. $4w - 8 + 3w + 20 = ?$

14. If m represents one month and $y = 12m$, express $y + 5m$ in terms of m.

15. If y (one yard) equals $3f$ ($f =$ one foot), express $2y + 7f$ in terms of f.

16. Express $4q + 3n$ in terms of n, if q (one quarter) equals $5n$ ($n =$ one nickel).

17. Express $2d + 15h$ in terms of h, if $d = 24h$.

18. Express $15h + 50m$ in terms of m, if $h = 60m$.

19. The side of a square is 5 inches. What is its area? its perimeter?

20. The side of a square is s inches. What represents its perimeter? its area?

21. The base of a rectangle is 12 feet and its altitude is 4 feet. What is its area? its perimeter?

22. If b represents the number of feet in the base of a rectangle and a the number of feet in its altitude, what is its area? its perimeter?

23. A rectangle is twice as long as it is wide. Let x represent the number of inches in its width. Then express (a) the length in terms of x; (b) the perimeter; (c) the area.

24. A man is three times as old as his son. If y is the number of years in the son's age, what will represent the father's age?

25. A father is 30 years older than his son. If y represents the son's age in years, what will represent the father's age?

26. A rectangle is 12 feet longer than it is wide. Let w represent the width in feet. Then represent the length and the perimeter in terms of w and some numbers.

27. A rectangle is 18 feet narrower than it is long. If w represents the width in feet, what will conveniently represent the length? the perimeter?

28. A rectangle is 4 feet longer than twice its width. Express the width, the length, and the perimeter in terms of a letter, or a letter and numbers.

Origin of symbols. Many of the symbols that are in common use in algebra at the present time have histories which not only are interesting in themselves, but which also serve to indicate the slow and uncertain development of the subject. It is often found that symbols which seem without meaning represent some abbreviation or suggestion long since forgotten, and that operations and methods which we find hard to master have sometimes required hundreds of years to perfect.

In the early centuries there were practically no algebraic symbols in common use; one wrote out in full the words *plus*, *minus*, *equals*, and the like. But in the sixteenth century several Italian mathematicians used the initial letters $\bar{p}$ and $\bar{m}$ for $+$ and $-$. Some think that our modern symbol $-$ came into use through writing the initial m so rapidly that the curves of the letter gradually flattened out, leaving finally a straight line. The symbol $+$ may have originated similarly in the rapid writing of the letter p. But in the opinion of others these symbols were first used in the German warehouses of the fifteenth century to mark the weights of boxes of goods. If a lot of boxes, each supposed to weigh 100 pounds, came to the warehouse, the weight would be checked, and if a certain box exceeded the standard weight by 5 pounds, it was marked $100 + 5$; if it lacked 5 pounds, it was marked $100 - 5$. Though the first book to use these symbols was published in 1489, it was not until about 1630 that they could be said to be in common use.

Both of the symbols for multiplication given in the text were first used about 1630. The cross was used by two Englishmen, Oughtred and Harriot, and the dot is first found in the writings of the Frenchman, Descartes. It is interesting to note that Harriot was sent to America in 1585 by Sir Walter Raleigh and returned to England with a report of observations. He made the first survey of Virginia and North Carolina and constructed maps of those regions.

It is strange that the line was used to denote division long before any of the other symbols here mentioned were in use. This is, in fact, one of the oldest signs of operation that we have. The Arabs, as early as 1000 A.D., used both $\frac{a}{b}$ and a/b to denote the quotient of a by b. The symbol $\div$ did not occur until about 1630.

Equality has been denoted in a variety of ways. The word *equals* was usually written out in full until about the year 1600, though the two sides of an equation were written one over the other by the Hindus as early as the twelfth century. The modern sign $=$ was probably introduced by the Englishman, Recorde, in 1557, because, he says, "Noe. 2. thynges can be moare equalle" than two parallel lines. This symbol was not generally accepted at first, and in its place the symbols $\parallel$, ∞, and $\propto$ are frequently met during the next fifty years.

3. The usefulness of symbols. Symbols enable one to abbreviate ordinary language in the solution of problems.

For example: Three times a certain number is equal to 20 diminished by 5. What is the number?

If n represents the number, the preceding statement and question can be written in symbols, thus:

$$3\,n = 20 - 5.$$
$$n = ?$$

The symbolic statement, $3\,n = 20 - 5$, is called an *equation* and n the *unknown number*.

If
$$3\,n = 20 - 5,$$
$$3\,n = 15,$$
and
$$n = 5.$$

The preceding example illustrates the algebraic method of stating and solving the problem. The method is brief and direct and its advantages will become more apparent as the student progresses.

EXAMPLE

1. The sum of two numbers is 112. The greater is three times the less. What are the numbers?

Solution: By the conditions of the problem,

$$\text{greater number} + \text{less number} = 112.$$

If we represent the less by l, then $3\,l$ must represent the greater, and the above statement becomes

$$3\,l + l = 112.$$

Collecting, $\qquad 4\,l = 112.$

Whence $\qquad l = \tfrac{112}{4} = 28,$

and $\qquad 3\,l = 3 \times 28 = 84.$

Therefore the greater number is 84 and the less 28.

PROBLEMS

1. The sum of two numbers is 160. The greater is four times the less. Find each.

2. A certain number plus five times itself equals 216. Find the number.

3. One number is seven times another. Their sum is 72. Find each.

4. The first of three numbers is twice the third, and the second is four times the third. The sum of the three numbers is 105. Find the numbers.

5. The sum of three numbers is 117. The second is twice the first, and the third three times the second. Find each.

6. There are three numbers whose sum is 192. The first is twice the second, and the third equals the sum of the other two. Find the numbers.

7. The sum of three numbers is 324. The second is five times the first, and the third is six times the second. Find the numbers.

8. The sum of three numbers is 104. The second is three times the first, and the third is the sum of the other two. Find the numbers.

9. What sum of money placed at interest for 1 year at 5% amounts to $378?

Solution: From arithmetic,

$$\text{principal} + \text{interest} = \text{amount}.$$

By the conditions of the problem,

$$\text{principal} + .05 \text{ principal} = \$378.$$

If p represents the principal, this last statement becomes

$$p + .05\,p = 378.$$

Collecting, $\qquad\qquad 1.05\,p = 378.$

Whence $\qquad\qquad p = \dfrac{378}{1.05} = 360.$

Therefore the required sum is $360.

10. What sum of money placed at interest for 1 year at 6% amounts to $265?

11. What sum of money placed at simple interest for 3 years at 4% will amount to $700?

12. In how many years will $225, at 6% simple interest, gain $27?

13. In how many years will $520, at 6½% simple interest, gain $169?

14. At what per cent simple interest will $375 gain $75 in 2 years?

Solution: Let $\qquad\qquad x = $ the rate of interest.

Then $\qquad\qquad \$375\,x = $ the interest for one year,

and $\qquad\qquad \$750\,x = $ the interest for two years.

But $\qquad\qquad \$75 = $ the interest for two years.

Therefore $\qquad\quad 750\,x = 75,$

and $\qquad\qquad x = \tfrac{1}{10}.$

Hence the money is lent at 10%.

15. At what per cent simple interest will $825 gain $165 in 4 years?

16. At what per cent simple interest will $250 amount to $317.50 in 6 years?

17. In how many years will $200 double itself at 4% simple interest?

18. In how many years will $150 treble itself at 5% simple interest ?

19. The perimeter of a certain square is 160 feet. Find the length of each side.

20. The perimeter of a certain rectangle is 256 feet. It is three times as long as it is wide. Find its dimensions.

21. The perimeter of the rectangle formed by placing two equal squares side by side is 198 inches. Find the dimensions and the perimeter of each square.

22. Two equal squares are placed side by side, forming a rectangle. If the perimeter of each square is 120 inches, find the perimeter of the rectangle.

4. Representation of numbers. In algebra numbers are represented by one or more numerals or letters or by both combined.

Thus 3, 25, a, $2b$, $4xy$, and $2x + 3$ are algebraic symbols for numbers.

Precisely what numbers $4xy$ and $2x + 3$ represent is not known until the numbers which x and y stand for are known. In one problem these symbols may have values quite different from those they have in another. To devise methods of determining these values in the various problems which arise is the principal aim of algebra.

5. Factors. A **factor** of a product is any one of the numbers which multiplied together form the product.

Thus $3ab$ means 3 times a times b. Here 3, a, and b are each factors of $3ab$. Similarly the expression $4(a + b)$ means 4 times the sum of a and b. Here 4 and $a + b$ are factors of $4(a + b)$.

6. Exponents. An **exponent** is a number written at the right of and above another number to show how many times the latter is to be taken as a factor.

(Later this definition will be modified so as to include fractions and other algebraic numbers as exponents.)

Thus $3^2 = 3 \cdot 3$; $5^3 = 5 \cdot 5 \cdot 5$. Also $a^4 = a \cdot a \cdot a \cdot a$, and $4\,xy^3 = 4 \cdot x \cdot y \cdot y \cdot y$. In a^b, b is the exponent of a. If a is 4 and b is 3, $a^b = 4^3 = 4 \cdot 4 \cdot 4$. The exponent 1 is not usually written.

7. Coefficients. If a number is the product of two factors, either of these factors is called the **coefficient** of the other in that product.

Thus in $4\,x^2y$, 4 is the coefficient of x^2y, y is the coefficient of $4\,x^2$, and $4\,y$ is the coefficient of x^2. The numerical coefficient 1 is usually omitted. If a numerical coefficient other than 1 occurs, it is usually written first. For instance, we write $5\,x$, not $x\,5$.

The following examples illustrate the difference in meaning between a coefficient and an exponent:

$$3\,x = x + x + x.$$
$$x^3 = x \cdot x \cdot x.$$

If, in each case, $x = 5$, $3\,x$ stands for the number 15, while x^3 stands for 125. If x is 10 in each case, $3\,x = 30$, while $x^3 = 1000$.

8. Use of parentheses. If two or more numbers connected by signs of operation are inclosed in a parenthesis, the entire expression is treated as a symbol for a single number.

Thus $3(6 + 4)$ means $3 \cdot 10$, or 30; $(17 - 2) \div (8 - 3)$ means $15 \div 5$, or 3; $(5 + 7)^2$ means 12^2, or 144; and $6(x + y)$ means six times the sum of x and y.

As in arithmetic, the symbol for square root is $\sqrt{\ }$, or $\sqrt[2]{\ }$, and the symbol for cube root is $\sqrt[3]{\ }$.

The name **radical sign** is applied to all symbols like the following: $\sqrt{\ }$, $\sqrt[2]{\ }$, $\sqrt[3]{\ }$, $\sqrt[4]{\ }$, etc. The small figure in a radical sign, like the 3 in $\sqrt[3]{\ }$, is often called the **index**.

Note. There has been a considerable variety in the symbols for the roots of numbers. The symbol $\sqrt{\ }$ was introduced in 1544 by the German, Stifel, and is a corruption of the initial letter of the Latin word *radix*, which means "root." Before his time square root was denoted by the symbol R, used nowadays by physicians on prescriptions as an abbreviation for the word *recipe*. Thus $\sqrt[3]{5}$ would have been denoted by $\mathrm{R}^4 5$. Some early writers used a dot to indicate square root, and expressed $\sqrt{2}$ by $\cdot 2$. The Arabs denoted the root of a number by an arabic letter placed directly over the number.

EXERCISES

Write in symbols:

1. The sum of three times a and five times b.

2. Three times a subtracted from five times b.

3. The square of a subtracted from the square of b.

4. Two times a squared subtracted from three times a squared.

5. The quotient of a divided by b.

6. The product of four times a squared and b.

7. The sum of a and b divided by their difference.

8. The product of a and $2b - c$.

9. The product of a by the sum of b and c.

10. The result of subtracting $a - b$ from $7x$.

11. The product of the sum of a and b by their difference.

12. The sum of the square root of $5a$ and the cube root of $7b$.

13. The product of $x - y$ and the square root of $7x$.

14. The square of the sum of a and b.

15. The square of the difference of a and b.

16. The quotient of three times a times the square of b by four times c times the cube of a.

17. The sum of the quotients of a by $3x$ and $4y$ by c.

18. Read Exercises 1–14, p. 11.

9. Order of fundamental arithmetical operations. If we read the expression $6 + 4 \cdot 9 - 12 \div 3$ from left to right, and perform each indicated operation as we come to its symbol, we obtain 10, 90, 78, and a final result of 26. If we perform the multiplication and division first, the expression becomes $6 + 36 - 4$, which equals 38. These results show that the value of the expression is determined largely by the order in which the operations are performed. When there is no statement to the contrary, it is understood that:

Do work in parenthesis first.

I. *A series of operations involving addition and subtraction alone shall be performed in the order in which they occur.*

Thus $8 + 12 - 10 + 6 = 20 - 10 + 6 = 10 + 6 = 16.$

It is incorrect to say $8 + 12 - 10 + 6 = 20 - 16 = 4.$

II. *A series of operations involving multiplication and division alone shall be performed in the order in which they occur.*

Thus $8 \cdot 12 \div 6 \cdot 4 = 96 \div 6 \cdot 4 = 16 \cdot 4 = 64.$

It is incorrect to say $8 \cdot 12 \div 6 \cdot 4 = 96 \div 24 = 4.$

III. *In a series of operations involving addition, subtraction, multiplication, and division the multiplications and divisions shall be performed in order before any addition or subtraction. Then the additions and subtractions shall be performed in accordance with I.*

Therefore $6 + 4 \cdot 9 - 12 \div 3 = 6 + 36 - 4 = 38.$

It is incorrect to say $6 + 4 \cdot 9 - 12 \div 3 = 10 \cdot 9 - 4 = 86.$

In a series of operations an expression inclosed in a parenthesis is regarded as a single number. Obviously, within any parenthesis I, II, and III apply.

Therefore $(3 + 2)6 = 5 \cdot 6 = 30,$

and $8 + (7 - 3)(9 - 6 \div 2) - 4 = 8 + 4 \cdot 6 - 4 = 8 + 24 - 4 = 28.$

EXERCISES

Simplify the following:

1. $20 - 5 + 6 - 10.$

2. $16 - (8 - 2).$

3. $14 - (16 - 8) + (12 - 4).$

4. $6 \div 3 - 2.$

5. $8 \cdot 6 \div 3 - 10.$

6. $18 \div (2 \cdot 3).$

7. $(6 - 3)(17 - 2 \cdot 5).$

8. $23 - 2 \cdot 6 - 4 \div 2 + 16.$

9. $18 \div (9 - 3).$

10. $(10 - 3)(16 - 3 \cdot 2 + 8 \div 4).$

11. $14 - 3 \cdot (16 - 2 \cdot 5) \div 6 + 8 \cdot 2.$

12. $(18 - 2) - 6 \div (4 + 2 \cdot 8 - 18 \div 9).$

13. $(16 - 6)(18 - 8) \div 100 \cdot 5 - 5.$

14. $(5 + 3)(5 - 3) \div 5 - 3.$

10. Evaluation of algebraic expressions. Finding the numerical value of an expression for certain values of the letters therein is frequently necessary. This process will be used later to test the accuracy of the results of algebraic operations.

EXERCISES

In Exercises 1–23 let $a = 3$, $b = 1$, $c = 5$, $d = 7$, and $e = 2$. Substitute for each letter its numerical value and then simplify the results according to the rules of § 9:

1. $4a + 3d$.

2. $a^2 + 2c$.

3. $ab + cd$.

4. $c^2 - 5ab$.

5. $abcd - 4e^2$.

6. $\dfrac{d + c}{e}$.

7. $\dfrac{cde}{5e} + \dfrac{ace}{2a}$.

8. $\dfrac{10b}{e} - \dfrac{c}{b}$.

9. $\dfrac{1}{c} + \dfrac{1}{d} + \dfrac{1}{e}$.

10. $\dfrac{e^2}{ac} + \dfrac{4cd}{ae}$.

11. $\dfrac{cd + ae + ce}{a - b + c}$.

12. $\dfrac{a^2 + b^2 + c^2 + d^2}{a + b + c + d}$.

13. $\dfrac{a^3 - ce^2 + 3cd}{d - a + c}$.

14. $5b^3 + 4b^2 - 2b - 5$.

15. $3b^5 - 14b^4 + 11b^3 + 11b^2 + 13b - 20$.

16. a^e.

17. c^a.

18. $d^e + e^a$.

19. $b^c + c^a$.

20. $d^e - c^2 + b^3$.

21. $e^2 \cdot c^a$.

22. $\dfrac{d + e^c}{2c + a}$.

23. $\dfrac{a^a + 3b}{c^e - d - e - b}$.

Find the numerical value of the following expressions when $a = 4$, $b = 0$, $c = 5$, $d = 7$, and $e = 8$:

24. $\dfrac{4a + 3b + 2d}{c + e + 2}$.

25. $\dfrac{b}{a + c + d}$.

26. $abc + acd - be$.

27. $\dfrac{ab}{c} + \dfrac{bd}{a} + \dfrac{be}{cd}$.

28. $\dfrac{a^2 - b^2 + c^3}{3\,d - 2\,e + c}$.

29. $\sqrt{a} + \sqrt{2\,e}$.

30. $2\sqrt{a} + \sqrt[3]{e}$.

31. $b\sqrt{a} + cd + \sqrt[3]{e}\cdot\sqrt{a}$.

32. $c\sqrt[2]{2\,ae} + d\sqrt[3]{2\,ae}$.

33. $\sqrt{b^2 + c^2 + d} + a$.

34. $\sqrt[3]{3\,d} + ec + a - 1$.

35. $de + ac\sqrt{ac^2 + 2\,e + c}$

36. $(a + c)\,c$.

37. $(a + e)(c + d)$.

38. $ab\,(a + b)$.

39. $acd\,(a + c + d)$.

40. $ac\,(e - c + b + d)$.

41. $(a + d)^2$.

42. $(e - a)^2$.

43. $(d - a)^3$.

44. $\dfrac{3\,ad\,(3\,a - 2\,c)^2(e - c)^3}{6\,ed}$.

45. $\dfrac{ab\,(c + d)(a + b)}{(e - a)}$.

46. $c^3 - 3\,e^2a + 3\,ca^2 - a^3$.

47. If $x = 2$ and $y = 3$, does $3\,x + 5\,y = 21$?

48. If $x = 8$, does $7\,x - 9 = 3\,x + 25$?

49. Does $x^2 + 5\,x + 6 = 0$, if $x = 2$? if $x = 3$? if $x = 4$?

50. Does $3\,x^2 - 14\,x - 5 = 0$, if $x = 5$? if $x = \frac{1}{3}$? if $x = 6$? if $x = 4$?

CHAPTER II

POSITIVE AND NEGATIVE NUMBERS

11. Arithmetical addition and subtraction. Let us suppose that equal distances are taken on a line and the successive points of division marked with the natural numbers as follows :

Such a scale of numbers may be used to illustrate both addition and subtraction as performed in arithmetic.

Thus in adding 5 to 3 we may begin at 3 and count 5 spaces to the right, obtaining the sum 8. We shall obtain the same result if we begin at 5 and count 3 spaces to the right. This process may be stated in general terms thus :

RULE. *To add the number* **a** *to the number* **b**, *begin at* **b** *and count* **a** *spaces to the right.*

In subtracting 4 from 7 we may begin at 7 and count 4 spaces to the left, thus obtaining 3. This process may be stated in general terms thus :

RULE. *To subtract the number* **a** *from the number* **b**, *begin at* **b** *and count* **a** *spaces to the left.*

If we attempt to subtract 5 from 4 by the preceding rule, we arrive at the first point of division to the left of zero. Arithmetic has no number to represent such a result ; in fact, the subtraction of 5 from 4 is there regarded as impossible. Arithmetically speaking, such a subtraction cannot be performed. We can, however, subtract 4 of the 5 units from the 4 units, leaving 1 unit unsubtracted. Now in algebra it is both convenient and necessary to speak of subtracting a greater

13

number from a less, and to call the portion of the greater
number which is unsubtracted the remainder. The fact that
such a subtraction is incomplete is indicated by writing a
minus sign before the result; thus $4 - 5 = - 1$. Hence the
first point of division to the left of zero may be thought of as
corresponding to $- 1$. Similarly $3 - 5 = - 2$; and to $- 2$ may
correspond the second point of division to the left of zero.

In like manner $5 - 8 = - 3$, which corresponds to the third
point to the left of zero. In the same way the fourth point of
division to the left of zero would correspond to $- 4$, the fifth
point to $- 5$, etc.

Such numbers as $- 1, - 2, - 3$, etc., are called **negative** numbers. The minus sign is never omitted in writing a negative
number, though a letter, as x, may stand for a negative number.

In opposition to negative numbers the ordinary numbers of
arithmetic are called **positive** numbers. If a number has no
sign before it, or a plus sign, it is a positive number.

The relative order of positive and negative numbers is
indicated in the following scale:

$$\cdots\cdots\cdot -7 \quad -6 \quad -5 \quad -4 \quad -3 \quad -2 \quad -1 \quad 0 \quad +1 \quad +2 \quad +3 \quad +4 \quad +5 \quad +6 \quad +7 \quad +8 \cdots\cdots \quad (B)$$

EXERCISES

Perform the following additions and subtractions by counting along the preceding scale according to the rules on page 13:

1. Add 4 to 2.   **3.** Add 5 to $- 3$.   **5.** Add 2 to $- 4$.

2. Add 4 to $- 2$.   **4.** Add 3 to $- 3$.   **6.** Add 5 to $- 7$.

7. Subtract 2 from 5.   **10.** Subtract 4 from $- 2$.

8. Subtract 5 from 2.   **11.** Subtract 3 from $- 4$.

9. Subtract 6 from 4.   **12.** Subtract 2 from $- 3$.

12. Practical use of positive and negative numbers. The scale
(B) of positive and negative numbers could be used to measure
many of the things with which we come in daily contact. In
fact, a practical equivalent is in many instances already in use.

Thus in graduating a thermometer a certain position of the mercury is taken as zero, and the degrees are marked both above and below this point. Hence a temperature reading of 18° is indefinite unless accompanied by the words *above zero* or *below zero*. Usually + 18° is taken to indicate the former, while − 18° indicates the latter.

Similarly any point on the earth's equator is in zero latitude. Then latitude 40° N. means 40° north of the equator. In like manner 30° S. means 30° south of the equator. Obviously + 40° and − 30° might be used to convey the same ideas.

EXERCISES

1. If the temperature is now + 10°, what will represent the temperature after a fall (*a*) of 5°? (*b*) of 10°? (*c*) of 18°?

2. If the temperature is now − 12°, what will it be after a rise (*a*) of 7°? (*b*) of 12°? (*c*) of 25°?

3. In the preceding exercise change the word *rise* to *fall* and then answer.

4. A ship sails south from latitude + 13° to latitude − 7°. If one degree is 69 miles, how far did it sail?

5. A ship sails south from latitude + 20° at the rate of 4° daily. In what latitude is it at the end of each of the next 6 days? In how many days will it reach latitude − 16°?

6. A man's property is worth $5200 and his debts amount to $2300. How can positive and negative numbers be used to represent (*a*) each of these amounts? (*b*) the man's financial standing?

Note. The first explanation of positive and negative numbers is, so far as is known, by means of the illustration of assets and debts. This is found in the writings of the Hindus before 700 A.D., long before negative numbers were accepted as having any definite meaning. In the use of this illustration the Hindus were nearly a thousand years in advance of the times.

7. If debts and property be reversed in 6, what would be the answer to (*a*) and (*b*)?

8. The temperature at 6.00 A.M. was $-12°$. During the morning it rose at the rate of 3° an hour. What was the temperature at 9.00 A.M.? 10.00 A.M.? 1.00 P.M.?

13. Addition of positive and negative numbers. As we have seen, subtraction by the use of scale (B) is performed by counting spaces to the left. Now a negative number represents an unperformed subtraction; therefore to add a negative number to another number means to perform this subtraction.

For example, in subtracting 8 from 5, -3 was obtained by beginning at zero and counting 5 to the right and then 8 to the left, leaving a remainder of 3 to the left. Thus when we wish to add -3 to any number, we count 3 spaces to the left from that number. Hence, in general, to *add* a *negative* number n to a given number, begin at the given number and count n spaces to the *left*.

Again, to add -8 to 24 we begin at 24 and count 8 spaces to the left, obtaining 16 as the result; that is,

$$+24 + (-8) = +16.$$

Similarly, to add -6 to -4 we begin at -4 and count 6 spaces to the left, obtaining -10 as the result; that is,

$$-4 + (-6) = -10.$$

The **numerical** or **absolute** value of a number is its value without regard to sign.

Thus the absolute values of -3, -5, and $+7$ are 3, 5, and 7 respectively. It should be noted that two different algebraic numbers, as $+6$ and -6, may have the same absolute value.

EXERCISES

Perform by the use of scale (B), p. 14, the operations:

1. $+3 + (+2)$.   **3.** $+3 + (-2)$.   **5.** $7 + (-4)$.

2. $-3 + (-2)$.   **4.** $-3 + (+2)$.   **6.** $-7 + (+5)$.

     7. $-6 + (-4)$.   **9.** $4 + (-7)$.

      8. $6 + (-5)$.   **10.** $-3 + (-6)$.

The preceding exercises illustrate the correctness of the following working rules:

I. *To add two or more positive numbers, find the arithmetical sum of their absolute values and prefix to this sum the plus sign.*

II. *To add two or more negative numbers, find the arithmetical sum of their absolute values and prefix to this sum the minus sign.*

III. *To add a positive and a negative number, find the difference of their absolute values and prefix to the result the sign of the one which has the greater absolute value.*

The **algebraic sum** of two or more numbers is the number obtained by adding them according to the preceding rules.

The algebraic sum of two numbers is often different from the sum of their numerical values; for example, the algebraic sum of $+9$ and -5 is $+4$, while the sum of their numerical values is 14.

Hereafter the word *add* will mean find the *algebraic sum.*

EXERCISES

Perform the indicated additions:

1. $+4+(+7).$

2. $-4+(-7).$

3. $+4+(-7).$

4. $-4+(+7).$

5. $+8+(-5).$

6. $-8+(+5).$

7. $-12+(-9).$

8. $-6+6.$

9. $-6+(-6).$

10. $-4+(+3)+(+6).$

11. $3+(-7)+(5)+(-4).$

12. $8+(-2)+(-4)+(+6).$

Answer the questions asked in the following:

13. $6+? = 9.$

14. $6+? = 2.$

15. $8+? = 12.$

16. $8+? = 4.$

17. $-8+? = -10.$

18. $-8+? = -6.$

19. $-10+? = -16.$

20. $-10+? = 7.$

21. $12+? = 4.$

22. $-12+? = 4.$

14. Subtraction of positive and negative numbers. If we wish to subtract 7 from 12, we may do so by answering the question, " What number added to 7 gives 12 ? " By answering a similar question we can subtract 8 from 15, or 25 from 43, or any number a from another number b. Exercises 13–22, p. 17, are therefore exercises in subtraction, for each asks a question similar to the one in the first sentence of this paragraph.

This point of view brings out the relation that the operation of subtraction bears to addition.

EXERCISES

Perform the following subtractions by answering in each case the question, " What number added to the first number gives the second number ? "

Subtract :

1. 5 from 8.
2. 9 from 13.
3. 8 from 5.
4. 13 from 9.
5. − 5 from − 8.

6. − 5 from 8.
7. 5 from − 10.
8. − 6 from − 4.
9. 12 from − 18.
10. 25 from 13.

11. Change the sign of the subtrahend (if + to − , if − to +) in Exercises 1–10 and then add the subtrahend to the minuend. Are the answers the same as were obtained before ?

The results obtained in Exercise 11 illustrate the following important principles :

I. *Subtracting a positive number is the same in effect as adding a negative number of the same absolute value.*

To illustrate : a decrease of $100 in a man's assets is equivalent to an increase of $100 in his liabilities, provided we consider his real financial standing in each case.

II. *Subtracting a negative number is the same in effect as adding a positive number of the same absolute value.*

To illustrate : a decrease of $75 in a man's liabilities is equivalent to an increase of $75 in his assets, as far as his net financial standing is concerned.

Hence, for the subtraction of positive and negative numbers, we have the

RULE. *Change the sign of the subtrahend (if it be + to −, if it be − to +) and then find the algebraic sum of the subtrahend (with its sign changed) and the minuend.*

This rule really turns algebraic subtraction into algebraic addition.

EXERCISES

Perform the indicated subtractions :

1. $8 - (+5)$.
2. $+8 - (-5)$.
3. $+5 - (-8)$.
4. $+5 - (+8)$.

5. $12 - (+9)$.
6. $12 - (-9)$.
7. $-12 - (9)$.
8. $-12 - (-9)$.

9. $+6 - (+6)$.
10. $-6 - (-6)$.
11. $6 - (-6)$.
12. $-6 - (+6)$.

13. $-14 - (-19)$.
14. $0 - (+1)$.
15. $-0 - (-1)$.
16. $1 - (-2)$.

17. $12 - (+3) - (+2)$.
18. $-12 - (+3) - (+2)$.
19. $-12 - (-3) - (-2)$.
20. $18 - (-5) - (7)$.

Answer the questions asked in :

21. $+6 + ? = 10$.
22. $-6 + ? = -10$.
23. $-3 + ? = 0$.
24. $+6 + ? = 0$.
25. $+6 + ? = 4$.

26. $-8 + ? = -3$.
27. $-8 + ? = -5$.
28. $-7 + ? = 7$.
29. $9 - ? = 3$.
30. $-7 - ? = -5$.

31. $+5 - ? = -6$.
32. $-7 - ? = 4$.
33. $-5 - ? = 0$.
34. $2 - ? = 0$.
35. $4 - ? = 18$.

Simplify :

36. $12 + (3) - (5)$.
37. $12 - (-3) + 6$.
38. $12 - (-4) + (-6)$.

39. $18 + (-6) - (+7)$.
40. $-16 + (-10) - (+11)$.
41. $-13 - (8) + (-14)$.

15. Multiplication of positive and negative numbers. In arithmetic, multiplication was defined as the process of taking one number, the multiplicand, as many times as there are units in another number, the multiplier. The original signification of *times* made this definition meaningless when the multiplier was a fraction; for in $8 \times \frac{3}{5}$, 8 could not be added $\frac{3}{5}$ of a time. The definition was then extended and the product of 8 multiplied by $\frac{3}{5}$ was defined to mean $\frac{8 \times 3}{5}$.

Similarly, since algebra deals with both positive and negative numbers, we must now extend the arithmetical definition of multiplication and **define** what is meant in each of the four cases which follow:

$$1. \ +4 \cdot +3 = ? \qquad 3. \ +4 \cdot -3 = ?$$
$$2. \ -4 \cdot +3 = ? \qquad 4. \ -4 \cdot -3 = ?$$

From the arithmetical definition of multiplication $+4 \cdot +3$ means
$$(+4) + (+4) + (+4) = +12;$$
that is, $\qquad +4 \cdot +3 = +12.$

Similarly $-4 \cdot +3$ means
$$(-4) + (-4) + (-4) = -12;$$
that is, $\qquad -4 \cdot +3 = -12.$

In $+4 \cdot -3$, we mean that 4 is to be subtracted three times. This is the same as subtracting 12 once.

Therefore $\qquad +4 \cdot -3 = -12.$

Lastly $-4 \cdot -3$ means that -4 is to be subtracted three times. This is the same as subtracting -12 once, and subtracting -12 once is the same as adding $+12$. Therefore
$$-4 \cdot -3 = +12.$$

Summing up,
$$+4 \cdot +3 = +12.$$
$$-4 \cdot +3 = -12.$$
$$+4 \cdot -3 = -12.$$
$$-4 \cdot -3 = +12.$$

Or, in general terms,

$$+ a \times + b = + ab.$$
$$- a \times + b = - ab.$$
$$+ a \times - b = - ab.$$
$$- a \times - b = + ab.$$

Therefore we have the

LAW. *The product of two numbers having like signs is a positive number, and the product of two numbers having unlike signs is a negative number.*

EXERCISES

Find the products in the following:

1. $+ 3 \cdot + 4.$	7. $- 12 \cdot + 9.$	13. $+ 4 \cdot - 5 \cdot + 6.$
2. $+ 4 \cdot + 12.$	8. $+ 6 \cdot - 4.$	14. $+ 4 \cdot - 5 \cdot - 6.$
3. $- 5 \cdot + 4.$	9. $- 6 \cdot - 6.$	15. $- 4 \cdot - 5 \cdot - 6.$
4. $+ 6 \cdot - 6.$	10. $+ 5 \cdot - 10.$	16. $12 \cdot + 0 \cdot - 5.$
5. $- 7 \cdot + 8.$	11. $+ 0 \cdot + 4.$	17. $9 \cdot - 10 \cdot - 0.$
6. $- 7 \cdot - 3.$	12. $- 7 \cdot 0.$	18. $- 4 \cdot + 3 \cdot - 6.$

19. $- 3 \cdot - 2 \cdot - 5.$ 20. $2 \cdot - 3 \cdot + 5.$

Note. The famous German mathematician, Leopold Kronecker (1823–1891), once observed that "the good Lord made the positive integers, but man is responsible for all the rest of the numbers." This expresses the truth about numbers as accurately as one can in a single sentence. We count objects from our earliest years, and so use the positive integers naturally. It is only when we come to study mathematics that the necessity for any other kind of numbers is forced upon us. Here we see that negative numbers are a great convenience if we wish to represent the relations between objects where oppositeness in any of its many forms is involved. But the artificial character of negative numbers delayed their intelligent use for many hundred years. To be sure, the Hindus said that "the square of negative is positive," but the statement probably did not mean anything to those who read it. It was not until after the time of Descartes (see p. 199) that the rules for operating on negative numbers were understood, even by great mathematicians.

16. Division of positive and negative numbers. When 18 is divided by 9 the result is 2. Here 18 is the dividend, 9 the divisor, and 2 the quotient. The three are connected by the following relation:

$$\text{quotient} \times \text{divisor} = \text{dividend}.$$

We can see that 2 is the correct value of $18 \div 9$, because $2 \times 9 = 18$. This simple test will be applied to determine whether the quotient is a positive or a negative number. All the cases which may arise are represented by the four following questions:

1. $+18 \div +9 = ?$	3. $+18 \div -9 = ?$
2. $-18 \div +9 = ?$	4. $-18 \div -9 = ?$

These questions are answered as follows:

$$+18 \div +9 = +2 \text{ because } +2 \cdot +9 = +18.$$
$$-18 \div +9 = -2 \text{ because } -2 \cdot +9 = -18.$$
$$+18 \div -9 = -2 \text{ because } -2 \cdot -9 = +18.$$
$$-18 \div -9 = +2 \text{ because } +2 \cdot -9 = -18.$$

In 1 and 4 the dividend and divisor have *like* signs and the sign of the quotient is *plus*. In 2 and 3 the dividend and divisor have *unlike* signs and the quotient is *minus*.

Therefore we have the

RULE. *The quotient of two numbers having like signs is a positive number, and the quotient of two numbers having unlike signs is a negative number.*

The result of multiplication by zero is given a definite meaning in arithmetic and algebra, namely zero; but in both subjects *division by zero is always excluded.* If zero were used as a divisor, numerous contradictions would arise of which the following is an illustration:

Obviously	$0 \cdot 4 = 0,$
and	$0 \cdot 6 = 0.$
Therefore	$0 \cdot 4 = 0 \cdot 6.$
Dividing each by zero,	$4 = 6.$

Note. The Hindus were the first to express the laws that govern the operations with the number 0. In fact, they were the first to have such a symbol. In the twelfth century a Hindu writer states that $a + 0 = a$, that $\sqrt{0} = 0$, and that $0^2 = 0$. Of course he did not express himself in terms of these symbols, but in the notation of his time.

EXERCISES

Perform the indicated division:

1. $+ 10 \div + 2.$

2. $- 10 \div - 2.$

3. $- 15 \div + 3.$

4. $+ 14 \div - 7.$

5. $- 18 \div - 2.$

6. $- 7 \div + 7.$

7. $0 \div + 5.$

8. $0 \div - 5.$

9. $+ 18 \div + 3 \div - 2.$

10. $+ 45 \div - 5 \div - 3.$

11. $- 64 \div + 8 \div - 2.$

12. $+ 96 \div - 6 \div + 4.$

13. $72 \div + 9 \div - 4.$

14. $60 \div - 5 \div - 12.$

15. $48 \div + 3 \div - 4.$

16. $\dfrac{-10}{?} = 2.$

17. $\dfrac{-12}{?} = -2.$

18. $\dfrac{+16}{?} = 8.$

If the first of several numbers connected by either plus or minus signs is a positive number, its sign is omitted; thus $+ 4 - 3 + 6$ is written $4 - 3 + 6$. If the sign of the 4 had been negative, its sign could not have been omitted.

If each of two or more numbers be inclosed in a parenthesis with no sign of operation connecting them, the sign of multiplication is always understood; thus $(6)(3)$, or even $6(3)$ or $(6)3$ means $6 \cdot 3$.

EXERCISES

Simplify the following:

1. $(7) + (5).$

2. $(7) - (5).$

3. $(7) + (- 5).$

4. $(7) - (- 5).$

5. $(- 7) + (5).$

6. $- 7 + 5.$

7. $(- 9) - (4).$

8. $- 9 - 4.$

9. $- 11 + (- 13).$

10. $- 6 - (- 10).$

11. $- 6 + 10.$

12. $8 + (- 10).$

13. $12 - 18$.　　**21.** $8(-3)$.　　　**29.** $12 \div (-2)$.

14. $-18 - 12$.　　**22.** $(-5)(-12)$.　　**30.** $-12 \div 2$.

15. $15 - 14$.　　**23.** $-3(-8)$.　　　**31.** $-39 \div (-3)$

16. $+7 - 0$.　　**24.** $-5 \cdot 4$.　　　**32.** $45 \div (-15)$.

17. $-0 - 3$.　　**25.** $5 \cdot 0$.　　　　**33.** $0 \div (-6)$.

18. $(-3)(6)$.　　**26.** $0 \cdot (-9)$.　　**34.** $0 \div 3$.

19. $(-5)6$.　　**27.** $4 \cdot 8$.　　　　**35.** $-27 \div 9$.

20. $(7)(-5)$.　　**28.** $-3 \cdot 6$.　　　**36.** $3 - 5 + 6$.

37. $-4 + 6 - 2 + 1$.　　　**38.** $-4 + 6 + 2 - 1$.

39. $2 - 3 + 4 - 5 - 6$.

Add:

40.	**41.**	**42.**	**43.**
7	6	-8	4
-2	-2	6	-9
3	-3	2	-3
-5	4	-5	6

Simplify:

44. $3 \cdot 6 \div 3$.　　　　　　**49.** 3^2.

45. $-4(7) \div (-2)$.　　　　**50.** $(-3)^2$.

46. $3(-6) \div 2$.　　　　　**51.** 2^3.

47. $4 \cdot 6(-8) \div (-16)$.　　**52.** $(-2)^3$.

48. $18 \div (-3) \cdot 6 \div 4$.　　**53.** $(-4)^3 + (4)^2$.

54. $(-1)^2 + (-1)^3 + (-2)^2 + (-2)^3$.

55. $6 + 3 \cdot 2 + 18 \div (-3)$.

56. $5^2 - 4 \div (-2) + 6(-3)$.

57. $3 \cdot 6 \div 9 - 2 \cdot 6 \div 4 + (-3)^2$.

58. $6 + 6 \cdot 3^2 - 5^2 \cdot 2 \div 10$.

If $x = 3$ and $y = -2$, find the value of:

59. y^2.　　　**61.** y^4.　　　**63.** $2y^2$.　　　**65.** $5x^2y^2$.

60. y^3.　　　**62.** y^5.　　　**64.** $2y^3$.　　　**66.** $4x^2y^4$.

67. $x^2 - y^2$.　　　　　　　　**69.** $x^2 + 2xy + y^2$.

68. $x^3 - y^3$.　　　　　　　　**70.** $x^2 - 2xy + y^2$.

71. $(x + y)(x - y)$.

72. $x^3 + 3x^2y + 3xy^2 + y^3$.

73. $y^3 - 3xy^2 + 3x^2y - x^3$.

74. Does $4x - 2 = 2x + 8$, if $x = 5$?

75. Does $3x - 5 = 2x + 8$, if $x = -9$?

76. Does $x^2 - x - 12 = 0$, if $x = 4$? if $x = -8$? if $x = -4$?

77. Does $3x^2 + 19x = 14$, if $x = \frac{2}{3}$? if $x = 2$? if $x = -7$?

78. At 7.00 A.M. on a certain day the thermometer registered 15 degrees above zero. The mercury then fell at the rate of 3 degrees per hour. What was the temperature at 9.00 A.M.? at noon? at 3.00 P.M.?

79. With reference to a certain assumed level, a surveyor found the heights of 5 points to be $+30$ feet, -7 feet, $+18$ feet, -10 feet, and $+16$ feet respectively. What was the average height of the 5 points? What meaning has the result?

80. A sixth point whose height was -38 feet was later included in the preceding survey. Find the mean height of the 6 points. What meaning has the result?

81. Later a seventh point was added to the preceding survey. The average height of the 7 points was then zero. Find the height of this last point.

82. Euclid lived about 300 B.C. Sir Isaac Newton died in 1727 A.D. If dates before Christ are considered negative and those after Christ be considered positive, how might these dates be written?

83. What is the meaning of the date -450? of $+1910$? What is the difference in time between these two dates?

84. In still water a gasoline launch can travel 8 miles per hour. Using positive and negative numbers, represent its rate both up and down a river which runs $1\frac{1}{2}$ miles per hour.

85. A boat is traveling 12 miles per hour. A man on its deck is walking 3 miles per hour. Using positive and negative numbers, represent the rate at which he approaches his destination when he walks toward the bow and when he walks toward the stern.

86. A balloon capable of supporting 500 pounds is held down by 10 men whose average weight is 150 pounds. Using positive and negative numbers, represent the weight of the balloon, the men, and the balloon and men together.

87. A man swims in still water at the rate of $1\frac{1}{2}$ miles per hour. If he swims in a river which flows 2 miles per hour, represent his rate (a) when he swims downstream; (b) when he swims upstream. What is the practical meaning of the last answer?

CHAPTER III

ADDITION

17. Addition of monomials. A number symbol consisting of a numeral, or a letter, or a product of letters alone, or the product of a numeral and one or more letters is called a **monomial** or **term**.

Thus 5, $-a$, b^4, a^2x, $-4cy^2$, $\frac{3}{5}a^2x^3y$, x^a, and x^{a+2} are terms. Frequently, where no confusion would arise, expressions like $(a+b)$, $3(x-y)$, $5\sqrt{x^3}$, and $\sqrt{a-x}$ are also called terms, for often they may be replaced by a single letter.

The **literal** part of a term is the portion composed of letters.

Similar terms are integers and fractions, like numerical roots, or such terms as have like literal parts.

Thus 3, -7, and 9 are similar terms as well as $\sqrt{2}$ and $3\sqrt{2}$. Also a, $4a$, and $-10a$ are similar terms as are a^2x, $-3a^2x$, and $7a^2x$.

Dissimilar terms are unlike numerical roots or such terms as have unlike literal parts.

Thus 4, $\sqrt{2}$, $\sqrt{3}$, and $\sqrt[3]{5}$ are dissimilar terms as well as $3a$, $4b$, and $6c^2$. Also $7a^2x$, $3ax^2$, and $5ax$ are dissimilar terms.

We know that 6 acres and 3 acres $= 9$ acres. Similarly $6a + 3a = 9a$, and $6a + (-3a) = 3a$, and $5xy + 6xy = 11xy$. In like manner the sum of $8y$, $-3y$, $2y$, and $-y$ is $6y$. Such terms as $-y$, x, ay, and $-c^2x$ are equivalent to $-1y$, $+1x$, $+1ay$, and $-1c^2x$, the coefficient 1 being always understood if no numerical coefficient is written.

Thus for adding similar terms we have the

Rule. *Find the algebraic sum of the numerical coefficients and prefix this result to the common literal part.*

EXERCISES

Find the algebraic sum of:

1. $18 - 5 + 6.$

2. $18\,a - 5\,a + 6\,a.$

3. $12 - 7 + 3 + 4.$

4. $12\,a^2 - 7\,a^2 + 3\,a^2 + 4\,a^2.$

5. $6 - 4 - 17 + 20.$

6. $6\,ab - 4\,ab - 17\,ab + 20\,ab.$

7. $15 - 17 + 8 - 12 - 25.$

8. $8\,abc - 17\,abc - 4\,abc + 15\,abc - 12\,abc.$

9. $11 + 5 - 9 - 3 + 16 - 25.$

10. $16\,ac - 9\,ac + 5\,ac - 2\,ac - 3\,ac + 11\,ac.$

11. $7\,x + 4\,x - 15\,x - 8\,x + 3\,x.$

12. $12\,y - 17\,y + 10\,y + 20\,y - 25\,y.$

13. $4\,xy - 8\,xy - 12\,xy + 13\,xy - xy.$

14. $14\,x^2 - 13\,x^2 + x^2 - 5\,x^2 + 4\,x^2.$

15. $5\,y^2 - 2\,y^2 - 11\,y^2 + y^2 - 7\,y^2.$

16. $7\,a^2b - 5\,a^2b + 8\,a^2b - a^2b + 9\,a^2b.$

Obviously $2 + 3 = 3 + 2,$ and $2 - 3 + 5 = 2 + 5 - 3 = -3 + 5 + 2,$ etc. This illustrates the law that in addition the terms may be arranged in any order. Hence $6\,d + 7\,c = 7\,c + 6\,d,$ and the sum of 3 and x is either $x + 3$ or $3 + x$; also $a + b = b + a,$ and $a + b + c = b + c + a = c + a + b,$ etc.

Algebraic expressions for numbers with unlike-literal parts, such as $6\,d$ and $7\,c,$ may be added by writing them one after the other with a plus sign between them; thus $6\,d + 7\,c.$ The addition of $6\,d$ and $-7\,c$ is indicated by writing $6\,d + (-7\,c),$ which is the same as $6\,d - 7\,c.$ Similarly the sum of $3\,x,$ $-2\,y,$ and $-7\,z$ may be written $3\,x + (-2\,y) + (-7\,z),$ or, more simply, $3\,x - 2\,y - 7\,z.$

Thus for adding dissimilar terms we have the

RULE. *Write the terms one after another in any order, giving to each its proper sign.*

If similar and dissimilar terms are to be added, the two preceding rules must be observed.

EXERCISES

Find the algebraic sum of:

1. a, $3b$, and $-c$.

2. $4x$, $-2b$, $3y$, and 10.

3. $3ab^2$, $2bx$, $-cy$, and $4a^2b$.

4. $5x^3y$, $-5xy^3$, c^3y, and $-2cy^3$.

5. $4x$, $-3a$, $2b$, $-5x$, and $3y$.

6. $5a$, $-4b$, $+3c$, $6b$, and $-2c^2$.

7. $3a^2$, $+2b^2$, $-5c^2$, $-4b^2$, and $5a^2$.

8. $4a^3b$, $-4ab^3$, $-3a^2b$, $3ab^2$, $4a^3b$, and $2ab^3$.

9. $-4a^2b + 6a^2b^2 - 15a^2b^2 + 3a^2b^2 + 0a^2b^2$.

10. $-b^3 - 23b^3 + 17b^3 + b^3 - 0b^3 + 13b^3$.

11. $12a^3b + 6a^3b - a^3b + 16a^3b - 13a^3b - 25a^3b$.

12. $11\sqrt{a} - 14\sqrt{a} + 21\sqrt{a} - \sqrt{a}$.

13. $3\sqrt{x-y} - \sqrt{x-y} + 9\sqrt{x-y} - 7\sqrt{x-y}$.

14. $3(a+b) - 2(a+b) + 8(a+b)$.

15. $-7(a-2b)$, $(a-2b)$, $12(a-2b)$.

16. $8(a+b) + 3(a-b) - 4(a+b) - 2(a-b)$.

17. $4(x-y) - 3(x+3) - 6(x-y) + 5(x-3)$.

18. $(2x-y)^2 - 3(2x-y)^2 + 4(2x-y)^2 - 7(2x-y)^2$.

18. Addition of polynomials. A **polynomial** is an algebraic expression consisting of two or more terms.

It is not usual to call an expression a polynomial if any of its terms contain a letter under a radical sign. Thus we shall not call expressions like $\sqrt{x-3} + 4$ polynomials.

A **binomial** is a polynomial of two terms.

A **trinomial** is a polynomial of three terms.

EXAMPLE

Add the following polynomials: $4a - 6b - a^2c$; $3b + 4a^2c$; $-3a - 7a^2c + 10$; $5a + 3b - 6$.

$$
\begin{array}{ll}
\text{Solution:} & \quad 4a - 6b - a^2c \\
& \qquad\quad\; 3b + 4a^2c \\
& -3a \qquad\quad - 7a^2c + 10 \\
& \underline{5a + 3b \qquad\quad - 6} \\
\text{Sum,} & \quad 6a \qquad\quad - 4a^2c + 4
\end{array}
$$

For the addition of polynomials we have the

RULE. *Write similar terms in the same column.*

Find the algebraic sum of the terms in each column and write the results in succession with their proper signs.

A **check** on an operation is another operation which tests the correctness of the first.

For example, in arithmetic the result of division is checked by multiplication; thus the check for $132 \div 6 = 22$, is $22 \cdot 6 = 132$.

In the following example the letters a, b, and c represent any numbers whatever. Therefore in order to check the result we may give them any numerical values we please. Let $a = 1$, $b = 1$, and $c = 1$.

EXAMPLE

Add the polynomials $5a - 3b - 3c$, $2a - 5b + 6c$, and $-3a + 2b - 4c$.

$$
\begin{array}{lll}
\qquad\quad \text{Solution:} & \qquad\qquad \text{Check:} \\
\quad 5a - 3b - 3c & = & \quad 5 - 3 - 3 = -1 \\
\quad 2a - 5b + 6c & = & \quad 2 - 5 + 6 = 3 \\
\underline{-3a + 2b - 4c} & = & \underline{-3 + 2 - 4 = -5} \\
\text{Sum,} \quad 4a - 6b - c & & \qquad\qquad\qquad -3 \\
\text{But} \quad\; 4a - 6b - c & = & \quad 4 - 6 - 1 = -3
\end{array}
$$

We conclude that the addition is correctly performed, since the numerical value of the sum is -3 and the sum of the numerical values of the three polynomials to be added is -3 also.

A numerical check will usually detect errors, though not always. Two errors may be made, one of which offsets the other; these errors would not be detected by a numerical check like the preceding one.

Thus if in the preceding exercise the incorrect sum $4\,a - 5\,b - 2\,c$ had been obtained, the substitution of 1 for a, b, and c in this result would have given -3, an apparent check.

The number of times that errors will thus balance one another, however, is small compared to the total number of errors made; hence the check illustrated is practically very useful. If a more reliable check is desired in similar exercises, it can be obtained by the substitution of a different number for every letter.

EXERCISES

Add the following polynomials and check the results:

1. $x + y + z$, $x - 2\,y + 3\,z$, and $3\,x + 4\,y - 7z$.

2. $2\,x + 5\,y - z$, $3\,x - 8\,y + 6\,z$, and $x - y - z$.

3. $3\,x + 5\,y$, $4\,x - 7\,y + 6\,z$, and $3\,x - 3\,y - 3\,z$.

4. $7\,x - y + 3\,z$, $5\,x - 4\,z$, and $2\,x + 6\,y - 5\,z$.

5. $4\,x - 3\,y - 5\,z$, $6\,y - 2\,z$, and $7\,x - 6\,y - 4\,z$.

6. $x + 2\,z + 3\,y$, $y - 3\,z + x$, and $z - 2\,x - 4\,y$.

7. $5\,x - y + 3\,z$, $2\,y - 11\,z + x$, and $9\,z - 7\,y$.

8. $8\,a - 7\,b - 6\,c$, $5\,c - 4\,a - 3\,b$, and $3\,b + 7\,c$.

9. $9\,ac - bc$, $8\,ab - 4\,ac$, and $-12\,ab - ac$.

10. $a^2 - 4\,a + 10$, $5\,a - 6\,a^2 + 4$, and $3\,a - 16 + 2\,a^2$.

11. $9 - a^2 + a$, $-7 + 6\,a^2 - 4\,a$, and $5\,a^2 - a$.

12. $\frac{1}{2}x - \frac{2}{3}y + \frac{2}{3}z$, $x - y + 2\,z$, and $\frac{1}{3}x - \frac{1}{2}y + \frac{1}{10}z$.

13. $\frac{1}{4}x - \frac{3}{20}z$, $\frac{1}{8}x + \frac{4}{9}y$, and $\frac{3}{5}z - \frac{5}{3}y$.

14. $a - 3(x-y) + z$, $5 - 10\,a + 4\,(x-y)$, and $-2\,(x-y) + 6$.

15. $a + d + 2\,(b-c)$, $7\,(b-c) + 6\,d - 12\,a$, and $11\,a - 5\,(b-c)$.

Combine similar terms in the following polynomials:

16. $7\,a^2 - 13\,b^2 + 12\,c^2 + 15\,b^2 - a^2 - 7\,c^2 + 3\,b^2 + 5\,c^2$.

17. $x^2 - 2\,xy + y^2 - 4\,xy - 4\,x^2 - y^2 - 16\,x^2 - 8\,xy + y^2 + y^3$.

18. $5\,ab - a^2 + b^2 - 4\,ab - 9\,b^2 + 5\,a^2 - 2\,ab + 2\,b^2$.

19. $3x^2 - 6x + 11 - 4x - 8 - 3x^2 + 5x - 16 + 13x.$

20. $12c^2 - 10bc + 8b^2 - bc - 6b^2 - c^2 + c^3 - 11c^2.$

21. $4x^2y - xy + y^2 - 3xy + 4xy^2 - 2x^2y + 4y^2 - 3xy + x^2y.$

22. $\frac{1}{2}a + \frac{1}{3}b - \frac{1}{4}c - c + \frac{1}{2}b - \frac{2}{3}a - b + \frac{1}{2}c - \frac{3}{4}a + 7.$

The sum of $5x$ and $2x$ may be written $(5 + 2)x$. This is not usual or necessary, as 5 and 2 can be combined and the result written $7x$. In adding $5x$ and ax, however, the 5 and the a cannot be combined and the result expressed by a single character, so the sum is written $(5 + a)x$. Similarly $ax - 3x = (a - 3)x$, $ax + bx = (a + b)x$, and $ax - bx + x = (a - b + 1)x$.

Write the following with polynomial coefficients:

23. $ax + bx + cx.$

24. $2ax - 3x + bx.$

25. $3ax - 4cx + x.$

26. $3ax^2 - bx^2 - x^2 + a^2x^2.$

27. $by - 4cy - y - 4by.$

28. $a(b + c) + 3(b + c).$

29. $4(a - x) - 3b(a - x).$

30. $8a(a + 3b) - 1(a + 3b).$

31. $7b(x^2 + y^2) - a(x^2 + y^2) + (x^2 + y^2).$

CHAPTER IV

SIMPLE EQUATIONS

19. Definitions and axioms. An **equation** is a statement of equality between two equal numbers or number symbols.

Thus $2 = 5 - 3$, $a - 2b = 3a + b - 2a - 3b$, $4x = x + 12$, and $x^2 - 5x + 6 = 0$ are equations.

The part of an equation on the left of the equality sign is called the *first* or *left member*, that on the right, the second or right member.

In an equation a letter whose value is sought is called the *unknown letter*, or simply the *unknown*.

An **axiom** is an evident truth which is accepted without proof.

In the solution of equations constant use is made of four axioms.

AXIOM I. *Adding the same number to each member of an equation does not destroy the equality.*

AXIOM II. *Subtracting the same number from each member of an equation does not destroy the equality.*

AXIOM III. *Multiplying each member of an equation by the same number does not destroy the equality.*

AXIOM IV. *Dividing each member of an equation by the same number (not zero) does not destroy the equality.*

If an equation is in a form as simple as $3x = 12$, it can easily be solved by dividing each member by the coefficient of x.

Thus dividing each member of $3x = 12$ by 3, the coefficient of x, we get $x = 4$.

If all terms containing the unknown letter are in one member and all numerical terms in the other, the like terms may be united and the equation solved as before.

Thus $5x - 2x + x = 8 + 15 - 3$ becomes, when like terms are united, $4x = 20$, and dividing each member by 4, we obtain $x = 5$.

Usually numerical terms as well as terms containing the unknown letter will be found in each member of an equation, as in $5x - 3 = 2x + 18$. By the use of one or more of the preceding axioms it is always possible to change the form of such equations until they are similar to the equation $3x = 12$, which, as we have seen, can easily be solved.

A **simple** or **linear** equation is one that may be put in a form in which:

(*a*) There is at least one unknown.

(*b*) The exponent of each unknown is 1.

(*c*) No term contains more than one unknown.

(*d*) No unknown occurs in any exponent.

(*e*) No unknown occurs in any denominator.

Thus $5x - 2 = 8$, $4x = y - 18$, $4n - 2 = 3n + 8$, and $x - 2y + 3 = 6$ are simple equations, while $2^x = 4$, $x - xy = 3$, and $\frac{1}{x} + \frac{2}{x+1} = 2$ are not.

EXAMPLE

Solve $5x - 4 = 2x + 17$.

Solution: $\qquad\qquad 5x - 4 = 2x + 17.$

Subtracting $2x$ from each member,

$\qquad\qquad\qquad 3x - 4 = 17.$ $\qquad\qquad$ Ax. II

Adding 4 to each member, $\quad 3x = 21.$ $\qquad\qquad$ Ax. I

Dividing each member by 3, $\quad x = 7.$ $\qquad\qquad$ Ax. IV

Checking the solution of an equation is often called **testing**, or **verifying**, the result. For this we have the

RULE. *Substitute the value of the unknown obtained from the solution in place of the letter which represents the unknown in the original equation. Then simplify the result until the two members are seen to be identical.*

Check: $\qquad\qquad 5x - 4 = 2x + 17.$

Substituting 7 for x, $\quad 5 \cdot 7 - 4 = 2 \cdot 7 + 17.$

Simplifying, $\qquad\qquad 35 - 4 = 14 + 17,$

or $\qquad\qquad\qquad\qquad 31 = 31.$

EXERCISES

Find the value of the unknown in the following equations and verify results:

1. $x + 5 = 11.$
2. $x - 4 = 12.$
3. $3x + 10 = 28.$
4. $5x - 6 = 19.$
5. $9x - 12 = 6.$
6. $4x = 12 + x.$
7. $6x = 20 + 2x.$
8. $9n = 40 - n.$
9. $13n = -5n + 36.$

10. $-4n = -13n + 27.$
11. $3y + 2 = y + 8.$
12. $5 + 4y = 3y + 20.$
13. $2y - 3 = 17 - y.$
14. $8x - 15 = 6x - 15.$
15. $-7h + 19 = 25 - 9h.$
16. $-7x + 18 = 4x + 18.$
17. $5k - 4 = 3k + 18.$
18. $8 - 6x + 12 + 10x = 26.$

19. $x + 2x + 18 + x + 2x + 18 = 116.$
20. $4x - 3 + 8x - 17 = 40 + 6x - 54.$

EXERCISES

1. A rectangle is three times as long as it is wide. If x represents the width, what will represent the length? the perimeter?

2. A rectangle is 10 feet longer than it is wide. If x represents the width in feet, what will represent the length? the perimeter?

3. A rectangle is 18 feet longer than it is wide. If x represents the length, what will represent the width? the perimeter?

4. The length of a certain rectangle is 4 feet more than twice the width. Represent the width, the length, and the perimeter in terms of one letter and numbers.

5. The numbers 3, 4, 5, 6, etc., are consecutive integers. How much greater is each than the preceding one?

6. If n represents an integer, what will conveniently represent the next consecutive one?

7. If n represents an integer, represent the next two consecutive integers. What will represent the sum of these two?

8. If n represents the first of four consecutive integers, what will represent the other three? the sum of the four?

9. The numbers 3, 5, 7, 9, 11, etc., are consecutive odd integers. How much greater is each than the preceding one?

10. If n is any odd number, what will represent the next greater odd number? What will represent the odd number preceding n?

11. Represent three consecutive odd numbers of which n is the first. What will represent the sum of the three?

12. Represent four consecutive even numbers. Find their sum.

13. Represent three numbers of which the second is twice the first, and the third three times the second.

14. Represent three numbers of which the second is 10 more than the first, and the third 7 less than the second.

15. If a man's age now is represented by x, what will represent his age 4 years ago? 6 years hence?

16. A's age is twice B's. Represent the age of each in terms of x: (a) now; (b) 7 years ago; (c) 12 years hence.

Express the following statements as equations:

17. The sum of 8 and x is 5.

18. x is 2 less than 10.   **20.** x is 5 more than y.

19. x is 3 greater than 5.   **21.** Three times x is 21.

22. Four times a is greater than 18 by 2.

23. Eight added to x gives the same result as x taken from 34.

24. Nine subtracted from $2x$ gives the same result as 14 added to x.

25. Twice x added to three times x is 48 more than x.

26. Twelve taken from three times x gives the same result as x added to 50.

PROBLEMS

1. One number is twice another, and the sum of the two is 135. Find both numbers.

2. One number is four times another, and the sum of the two is 105. Find both numbers.

3. One number is five times another, and the difference of the two is 52. Find both numbers.

4. One number is 5 greater than another, and their sum is 129. Find both numbers.

5. One number is 18 greater than another, and their sum is 168. Find both numbers.

6. A rectangle is five times as long as it is wide, and its perimeter is 156 feet. Find the length and the width.

7. A rectangle is 12 feet longer than it is wide, and its perimeter is 96 feet. Find the length and the width.

8. The perimeter of a rectangle is 98 feet, and its length is 4 feet more than twice the width. Find the length and the width.

9. Find the dimensions of a rectangle whose perimeter is 88 feet, and whose length is 20 feet less than three times the width.

10. Find three consecutive numbers whose sum is 45.

11. Find four consecutive numbers whose sum is 106.

12. Find five consecutive numbers whose sum is 85.

13. Find three consecutive odd numbers whose sum is 291.

14. Find three consecutive even numbers whose sum is 66.

15. Find five consecutive odd numbers whose sum is 315.

16. A's age is two years less than B's, and the sum of their ages is 43 years. Find the age of each.

17. B's age is twice A's. Six years from now the sum of their ages will be 54 years. How old is each now?

18. The United States has 52,000 more miles of railway than Europe, and together they have 402,000 miles. Find the mileage of each.

19. The Nile is 500 miles longer than the Amazon and 300 miles shorter than the Mississippi (entire). The sum of the lengths of the three is 11,500 miles. Find the length of each.

20. Mount McKinley is 6313 feet higher than Pike's Peak. The sum of the heights of the two mountains is 34,607 feet, which is 5605 feet more than the height of Mount Everest. Find the height of each.

21. The combined horse power of a Mallet Compound freight engine (Erie R. R.), of a Pacific passenger engine (Pennsylvania R. R.), and of a Baltimore and Ohio electric tractor is 11,200. The horse power of the freight engine is 1800 more than that of the electric tractor and 1000 less than that of the passenger engine. Find the horse power of each.

Note. The process of developing a simple and clear means of expressing an equation has been a slow one. The very first writer on mathematics of whom we know anything, an Egyptian priest named Ahmes, who lived nearly two thousand years before Christ, called the unknown *heap* instead of *x*. One of his problems is as follows: "Heap; its seventh, its whole, it makes nineteen." This we should express by the equation $\frac{x}{7} + x = 19$. The Hindus often used the word *color* for the unknown, and if there was more than one unknown in the equation, the names of different colors would be used; thus they might express the product *xy* by "black times yellow." The Arabs used the word *root* with a similar meaning, and to this day we call the result of solving an equation its root (see p. 44). The early European mathematicians usually called the unknown *res*, the Latin word for *thing*, and it was not until after the time of Vieta (see p. 257) that the unknown was regularly denoted by a letter. The use of *x* for this purpose originated with Descartes in 1637.

CHAPTER V

SUBTRACTION

20. Subtraction of monomials. The principles stated on page 18 apply to the subtraction of monomials as well as to the positive and negative numbers there used.

For subtracting one monomial from another we have the

RULE. *Change the sign of the subtrahend; then find the algebraic sum of this result and the minuend.*

EXAMPLES

1. From $+ 8\,a$ take $+ 3\,a$.

Solution: $+ 8\,a$ minus $+ 3\,a = 8\,a - 3\,a = 5\,a$.

2. From $6\,ax$ take $- 4\,ax$.

Solution: $6\,ax$ minus $- 4\,ax = 6\,ax + 4\,ax = 10\,ax$.

3. Subtract $7\,a^2b$ from $- 10\,a^2b$.

Solution: $- 10\,a^2b$ minus $7\,a^2b = - 10\,a^2b - 7\,a^2b = - 17\,a^2b$.

4. Subtract $- 9\,ay^3$ from $3\,ay^3$.

Solution: $3\,ay^3$ minus $- 9\,ay^3 = 3\,ay^3 + 9\,ay^3 = 12\,ay^3$.

The difference of two dissimilar monomials cannot be written as a single term, but is expressed by a binomial, as follows:

5. Subtract $+ a$ from $+ b$.

Solution: $+ b$ minus $+ a = b - a$.

6. Subtract $- 5\,b$ from $3\,c$.

Solution: $3\,c$ minus $- 5\,b = 3\,c + 5\,b$.

7. Subtract $4\,xy$ from $- 3\,x^2z$.

Solution: $- 3\,x^2z$ minus $4\,xy = - 3\,x^2z - 4\,xy$.

As soon as possible the student should learn to change the sign of the subtrahend *mentally*.

EXERCISES

Subtract the first monomial from the second, and also the second monomial from the first, in each of the following:

1. $2x, 3x.$
2. $4x, 3x.$
3. $-2x, -3x.$
4. $-5x, -3x.$
5. $-x, 4x.$
6. $-x, -3x.$

7. $-c, 5c.$
8. $-ac, -5ac.$
9. $8a^2c, -11a^2c.$
10. $6x^2y^2, -6x^2y^2.$
11. $3x, 0.$
12. $-4ab, 0.$

13. $a, b.$
14. $c, 2x.$
15. $x, -4y.$
16. $-3a, 2b.$
17. $-2a, -5b.$
18. $-2a, -2a.$

21. Subtraction of polynomials. For the subtraction of polynomials we have the

RULE. *Write the subtrahend under the minuend so that similar terms are in the same column.*

Change the sign of each term of the subtrahend.

Find the algebraic sum of the terms in each column and write the results in succession with their proper signs.

EXAMPLE

Subtract $5x - 2y - 7z + 2$ from $3x + 8y - 5z$, and check the result by letting $x = 1$, $y = 1$, and $z = 1$.

Solution and **Check:**

$$\begin{array}{ll} 3x + 8y - 5z & = 3 + 8 - 5 & = 6 \\ 5x - 2y - 7z + 2 = 5 - 2 - 7 + 2 = -2 \\ \hline \textit{Difference,} \quad -2x + 10y + 2z - 2 = & & 8 \\ \quad -2 + 10 + 2 - 2 = 8 \text{ also.} \end{array}$$

We might also apply the check:

$$\text{difference} + \text{subtrahend} = \text{minuend}.$$

EXERCISES

Subtract the first number from the second, and also the second number from the first, in Exercises 1–9:

1. $a + 2, a + 3.$
2. $a - 4, a - 2.$
3. $2a - 3, 3a + 5.$

4. $3a + 7, 9 - 4a.$
5. $4a, 4a - 3.$
6. $2ab - 5c, 5c.$

7. $3xy - a, 5xy.$
8. $0, x + 3.$
9. $2x - 3, 0.$

Subtract the first polynomial from the second in Exercises 10–17, and check the work numerically:

10. $x - 2y + 3z,\ 2x - 2y + z.$

11. $4x - 8y - 2z,\ 4x - 5y + 3z.$

12. $3a - 2b,\ 4a - b + 2c.$

13. $5a - 4b - 3c,\ 3a - 5b.$

14. $a - x - y,\ b - x + y.$

15. $3a - 2b - c + 6,\ 4a - b + 5c.$

16. $2a - 2b - 2c + 4,\ a - 3b.$

17. $a + b - c,\ c - d + e.$

Find the expression which added to the first will give the second in:

18. $x - 2y + z,\ 2x + 5y - 3z.$

19. $7x - 9y + 3z,\ 5x - 2y - 4z.$

20. $5a - 4b - 6c,\ 6a + 3b.$

21. $a + b - 2c,\ 5.$

22. $3ab + c,\ 3xy + z.$

23. $2x - 4y - z,\ 0.$

24. $2x^2y - 3xy^2,\ y^2x + yx^2 + z.$

Find the expression which subtracted from the first will give the second in Exercises 25–30:

25. $x - 2y + z,\ 3x + 2y - z.$

26. $x^2 - 7x + 10,\ 14x - 8 + 3x^2.$

27. $x - y + z,\ 5x + 3y - 8z.$

28. $4 - 8x^2,\ x^2 - 5x + 6.$

29. $3a - 5b + c,\ 0.$

30. $4a - 6b + 8y,\ x - 12.$

31. Subtract the sum of $a^2 - 2ab + b^2$ and $a^2 - 12ab + 20$ from $a^2 - 13a + 30.$

32. Subtract the sum of $a - 3b + c$ and $4a + 5b - 6c + 4$ from $a - b + c - x$.

33. From the sum of $5x + 3x^2y - 15xy^2$ and $-6x - 12y^2x + 7yx^2$ subtract $11x - 5x^2y + 7y^2x$.

34. From the sum of $4abc^2 - 3ab^2c + 2a^2bc$ and $6ac^2b - 5acb^2 - 4a^2b^2c$ subtract $2c^2ab - 3a^2bc + 7acb^2$.

35. From the sum of $3x - 4xy - 2z$ and $7xy - 4z - 3x$ take the sum of $5z - 2xy - a^2bc$ and $9x - 6ba^2c - z$.

36. Simplify $(4x - 3y + 6) + (3x + 5y - 10)$.

37. Simplify $(7c + 5d - e) - (4c + 5d - 9e)$.

38. Simplify $(x^2 + 2x + 5) + (2x^2 + x - 10) - (x^2 - 5x + 3)$.

39. Simplify $(x + 3y - 2z) + (4x - 5y + 3z) - (3x - 2y - 6z)$.

Find the algebraic sum of :

40. $(5x + 3y - z) + (4y + 7z) - (x - y + 3z)$.

41. $4x - 3y + 7 - (2x - 5y - 4) + (4x - 8)$.

42. $3c - 5d - e - (5 + 6d + 11e) - (5c + 4e)$.

43. $3a + 3b - 4c - (-3b - 3c - 4) - (4a + x - 8c)$.

CHAPTER VI

IDENTITIES AND EQUATIONS OF CONDITION

22. Kinds of equations. Equations are of two kinds, — **identities** and **equations of condition**.

An **identity** is an equation in which, if the indicated operations are performed, the two members become precisely alike, term for term.

Thus $4 \cdot 5 + 3 \cdot 4 = 8 \cdot 5 - \dfrac{4 \cdot 6}{3}$ is an identity, for, performing the indicated operations, it becomes $20 + 12 = 40 - 8$, or $32 = 32$.

Similarly the equation $2a + 3b - 4 = 3a - 2b + (5b - a - 4)$ is an identity, for, performing the indicated addition in the second member, it becomes $2a + 3b - 4 = 2a + 3b - 4$, in which the two members are alike, term for term.

A **literal identity** is true for *any* numerical values of the letters in it.

Thus the literal identity $(a + 3)^2 = a^2 + 6a + 9$ becomes, when $a = 5$, $(5 + 3)^2 = 5^2 + 6 \cdot 5 + 9$, or $8^2 = 25 + 30 + 9$, or $64 = 64$. If a is zero, the identity becomes $(0 + 3)^2 = 0 + 6 \cdot 0 + 9$, or $9 = 9$. If a is 2, we obtain $(2 + 3)^2 = 2^2 + 6 \cdot 2 + 9$, or $25 = 25$.

Similarly $(a + b)^2 = a^2 + 2ab + b^2$ is an identity, and is true for all values of a and b. If $a = 2$ and $b = 3$, this identity becomes $25 = 25$. If $a = -3$ and $b = 5$, it becomes $4 = 4$. If $a = 0$ and $b = 3$, it becomes $9 = 9$. If $a = -4$ and $b = 5$, it becomes $1 = 1$. In this way the literal identity becomes a numerical identity for any numerical values of a and b.

An equation which is true only for certain values of a letter in it, or for certain sets of related values of two or more of its letters, is an **equation of condition**, or simply an equation.

Every equation of condition may be regarded as asking a question. Thus the equation $3x + 2 = 15$ asks, "What number when multiplied by 3 and the product increased by 2 gives 15 as the result?"

The equations used in solving the problems on pages 5–7 are equations of condition. The condition there expressed in ordinary language in the problem was translated into the algebraic language of the equation.

The equation $4x = x + 12$ is true only when $x = 4$. If 4 is put for x, the equation becomes the identity $4 \cdot 4 = 4 + 12$, or $16 = 16$. Clearly the result is false if 0, or 3, or any value other than 4 is put for x; the equation is true on condition that x be 4, and on no other.

Similarly $x^2 - 5x + 6 = 0$ is true when $x = 2$ or when $x = 3$. In the first case $x^2 - 5x + 6 = 0$ becomes $2^2 - 5 \cdot 2 + 6 = 0$, or $4 - 10 + 6 = 0$, or $0 = 0$. In the second case we obtain $3^2 - 5 \cdot 3 + 6 = 0$, or $9 - 15 + 6 = 0$, or $0 = 0$. Plainly the statement obtained is false when -2 is put for x, for then it becomes $(-2)^2 - 5(-2) + 6 = 0$, or $4 + 10 + 6 = 0$, or $20 = 0$. Similarly any value other than 2 or 3, when put for x, gives a relation between numbers which is not true.

Instead of the equality sign, the sign $\equiv$, read *is identical with,* or *is identically equal to,* is often used for emphasis if the equation is an identity.

Thus $3a = 2a + a$ may be written $3a \equiv 2a + a$.

A number or literal expression which, being substituted for the unknown letter in an equation, reduces it to an identity, is said to **satisfy** the equation.

Thus it has been shown that 4 satisfies the equation $4x = x + 12$, and both 2 and 3 satisfy the equation $x^2 - 5x + 6 = 0$. Similarly the literal expression $3a$ satisfies the equation $x - 5 = 3a - 5$.

*A number or number symbol is called a **root** of an equation, if, on substituting it in place of the unknown, the equation becomes an identity.*

A root of an equation satisfies the equation.

The process of finding the root or the roots of an equation is called solving the equation.

The process of checking the solution is really finding out whether the result obtained is a root of the equation or not.

In solving the equation $5k - 4 = 3k + 18$, in Exercise 17, p. 35, the student added 4 to each member and subtracted $3k$ from each member. If we indicate this addition of 4 to each member and this subtraction of $3\,k$ from each member, the equation becomes

$$5\,k - 4 + 4 - 3\,k = 3\,k + 18 + 4 - 3\,k.$$

Now in the first member $-4 + 4 = 0$, and in the second member $3\,k - 3\,k = 0$. Omitting these, the equation becomes $5\,k - 3\,k = 18 + 4.$

Comparing this with the original equation, it is seen that -4 has vanished from the first member of the original equation and $+4$ appears in the second member of the last; and that $3\,k$ has vanished from the second member of the original equation and $-3\,k$ appears in the first member of the last.

It thus appears that a term may be omitted from one member of an equation, provided the same term, with its sign changed, is written in the other member. This process is called **transposition**.

Hereafter, instead of the method illustrated on page 34, the student will use transposition, as it is more rapid and convenient. He should, however, always remember that the transposition of a term is really the subtraction of that term from each member of the equation.

Like terms in the same member of an equation should be combined before transposing any term.

If we transpose each term of the equation

$$5\,k - 4 = 3\,k + 18,$$

it becomes $\qquad -3\,k - 18 = -5\,k + 4,$

or, reversing the two members,

$$-5\,k + 4 = -3\,k - 18.$$

It thus appears that the signs of all the terms of an equation may be changed without destroying the equality. Such a change may also be looked upon as equivalent to multiplying each term of the equation by -1.

Note. Our word *algebra* is derived from the Arabic word for *transposition*. The process by which one passes from the equation $px - q = x^2$ to the equation $px = x^2 + q$ was known as *al-jabr*. This is the first word in the title of an Arabic book on algebra which was translated into Latin. For some reason only this part of the title remained, and by the early part of the seventeenth century *al-jabr*, or algebra, was the common name given to the whole subject.

EXAMPLE

Solve the equation $8x - 5 + 4x + 12 = 13x - 10 - 3x + 29$.

Solution:	$8x - 5 + 4x + 12 = 13x - 10 - 3x + 29$.
Combining like terms,	$12x + 7 = 10x + 19$.
Transposing,	$12x - 10x = 19 - 7$.
Combining like terms,	$2x = 12$.
Dividing by 2,	$x = 6$.
Check:	$8x - 5 + 4x + 12 = 13x - 10 - 3x + 29$.
Substituting 6 for x,	$48 - 5 + 24 + 12 = 78 - 10 - 18 + 29$.
Combining,	$79 = 79$.

EXERCISES

Solve the following equations and check results:

1. $8x - 2 = 6x + 6$.

2. $4x - 5 = 2x + 10$.

3. $6y - 5 = 9y + 2$.

4. $7y + 3 = 10 + 8y$.

5. $5n - 3 + 21 = 18 + 4n$.

6. $6 + 4n - 15 = 15 - n$.

7. $5n + 3 - 2n = 7 - 4$.

8. $3k + 9 + 5k + 31 = 0$.

9. $6k + 3 - 2k = 27$.

10. $3x - 6 = 34 + 8x$.

11. $2x - 14 - 5x + 4 = 0$.

12. $x + 12 - 11x = -15x + 22$.

13. $5y + 3 = 17 + 3y + 8$.

14. $3y + 5 + 8y + \frac{1}{2} = 0$.

15. $2 - 4h = 3 - 8h + 8$.

16. $3 - 5h + 2 = 7h + 5$.

17. $3h - 25 + 8h - 20 = 0$.

18. $14x - 6x = 22 + 17x - 11x$.

19. $7x - 13 + 8 = x - 27 - 5x$.

20. $4x - 15 - 11x - 18 + 16x - 17 = 0$.

21. $5y - 6 + 3y + 18 - 2y - 25 + 1 = 0$.

22. $0 = 9x - 3 - 4x + 27 + 16x + 18$.

23. $7n - 5 - 4n + 8 = 3n + 18 - 2n - 3$.

EXERCISES

Represent a number:

1. Greater than n by 5.   5. Four times n.

2. Greater than n by a.   6. Three greater than $a + b$.

3. Less than n by 3.   7. c greater than $a + b$.

4. Less than n by b.   8. Five less than $2a - b$.

9. c less than $2a - b$.

10. b less than two times n.

11. a greater than five times n.

12. Seven less than four times n.

13. Eight greater than three times n.

14. One part of 10 is 6. What is the other part?

15. One part of x is 4. What is the other part?

16. One part of 12 is y. What is the other part?

17. One part of x is a. What is the other part?

18. One part of a is x. What is the other part?

19. One part of $x + y$ is z. What is the other part?

20. The sum of two numbers is 18. If one of them is 7, what is the other?

21. The sum of two numbers is 18. If one of them is n, what is the other?

22. The difference of two numbers is 18. If the greater is 34, what is the other?

23. The difference of two numbers is 18. If the greater is n, what is the other?

24. The sum of two numbers is 30. If the smaller is b, what is the other?

25. The sum of two numbers is a. If one of them is 7, what is the other?

26. The sum of two numbers is a. If one of them is x, what is the other?

27. The difference of two numbers is d. If one of them is 6, what is the other?

28. The difference of two numbers is d. If one of them is n, what is the other?

29. What is the excess of 10 over 4? 10 over x?

30. By how much does 25 exceed 9? 25 exceed y? 16 exceed $a + b$?

31. How much greater is 40 than 27? than 40? than a? a than b?

32. How much smaller is 22 than 36? 14 than a? x than y?

33. By how much does $a + 6$ exceed $a - 6$? $a + 6$ exceed $b - 6$? $4x - 3$ exceed $3x - 4$?

34. A is n years old. What will be his age 4 years hence? x years hence? What was his age 3 years ago?

35. A's age is $2n - 3$ years. What will be his age 10 years from now? a years from now? What was his age 8 years ago? a years ago?

36. A and B each have x dollars. If A gives B four dollars, how much will each then have?

37. A and B each have $x + 50$ dollars. If B gives A y dollars, how much will each then have?

38. If A has $x + 30$ dollars and B has $3x - 4$ dollars, express as equations:

(*a*) A and B together have \$200.

(*b*) A has as many dollars as B.

(*c*) A has \$10 less than B.

(*d*) If A gains \$100 and B loses \$50, they have equal amounts.

39. If A's age is x years, B's $2x + 7$ years, and C's $3x - 8$ years, express:

(*a*) The ages of A, B, and C five years hence.

(*b*) The ages of A, B, and C three years ago.

Express each of the following as equations:

(c) The sum of the ages of A and B, four years hence, will be 40.

(d) The difference of the ages of A and C, six years ago, was 24.

(e) In 10 years A will be as old as B is now.

(f) Four years ago C was as old as B will be in 10 years.

(g) In x years B will be 40.

(h) In 2 years the sum of the ages of A, B, and C will be 100.

Translate the following equations into words:

40. $n - 2 = 8$.   **42.** $3n = 27$.   **44.** $18 - n = n - 4$.

41. $n + 3 = 5$.   **43.** $4n - 2 = 16$.   **45.** $3n - 4 = 2n + 8$.

Translate Exercises 46–57 into English, calling m "a number" and n "a second number":

46. $m + n = 20$.   **52.** $m + a = n$.

47. $m - n = 2$.   **53.** $m - b = n$.

48. $2m = n + 6$.   **54.** $3m = 2n$.

49. $3m - 2n = 8$.   **55.** $m = 2n - 6$.

50. $m + n = a$.   **56.** $4 + 3m = 2n + 4$.

51. $m - n = b$.   **57.** $80 - m = 30 + n$.

23. Solution of problems. In the solution of problems in simple equations the following steps are necessary:

1. Read the problem carefully.

2. Represent the unknown number by a letter.

3. Express the conditions stated in the problem as an equation involving this letter.

4. Solve the equation.

5. Check by substituting in the problem the value found for the unknown.

This last is of importance, for substitution in the equation would not detect any errors made in translating the words of the problem into the equation.

The preceding directions for the solution of the various problems leading to simple equations are as definite as can be given. The student will obtain much aid from the study of the typical solutions which occur from time to time. Then one or more careful readings of each problem, a little fixing of the attention upon it, and an application of common sense will insure progress.

In the solution of problems the writing of the equation is nothing more than translating from ordinary speech into the language of algebra. Sometimes it is possible to translate the statement of the problem, word by word, into algebraic symbols.

For example,

Four times a certain number, diminished by 6, gives the same
4 × n − 6 =
result as the number increased by 30.
n + 30.

Again,

Seven times A's age two years ago equals five times his age ten years
7 × (a − 2) = 5 × (a + 10).
hence.

PROBLEMS

Solve and check the following:

1. To what number must 22 be added so that the sum may be 50?

2. From what number must 15 be subtracted so that the remainder may be 47?

3. What number increased by 9 equals 28?

4. What number diminished by 17 equals 35?

5. What number if doubled and the result diminished by 27 gives 49 as a remainder?

6. What number if trebled and the result diminished by 36 gives twice the original number?

7. Three times a certain number, less 17, equals twice the number, less 1. Find the number.

8. Five times a certain number, increased by 6, equals twice the number, increased by 15. Find the number.

9. Four times a certain number, plus 9, equals seven times the number, minus 33. Find the number.

10. A certain number added to 9 gives the same result as that obtained when the number is subtracted from 71. Find the number.

11. If 6 is added to twice a number, and 10 be subtracted from four times the number, the results are the same. Find the number.

12. The sum of two numbers is 67, and their difference is 5. Find the numbers.

Solution: There are *two* unknowns in this problem, but both can be represented in terms of the same letter, thus:

Let n = the smaller number.

Then $n + 5$ = the greater number, since the smaller is 5 less than the greater.

The sum of the two numbers is 67.

Therefore $n + n + 5 = 67$.

Combining, $2n + 5 = 67$.

Transposing, $2n = 67 - 5$.

Combining, $2n = 62$.

Dividing by 2, $n = 31$, the smaller number,

and $n + 5 = 36$, the greater number.

Check: $31 + 36 = 67$; $36 - 31 = 5$.

13. The sum of two numbers is 74, and their difference is 12. Find the numbers.

14. The sum of two numbers is 45; the second is 3 less than the first. Find the numbers.

15. The sum of two numbers is 44, and one exceeds the other by 8. Find the numbers.

16. The sum of three numbers is 83. The second is 4 less than the first, and the third is 9 greater than the first. Find the numbers.

17. The sum of three numbers is 66. The second is 3 less than the first, and the third is 18 greater than the second. Find the numbers.

18. The sum of two consecutive numbers is 37. Find the numbers.

19. Find three consecutive numbers whose sum is 39.

20. Find four consecutive numbers whose sum is 90.

21. Find two consecutive even numbers whose sum is 30.

22. Find three consecutive odd numbers whose sum is 87.

23. Find four consecutive even numbers whose sum is 100.

24. A rectangle whose perimeter is 38 feet is 3 feet longer than it is wide. Find its dimensions.

25. A rectangle whose perimeter is 128 feet is 16 feet longer than it is wide. Find the dimensions.

26. The length of a rectangle is 7 feet more than twice the width. Its perimeter is 104 feet. Find the dimensions.

27. The length of a rectangle is 5 feet more than four times its width. Its perimeter is 90 feet. Find the dimensions.

28. At Pittsburg on June 21 the day is 6 hours and 6 minutes longer than the night. How long is the night? the day?

29. A's age is twice B's, and C is 7 years older than A. The sum of their ages is 67 years. Find the age of each.

30. A's age is three times B's, and C is 10 years older than B. Five years hence the sum of their ages will be 60 years. Find the age of each now.

31. A is 10 years older than B, and C is 6 years younger than B. Four years ago the sum of their ages was 46 years. Find the age of each now.

32. A's age is 2 years more than twice B's age, and C's age is 7 years less than A's. Six years hence the sum of their ages will be 70 years. Find the age of each now.

33. In 1907 the yield of corn in the United States exceeded the yield of oats by 1838 million bushels, and the yield of wheat was 120 million bushels less than the yield of oats.

The total yield was 3981 million bushels. Find the number of bushels of each.

34. The north frigid zone and the south frigid zone have the same width, as have also the north temperate zone and the south temperate zone. The torrid zone is 47 degrees wide, or twice the width of the north frigid zone. Together the width of the five zones is 180 degrees. Find the width of each.

35. If the whole number of people in the United States is taken as 100%, 12% more people are engaged in agriculture than in the industries, 8% more in the industries than in commerce, and the rest, 24%, in other pursuits. Find the per cent of people engaged in agriculture, industries, and commerce.

36. In a certain year Montana produced 110 million pounds of copper more than Michigan, and 139 million pounds more than Arizona. If the total production of the three was 514 million pounds, find the amount each produced.

37. The height of the Eiffel Tower, Paris, is 120 feet less than twice the height of the Washington Monument. The latter is 105 feet higher than the Great Pyramid in Egypt, and 107 feet higher than St. Peter's in Rome. If the sum of their heights is 2443 feet, find the height of each.

38. The area of the coal fields of China and Japan is 6000 square miles greater than the area of the coal fields of the United States. The area of the latter exceeds twice that of all other countries (except China and Japan) by 38,400 square miles. If the total area of the coal fields of the world is 471,800 square miles, find the area of the coal fields of China and Japan, of the United States, and of the other countries.

39. In a certain year the production of copper in the United States was 5573 tons less than five times that of Spain and Portugal. These two countries produced 808 tons less than twice the output of Japan. The other countries of the world produced 4615 tons less than five times the output of Japan.

If the world produced 486,084 tons, find the output of the United States, Spain and Portugal, Japan, and the other countries.

40. The area of Asia is 982,000 square miles more than twice that of North America. The area of North America exceeds that of South America by 1,186,000 square miles, and that of Europe by 4,382,000 square miles. The total area of the four continents is 35,692,000 square miles. Find the area of each.

41. The number of United States troops engaged in the Civil War was 15,621 less than nine times the number engaged in the War of the Revolution, which was 266,841 less than the number engaged in the War of 1812. If the total number of United States troops engaged in the three wars was 3,658,811, find the number engaged in each.

42. St. Peter's Cathedral (Rome) has a capacity 29,000 greater than that of St. Paul's Cathedral (London), and 17,000 and 22,000 greater respectively than the Cathedral at Milan and St. Paul's church (Rome). The combined capacity of all is 148,000. Find the capacity of each.

CHAPTER VII

PARENTHESES

24. Removal of parentheses. In solving exercises and problems it is often necessary to inclose several terms in a parenthesis. Sometimes it is necessary to inclose this parenthesis with other terms in a second parenthesis, or even in a third. To avoid confusing the different parentheses, *brackets*, [ ], and *braces*, { }, are also used.

The parenthesis, the brackets, and the braces are called *signs of aggregation*. For convenience, brackets and braces are often spoken of as parentheses.

In the solution of equations and in other exercises it is frequently necessary to remove all signs of aggregation; this removal requires some special study.

The value of $12 + (5 - 3)$ is the same as that of $12 + 5 - 3$, or 14. Similarly $a + (b - c) = a + b - c$.

The plus signs preceding the parentheses in $12 + (5 - 3)$ and $a + (b - c)$ belong to the parentheses and vanish with them, whereas the plus signs *understood* before 5 and b within the parentheses are supplied when we write $12 + 5 - 3$ and $a + b - c$. In the expression $12 + (- 5 - 3)$ the sign of 5 must be retained, and we have $12 + (- 5 - 3) = 12 - 5 - 3 = 4$.

Therefore we have the

PRINCIPLE. *A parenthesis preceded by a plus sign may be removed from an expression without changing the signs of the terms which were inclosed by the parenthesis.*

In the expression $12 - (5 - 3)$ the binomial $(5 - 3)$ is to be subtracted from 12. Hence we change the sign of the subtrahend and find the sum of the resulting terms.

Thus $12 - (5 - 3) = 12 - 5 + 3 = 10$. This is obviously correct, for $12 - (5 - 3) = 12 - 2 = 10$.

Similarly $a - (b - c)$ becomes $a - b + c$ when the signs of the subtrahend, $(b - c)$, are changed.

The minus signs preceding the parentheses in $12 - (5 - 3)$ and $a - (b - c)$ vanish with the parentheses, and the plus signs understood before 5 and b within the parentheses are changed when we write $12 - 5 + 3$ and $a - b + c$.

Therefore we have the

PRINCIPLE. *A parenthesis preceded by a minus sign may be removed from an expression, provided the sign of each term which was inclosed by the parenthesis be changed.*

These principles may also be applied to remove the parentheses used to inclose the numbers in Chapter II.

When one parenthesis incloses another, either the outer or the inner parenthesis may be removed first. It is best for the beginner to use the

RULE. *Rewrite the expression, omitting the innermost parenthesis and changing the signs of the terms which it inclosed if the sign preceding it be minus, leaving them unchanged if it be plus.*

Combine like terms that may occur within the new innermost parenthesis.

Repeat this process until all the parentheses are removed.

EXAMPLES

Remove the parentheses from:

1. $8 - (3 - 2a) + (4 - 5a)$.

Solution: $8 - (3 - 2a) + (4 - 5a) = 8 - 3 + 2a + 4 - 5a$
$$= 9 - 3a.$$

2. $5a - [2a + (-3a - 4b) - (a - 8b) + 4a]$.

Solution: $5a - [2a + (-3a - 4b) - (a - 8b) + 4a]$
$$= 5a - [2a - 3a - 4b - a + 8b + 4a]$$
$$= 5a - [2a + 4b]$$
$$= 5a - 2a - 4b$$
$$= 3a - 4b.$$

EXERCISES

Remove the parentheses and combine like terms :

1. $14 - (6 - 3) - 5$.
2. $10 + (7 - 4) - (9 - 7)$.
3. $(7 - 3 + 2) - (6 - 4) + 11$.
4. $11\,a - (4\,a - 9\,a) + (6\,a - a)$.
5. $(2\,a - 5\,a) - (4\,a - a - 7\,a)$.
6. $a - (b - c) + (2\,b - 3\,c)$.
7. $a - b - (c - d) + (a + b) - (b - c)$.
8. $(x - y) - (2\,y - 3\,x) + (x - 4\,y)$.
9. $x - (x - y + 2\,z) - (3\,z - y + 4) + (x - 6)$
10. $7 - [8 - (3 - 10)] - (13 - 25)$.
11. $a + [2\,a - (3\,a - 2\,b)] + (3\,b - 2\,a)$.
12. $(5\,x - 6\,y) - [-2\,x - (4\,z - y) - 2\,z]$.
13. $[3\,x - (2\,y - z)] - [-(3\,y - 2\,x) - 5\,x]$.
14. $[(a + 3) - (x - 5)] - [a + 3 + (x - 5)]$.
15. $7 - [-6 - \{-4 + (6 - 10)\} + 11]$.
16. $-5\,x + [+10\,x - \{+11\,x - (2\,x - 7\,x + 4) - 3\,x\} - 22]$.
17. $\{4\,a - [2\,a - (3\,a - 2\,b) + 4\,a] - (4\,b - 6)\}$.
18. $2\,x - 3\,y - [\{+3\,z - 7\,x - (y + 4\,z) - 9\,x\} + z]$.
19. $(4\,y - 7\,x) - \{3\,x - [4\,x + (7\,y - 4\,x) - (3\,y - 3\,x)]\}$.

Sometimes it is necessary to remove some of the signs of aggregation in an expression, leaving others. In the following remove the parentheses, leaving the brackets, and simplify the results as much as possible :

20. $[(a + b) + c]$, $[(a + b) - c]$.
21. $[4\,x + (3\,z - 5\,y)]$, $[4\,x - (3\,z - 5\,y)]$.
22. $[(a - 2\,b) + (3\,c - d)]$, $[(a - 2\,b) - (3\,c - d)]$.
23. $[(4\,x - 3) + (5\,y - 7)]$, $[(4\,x - 3) - (5\,y - 7)]$.
24. $[(x^2 - a^2) + (y^2 - 2\,a^2)]$, $[(x^2 - a^2) - (y^2 - 2\,a^2)]$.

25. Inclosing terms in parenthesis. Obviously

$$16 + 9 - 5 = 16 + (9 - 5) = 16 + 4 = 20.$$

Similarly $\qquad a + b - c = a + (b - c).$

From this we have the

PRINCIPLE. *Two or more terms may be inclosed in a parenthesis preceded by a plus sign, without changing the sign of any of the terms.*

The expression

$$17 + 8 - 3 = 17 - (-8 + 3) = 17 - (-5) = 17 + 5 = 22.$$

Similarly $\qquad a + b - c = a - (-b + c).$

From this we have the

PRINCIPLE. *Two or more terms may be inclosed in a parenthesis preceded by a minus sign, provided the sign of each term thus inclosed be changed.*

EXERCISES

In the following inclose in a parenthesis preceded by a plus sign all the terms containing the letters x or y, and inclose in a parenthesis preceded by a minus sign all the terms containing the letters a or b:

1. $x^2 - a^2 - 2\,ab - b^2.$ **3.** $y^2 - 4\,b^2 + 4\,ab - a^2.$

2. $12\,ab + x^2 - 9\,b^2 - 4\,a^2.$ **4.** $10\,ab + x^2 - a^2 - 25\,b^2.$

5. $x^2 - b^2 - 4\,a^2 + 4\,y^2 - 4\,ab - 4\,xy.$

6. $4\,ab + x^2 - 4\,b^2 + y^2 - a^2 - 2\,xy.$

7. $16\,x^2 - a^2 - 16\,xy - b^2 + 2\,ab + 4\,y^2.$

8. $x^2 - b^2 - 10\,xy + 12\,ab - 36\,a^2 + 25\,y^2.$

CHAPTER VIII

MULTIPLICATION

26. Product of terms containing unlike letters. We assume that the factors of a product may be written in any order. This principle is called the *Commutative Law of Multiplication*.

That is, $\qquad\qquad 2 \cdot 4 = 4 \cdot 2.$

Similarly $\qquad\qquad a \times b = b \times a.$

As $3 \times b$ is written $3\,b$, $a \times b$ is written ab, $x^2 \times y^2$ is written $x^2 y^2$, and $a \times b \times c$ is written abc.

Further $\qquad\qquad 2\,a^2 \times 3 = 2 \times 3 \times a^2 = 6\,a^2,$

and $\qquad\qquad 2\,a \times 3\,b = 2 \times 3 \times a \times b = 6\,ab.$

Similarly $\qquad 6\,x^2 \cdot 5\,y^3 = 6 \cdot 5 \cdot x^2 \cdot y^3 = 30\,x^2 y^3.$

Also $\qquad\qquad 4\,ab \cdot 3\,z^2 = 4 \cdot 3 \cdot ab \cdot z^2 = 12\,abz^2.$

We have also assumed that the various operations of multiplication in any product may be performed in any order. This principle is called the *Associative Law of Multiplication*.

That is, $(3 \cdot 2)\,4 = 3\,(2 \cdot 4)$. Similarly $a\,(b \cdot c) = (a \cdot b)\,c$. This merely tells us that a multiplied by the product of b and c is the same as the product of a and b multiplied by c.

Biographical note. SIR WILLIAM ROWAN HAMILTON. It is strange that of all the topics treated in this book, the last to be thoroughly understood by mathematicians are those appearing in the first chapters. But in all the sciences it is often most difficult to answer the questions that at first sight seem quite obvious. Any child can ask what electricity is, but the wisest scientist cannot tell. He can only explain what electricity does. It is easy to ask how the earth came to be revolving around the sun with the moon revolving around it, but even the deepest students of astronomy differ in their theories of how it came to be. And so in mathematics, long after many of the more complicated processes of algebra were completely understood, the simple laws of operation of numbers were surrounded with haze. One of the men who did most to clarify the nature of these laws was Sir William Rowan Hamilton (1805–1865). He was born in Dublin, Ireland, where he lived most of his life. He was a precocious boy, and at the age of twelve was familiar with thirteen languages. He devised kinds of numbers that do not follow the same laws as those that we use in algebra, and so threw a flood of light on the nature and properties of these common numbers. He was the first to recognize the importance of the Associative Law, and called it by that name. Most of his works are very advanced in character and are difficult to read.

27. Product of terms containing like letters. By the definition of an exponent (§ 6), $a^2 = a \cdot a$, and $a^3 = a \cdot a \cdot a$.

Therefore $\qquad a^2 \times a^3 = a \cdot a \times a \cdot a \cdot a = a^5 = a^{2+3}$.

Similarly $\qquad b \times b^3 \times b^5 = b \times b \cdot b \cdot b \times b \cdot b \cdot b \cdot b \cdot b = b^9 = b^{1+3+5}$.

In like manner $3^2 \times 3^4 \times 3^5 = 3 \cdot 3 \times 3 \cdot 3 \cdot 3 \cdot 3 \times 3 \cdot 3 \cdot 3 \cdot 3 \cdot 3 = 3^{11}$
$$= 3^{2+4+5}.$$

Also $\qquad ay^2 \times y^3 = ay^5 = ay^{2+3}$,

and $\qquad 2\, ab \times 3\, a^2 = 6\, a^3b = 6\, a^{1+2}b$,

and $\qquad 4\, x^2yz \times 5\, xy^3 = 20\, x^3y^4z = 20\, x^{2+1}y^{1+3}z$.

Therefore we have the

PRINCIPLE. *The exponent of any letter in the product is equal to the sum of the exponents of that letter in the factors.*

This is expressed in general terms, thus:

$$n^a \times n^b = n^{a+b}.$$

The law of signs for the multiplication of positive and negative numbers, given in § 15, applies to literal terms as well.

Thus $\qquad + 2\, a^2 \times (+ 3\, a^5) = + 6\, a^7.$
$$+ 2\, a^2 \times (- 3\, a^5) = - 6\, a^7.$$
$$- 2\, a^2 \times (+ 3\, a^5) = - 6\, a^7.$$
$$- 2\, a^2 \times (- 3\, a^5) = + 6\, a^7.$$

For the multiplication of two monomials we have the

RULE. *Keeping in mind the rule of signs for multiplication, write the product of the numerical coefficients followed by all the letters that occur in the multiplier and the multiplicand, each letter having as its exponent the sum of the exponents of that letter in the multiplier and the multiplicand.*

SIR WILLIAM ROWAN HAMILTON

ORAL EXERCISES

Perform the following indicated multiplications:

1. $(3)(-8)$.
2. $(-2)(5)$.
3. $(-7)(-3)$.
4. $(-4x)(3)$.
5. $(-4x)^2$.
6. $(7)(-5a)$.
7. $(3a)(-6)$.
8. $(-2y)^2$.
9. $(-9a)(-10)$.
10. $(-3ax)^2$.
11. $(4a)(-2a)$.
12. $(6abc)^2$.
13. $(-11x)(2x)$.
14. $(7x)(-3x)$.
15. $(-2a)^3$.
16. $(-2a)(-3a^2)$.
17. $(5a^4)(7a^3)$.
18. $(-4x)^3$.
19. $(a^8)(-20a)$.
20. $(-4a^5)(-6a^2)$.
21. $(+6y)^3$.
22. $(4x)(5y)$.
23. $(-3a^2x)^2$.
24. $(3x^2)(-y)$.

25. $(5x^2y)(-2x^3)$.
26. $(-6x^3y^2)^2$.
27. $(-x^4y)(-x^2y^4)$.
28. $(2ax^2)^3$.
29. $(5a^3)(-4a^2)(-3a)$.
30. $(3ax)(-4a^2x)(-2ax^3)$.

28. Multiplication of a polynomial by a monomial. Clearly $2(5+3)$ is equivalent to $2 \cdot 5 + 2 \cdot 3$, each being equal to 16.

Similarly $a(b+c) = ab + ac$. This principle is called the *Distributive Law of Multiplication*.

Therefore, for the multiplication of a polynomial by a monomial, we have the

RULE. *Multiply each term of the polynomial by the monomial and write in succession the resulting terms with their proper signs.*

Example :

$$3x^2 - 2xy + 4y - 5a - 6$$
$$2xy$$

Product, $\quad 6x^3y - 4x^2y^2 + 8xy^2 - 10axy - 12xy$

Note. It should be kept in mind that the laws of operation that have been mentioned in this chapter, though evident from arithmetic only when the letters represent positive integers, are also valid when the letters stand for negative numbers, fractions, algebraic expressions, or other kinds of numbers that we shall introduce later. The principle which states that the operations on all numbers follow the rules expressed by the commutative, associative, and distributive laws is often called the *Law of Permanence*.

EXERCISES

Multiply :

1. $x + 3$ by $2x$.

2. $7x^2 - 5$ by $3x^3$.

3. $5x^2 - 2x$ by $-4x^2$.

4. $7xy - z$ by $3xy$.

5. $-4x^2 + 5x - 6$ by $6x^3$.

6. $x^3 - 3x^2 + 4$ by $-5x^4$.

7. $x^2 - 2xy + y^2$ by $-3xy$.

8. $a^4 - a^2b^2 + b^4$ by $-a^2b^2$.

9. $-a^2x^2 + 2ax - 7b^2$ by $-4abx$.

10. $7x^3 - 8x^2 - 12x + 6$ by $-\frac{3}{4}x^3$.

11. $-9a^2 - 12ax + 42x^2$ by $\frac{7}{3}ax^3$.

Perform the multiplication indicated :

12. $4(2x - 3)$.

13. $2x(x - y)$.

14. $-8(3x - 7)$.

15. $-9(-4a + b)$.

16. $-3x(2x - 7)$.

17. $-3(x^2 - 2x - 6)$.

18. $5xy(x^2 - 6x + 9)$.

19. $-3x(ax - bx + 3cx^2)$.

20. $-7ab(ax^2 + bx + c)$.

29. Multiplication of polynomials. Clearly $(5 + 3)(7 - 4) = 8 \cdot 3 = 24$. The multiplication may also be performed as follows : $(5 + 3)(7 - 4) = 5(7 - 4) + 3(7 - 4) = 35 - 20 + 21 - 12 = 24$.

Similarly $(2x + 3)(4x - 5) = 2x(4x - 5) + 3(4x - 5) = 8x^2 - 10x + 12x - 15$, or $8x^2 + 2x - 15$.

In general terms $(a + b)(c + d) = a(c + d) + b(c + d) = ac + ad + bc + bd$.

This gives for the multiplication of polynomials the

RULE. *Multiply the multiplicand by each term of the multiplier in turn, and add the partial products.*

Example:

$$3x - 2y$$
$$2x + 3y$$

Multiplying by $2x$,	$6x^2 - 4xy$	first partial product.
Multiplying by $3y$,	$+ 9xy - 6y^2$	second partial product.
Complete product,	$6x^2 + 5xy - 6y^2$	sum of partial products.

30. Powers. A **power** of a number is the product obtained by using the number as a factor one or more times.

For example, 8, or 2^3, is the third power of 2; 81, or 3^4, is the fourth power of 3, and $32\,x^5$, or $(2\,x)^5$, is the fifth power of $2\,x$.

31. Arrangement. A polynomial is said to be **arranged** according to the *descending* powers of a certain letter when the exponents of that letter in successive terms decrease from left to right. Thus $2\,x^4 - 5\,x^2 - 6\,x + 8$ is arranged according to the descending powers of x. Again, $4 - 2\,y + y^2$ and $x^3 - 3\,x^2y + 3\,xy^2 - y^3$ are arranged according to the *ascending* powers of y.

Whenever it is possible to arrange the multiplier and the multiplicand in a similar order it should be done, as the addition of the partial products is then much more easily performed.

32. Check of multiplication. The work of multiplication can be checked by giving a convenient numerical value to each letter involved and finding the corresponding numerical values of the multiplier, the multiplicand, and the product. The product of the numerical values of the multiplier and the multiplicand should equal the numerical value of the product.

The number 1 is more convenient than any other number to use in checking, but it will not check exponents, since $x^3 = x^5 = x^{10}$, etc., if $x = 1$. It checks merely the coefficients.

If a check on both coefficients and exponents is wanted, the number 2 is the most convenient.

EXAMPLES

1. Multiply $3\,x^3 - 5 + x^2 - 2\,x$ by $6 + x^2 - 5\,x$.

Solution: Arranging both multiplier and multiplicand in descending powers of x and multiplying, we obtain: **Check:** $x = 1$.

$$
\begin{array}{rr}
3\,x^3 + x^2 - 2\,x - 5 & = -3 \\
x^2 - 5\,x + 6 & = +2 \\
\hline
3\,x^5 + \quad x^4 - \quad 2\,x^3 - \quad 5\,x^2 & -6 \\
-\,15\,x^4 - \quad 5\,x^3 + 10\,x^2 + 25\,x & \\
+\,18\,x^3 + \quad 6\,x^2 - 12\,x - 30 & \\
\end{array}
$$

$Product,$ $\quad 3\,x^5 - 14\,x^4 + 11\,x^3 + 11\,x^2 + 13\,x - 30 = -6$

2. Multiply $10\,x^3y^2 - 2\,y^5 + 5\,x^4y - 4\,x^2y^3$ by $3\,x^3 - 7\,y^3 - 6\,x^2y$.

Solution:

Arranging terms and multiplying,   **Check:** $x = y = 1$.

$$
\begin{array}{ll}
5\,x^4y + 10\,x^3y^2 - 4\,x^2y^3 - 2\,y^5 & = 9 \\
3\,x^3 - 6\,x^2y - 7\,y^3 & = -10 \\
\hline
15\,x^7y + 30\,x^6y^2 - 12\,x^5y^3 - 6\,x^3y^5 & -90 \\
 - 30\,x^6y^2 - 60\,x^5y^3 + 24\,x^4y^4 + 12\,x^2y^6 & \\
 - 70\,x^3y^5 - 35\,x^4y^4 + 28\,x^2y^6 + 14\,y^8 & \\
\hline
15\,x^7y - 72\,x^5y^3 - 76\,x^3y^5 - 11\,x^4y^4 + 40\,x^2y^6 + 14\,y^8 & = -90
\end{array}
$$

33. Degree. The **degree** of a term with respect to any letter which does not appear in the denominator is determined by the exponent of that letter in the term.

Thus x, $3\,xy$, and $4\,a^2xz$ are of the first degree in x, and $3\,xy^2$ is of the second degree in y.

The degree of a term with respect to *two or more* letters which do not appear in the denominator is determined by the sum of the exponents of those letters in that term.

Thus $5\,x^3y$ is of the fourth degree in x and y; $4\,a^2bc^3$ is of the sixth degree in a, b, and c.

34. Homogeneous expressions. Terms are homogeneous if they are of the same degree with respect to the same letter or letters.

Thus $3\,a^2b^3$, $4\,ab^4$, and a^4b are homogeneous terms.

A polynomial is homogeneous if its terms are homogeneous.

For example, $x^3y - 3\,x^2y^2$ and $3\,a^4 + a^2b^2 + b^4$ are homogeneous polynomials.

An important property of homogeneous expressions is:

The sum, the difference, the product, or the quotient of any two homogeneous expressions is a homogeneous expression.

This property is useful in checking exponents in multiplication.

Thus, if it be required to multiply $x^2 - 2\,xy + y^2$ by $x^3 - 3\,x^2y + 3\,xy^2 - y^3$, we know beforehand that every term of the product will be of the fifth degree.

EXERCISES

Multiply and check results:

1. $x + 4$ by $x + 3$.
2. $2x + 3$ by $x + 3$.
3. $4x + 7$ by $3x + 2$.
4. $3x - 5$ by $3x + 8$.
5. $3x - 2$ by $2x + 3$.
6. $6 - 4a$ by $5a - 7$.
7. $2x + y$ by $x + 3y$.
8. $2x - 3y$ by $3x - 2y$.

9. $3x - \frac{1}{2}$ by $2x - \frac{1}{3}$.
10. $-3x + 11a$ by $5x - a$.
11. $ax - bx$ by $cx + dx$.
12. $-cx + d$ by $bx - cx^2$
13. $4x - \frac{1}{3}$ by $6x + \frac{2}{5}$.
14. $x^2 - 5x + 6$ by $x - 3$.
15. $3x^2 - 3x - 7$ by $2x + 4$.
16. $x^2 - xy + y^2$ by $x + y$.

17. $a^2x^2 - 2a^2x + 4a^2$ by $ax + 2a$.
18. $3x^3 - x^2 - 5x$ by $2x^3 - 5x^2$.
19. $2x^2 - 7x + 12$ by $x^2 - 3x - 5$.
20. $a^2 - \frac{1}{2}a + \frac{1}{4}$ by $a^2 - a + \frac{1}{3}$.
21. $x^2 - xy + y^2$ by $x^2 + xy + y^2$.
22. $3x^3 + 5x^2 - x + 2$ by $x^2 - 2x + 1$.

Expand:

23. $(x^3 - x - 5)(2x^2 - 3x - 4)$.
24. $(3x - x^3 + x^2 - 6)(5 - x^2 - 3x)$.
25. $(4a - 5a^2 + 7 + a^3)(6 + a^3 - a + a^2)$.
26. $(5x - 4 + 8x^3)(8 - 5x^2 + 2x^3 - 9x)$.
27. $(x^2y - y^2x)(4xy - 5x^2y)(3x^2y - 7xy^2)$.
28. $(x^2 + y^2 + z^2 - xy - xz - yz)(x + y + z)$.

29. $(a + b + c)^2$.
30. $(c + d - \frac{1}{2})^2$.
31. $(a - 2b + 3c - 4d)^2$.
32. $(x + y + z)^3$.
33. $(x + y)^3 + (x - y)^3$.
34. $(2a - b + 3)^2$.
35. $(2x - 3ay)^3$.

36. $(x + 2y)^2 - (x - 2y)^2$.
37. $(4x - 3y)^2 - (3x + 4y)^2$.
38. $(x - 3)^3 - (2x - 1)^2$.
39. $(x^a - 3)(x^a + 4)$.
40. $(x^{2a} + 5)^2$.
41. $(2x^a - 3)^3$.
42. $(2x^{2a} - 3x)^2$.

CHAPTER IX

PARENTHESES IN EQUATIONS

35. Simple equations involving parentheses. The removal of parentheses is really an easy matter which is governed by simple rules. In handling parentheses, however, it is very easy to acquire careless habits, which are difficult to overcome. Accuracy in such work can be attained only by especial care in removing each parenthesis that is preceded by a minus sign.

EXAMPLES

1. Solve the equation $5(2x-1)-3(4x-6)=7$.

Solution: Multiplying by the coefficients 5 and 3, this becomes
$$(10x-5)-(12x-18)=7.$$
Removing parentheses,
$$10x-5-12x+18=7.$$
Combining, $\qquad -2x+13=7.$
Transposing, $\qquad -2x=7-13=-6.$
Dividing by -2, $\qquad x=3.$
Check: $\quad 5(2\cdot3-1)-3(4\cdot3-6)=7.$
Simplifying, $\qquad 25-18=7,$
or $\qquad\qquad\qquad 7=7.$

Sometimes the square of the unknown number appears and then vanishes, as in the following.

2. Solve the equation $4+(n-3)(n-5)=15-(7-n)(2+n)$.

Solution: Expanding,
$$4+(n^2-8n+15)=15-(14+5n-n^2).$$
Removing parentheses,
$$4+n^2-8n+15=15-14-5n+n^2.$$
Subtracting n^2 from each member and combining,
$$19-8n=1-5n.$$

66

Transposing and combining,
$$-3n = -18.$$
Dividing by -3, $n = 6.$
Check: $4 + (6-3)(6-5) = 15 - (7-6)(2+6).$
Simplifying, $4 + 3 = 15 - 8,$
or $7 = 7.$

EXERCISES

Solve and check:

1. $5(x-1) = 30.$

2. $3 + 2(x-3) = 1.$

3. $7(3x-2) + 11 = 60.$

4. $4(2x-5) + 15 = 3(x+10).$

5. $12y - 2(4y-7) - 16 = 0.$

6. $9y - 3(2y-4) = 2(5-4y) + 2.$

7. $4 - 2(4y-3) = 3(y-5).$

8. $7(y-3) - 2(4+y) = 9.$

9. $5(n-7) + 24 + 4n = 0.$

10. $5n - 9(2n+4) = 2(n-9).$

11. $7n - 12 - 2(n-5) = n - 19.$

12. $4(2n-7) - 3(4n-8) + 4 = 2n - 3.$

13. $3h - 2(4h+8) = 3h - 24.$

14. $5(3h+1) - 7h = 3(h-7) + 4.$

15. $(h-2)(h-5) = (h+3)(h+2).$

16. $(h+4)(h+3) - (h+2)(h+1) - 42 = 0.$

17. $(x+4)(x+6) = (x+18)(x+13).$

18. $(k-7)(5+k) - (k-5)(k+7) + 5 = 0.$

19. $(2x-5)(4x-7) = 8x^2 + 52.$

20. $(3y+5)(4y+7) - (2y+3)(6y+11) - 2 = 0.$

21. $(n+3)(6n+5) - (2n+4)(3n-8) = 38.$

22. $(x+3)^2 - (x+5)^2 = -40.$

23. $(x+2)^2 - (x-4)^2 + 48 = 0.$

EXERCISES

1. The length of a rectangle is a and its breadth is b. What is its area? its perimeter?

2. The length of a rectangle is $x - 4$ and its width is 3. What is its area? its perimeter?

3. What is the area of a rectangle whose length is $2x - 4$ and whose breadth is $x + 2$? the perimeter?

4. Each of four horses cost $100. What was the cost of all?

5. Each of n horses cost $80. What represents the cost of all?

6. Each of a books cost b cents. What represents the cost of all?

7. What is the total cost of x hats at a cents each, and y hats at b cents each?

8. What is the cost of x horses at $b + 10$ dollars each?

9. Represent the total cost of x chairs at $b + 2$ dollars each, and y chairs at a cost of $c - 3$ dollars each.

10. What is 5% of 16? of x?

11. What is 3% of $x + 120$? of $12x - 300a$?

12. A is n years old. What will three times his age 4 years from now be?

13. If two sums of money are x dollars and $1000 - x$ dollars respectively, express the following as equations:

(a) 4% of the first sum equals $180.

(b) 3% of the first sum equals 5% of the second.

(c) 5% of the first sum is $20 less than 4% of the second.

14. A picture is 10 inches wide and 12 inches long and has a frame 2 inches wide. What are the outside dimensions of the frame?

15. If the frame in the preceding were x inches wide, what would represent the outside dimensions of the frame? the area of the picture and frame ? the area of the picture ? the area of the frame ?

36. Problems involving parentheses. The following problems involve two or more unknowns and the use of parentheses. One of the unknowns can always be represented by a single letter and the others by binomials involving this letter and one or more numbers. It may be necessary in some of the problems to inclose each of these binomials in a parenthesis and to think of them and use them as if they represented a single number. When the student can use a binomial in this way as readily as he uses a single letter, like x, he has made considerable progress in the algebraic way of thinking.

PROBLEMS

1. The sum of two numbers is 88. Three times the less equals twice the greater, plus 29. Find the numbers.

Solution: Here are two unknowns, the greater number and the less. Each can be represented in terms of a single letter as follows :

Let n represent the less number.

Then $88 - n$ must represent the greater.

By the conditions of the problem :

Three times the less   = twice the greater + 29.

Hence $3n = 2(88 - n) + 29.$

Simplifying, $3n = 176 - 2n + 29.$

Combining, $3n = 205 - 2n.$

Transposing, $3n + 2n = 205.$

Whence $n = 41$, the less number,

and $88 - n = 47$, the greater number.

Check : $41 + 47 = 88$; $3 \cdot 41 = 2 \cdot 47 + 29$, or $123 = 123.$

2. The sum of two numbers is 49. Twice the greater, minus 13, equals five times the less. Find the numbers.

3. The sum of two numbers is 143. Ten times the less added to five times the greater equals 950. Find the numbers.

4. Separate 45 into two parts such that five times the greater plus four times the less may equal 207.

5. The sum of two numbers is 88. Three times the greater equals five times the less, plus 29. Find the numbers.

6. Separate 93 into two parts so that seven times the less, minus 7, equals six times the greater.

7. Separate 48 into two parts so that twice the greater, minus 7, equals three times the less, minus 5.

8. The sum of two numbers is $12\frac{1}{2}$. Seven times one number minus ten times the other equals 45. Find the numbers.

9. Separate 121 into two parts so that four times the one, increased by 8, equals three times the other.

10. Twice a certain number minus five times another number equals 240. The sum of the numbers is 15. Find the numbers.

11. The sum of two numbers is 14. Nine times the one minus eleven times the other equals zero. Find the numbers.

12. The square of a number plus the square of the next consecutive number is 17 greater than twice the square of the smaller number. Find the numbers.

13. The difference of the squares of two consecutive numbers is 75. Find the numbers.

14. The difference of the squares of two consecutive numbers is 23. Find the numbers.

15. The difference of the squares of two consecutive odd numbers is 104. Find the numbers.

16. The difference of the squares of two consecutive odd numbers is 40. Find the numbers.

17. The product of two consecutive even numbers is 56 less than the square of the greater number. Find the numbers.

18. The product of two consecutive odd numbers equals the square of the smaller increased by 46. Find the numbers.

19. A square has the same area as a rectangle whose length is 8 inches greater and whose breadth is 4 inches less than the side of the square. Find the area of each.

Solution: There are three unknowns in this problem, — the side of the square, the length of the rectangle, and the breadth of the rectangle. The three can be represented in terms of the same letter as follows:

Let s = the side of the square in inches.

Then $s + 8$ = the length of the rectangle in inches,

and $s - 4$ = the breadth of the rectangle in inches.

Now the area of the square is $s \cdot s$, or s^2 square inches.

Similarly the area of the rectangle is $(s + 8)(s - 4)$, which, expanded, equals $s^2 + 4s - 32$.

By the conditions of the problem the area of the square equals the area of the rectangle.

Therefore $s^2 = s^2 + 4s - 32$.

Subtracting s^2 from each member,

$$0 = 4s - 32.$$

Whence $s = 8$, the side of the square,

and $s + 8 = 16$, the length of the rectangle,

and $s - 4 = 4$, the breadth of the rectangle.

Therefore the area of the square is $8 \cdot 8$, or 64, square inches, and the area of the rectangle is $16 \cdot 4$, or 64, square inches.

The check is obvious.

20. A square field has the same area as a rectangular field whose length is 30 rods greater, and whose breadth is 20 rods less, than the side of the square. How many acres are there in each field?

21. A tennis court, for two players, is 24 feet longer than twice its breadth. The distance around the court is 210 feet. Find the length and the breadth of the court.

22. A tennis court, for 4 players, is 6 feet longer than twice its breadth. The perimeter of the court is 228 feet. Find the dimensions of the court.

23. The breadth of a basket-ball court is 20 feet less than its length. The perimeter of the court is 80 yards. Find the dimensions.

24. The perimeter of a football field is 780 feet. Its length is 50 yards less than three times its breadth. Find the length and the breadth.

25. The value of 15 pieces of money, consisting of nickels and dimes, is 90 cents. Find the number of each.

Solution: There are two unknowns in this problem, the number of nickels and the number of dimes. Since their sum is 15, the two can be represented in terms of one letter, thus:

Let $d =$ the number of dimes.

Then $15 - d =$ the number of nickels,

and $10 \cdot d =$ the value of the dimes in cents.

Also $(15 - d)\,5 =$ the value of the nickels in cents.

The value of the nickels and dimes together is represented by $10\,d + (15 - d)\,5$.

By the conditions of the problem the value of the nickels and dimes together is 90 cents.

Therefore $10\,d + (15 - d)\,5 = 90$.

Solving, $d = 3$, the number of dimes,

and $15 - d = 12$, the number of nickels.

Check: $3 \cdot 10 + 12 \cdot 5 = 30 + 60 = 90$.

26. The value of 38 coins, consisting of dimes and quarters, is $5.30. Find the number of each.

27. A collection of nickels, dimes, and quarters amounts to $6.05. There are 5 more nickels than dimes, and the number of quarters is equal to the number of nickels and dimes together. Find the number of each.

28. The value of 40 coins, consisting of nickels and dimes, is $2.90. Find the number of each.

29. A is 20 years older than B. In 10 years A will be twice as old as B. Find the age of each now.

30. A is four times as old as B. In 20 years A will be twice as old as B. Find the present age of each.

31. A's age is 8 years more than twice B's age. Sixteen years ago A was four times as old as B. Find the age of each now.

32. A part of $800 is invested at 3% and the remainder at 4%. The yearly income from the two investments is $30. Find each investment.

Solution: Let $x =$ the number of dollars invested at 3%.

Then $800 - x =$ the number of dollars invested at 4%.

Hence $.03 x =$ the yearly income from the 3% investment,

and $.04 (800 - x) =$ the yearly income from the 4% investment.

Therefore, by the conditions of the problem,

$$.03 x + .04 (800 - x) = 30. \tag{1}$$

Multiplying each member of (1) by 100, in order to free the equation of decimals, we obtain

$$3 x + 4 (800 - x) = 3000. \tag{2}$$

Solving (2), $x = 200,$

and $800 - x = 600.$

Hence the 3% investment is $200 and the 4% is $600.

Check:

200	600	
.03	.04	
6.00	24.00	$6 + $24 = $30.

33. A part of $1400 is invested at 5% and the remainder at 6%. The total annual income from the two investments is $76. Find the amount of each investment.

34. A sum of money at 6% interest and a second sum at 8% yield a total annual income of $53. The first sum exceeds the second by $125. Find each.

35. A 5% investment yields annually $15 less than a 6% investment. If the sum of the two investments is $1240, find each.

CHAPTER X

DIVISION

37. Division of monomials. Division of numerical terms was explained under Positive and Negative Numbers. On page 22 will be found the rule for this division.

Just as $2 \div 3$ is written $\frac{2}{3}$, so $a \div b$ is written as a fraction, $\frac{a}{b}$, and this result can be simplified no farther.

Similarly $$a^2 \div x^2 = \frac{a^2}{x^2},$$

and $$2\,a \div 3\,b = \frac{2\,a}{3\,b}.$$

But $$12\,c^2 \div 4\,b^2 = \frac{3\,c^2}{b^2}.$$

In like manner, $-12\,a \div 6\,b = -\dfrac{2\,a}{b}$ Here the quotient is a fraction, and the minus sign indicates that the fraction is negative.

Similarly $$9\,x \div (-3\,y) = -\frac{3\,x}{y},$$

and $$-24\,a^2y \div (-6\,z^3) = +\frac{4\,a^2y}{z^3}.$$

By the definition of an exponent, $a^5 = a \cdot a \cdot a \cdot a \cdot a$ and $a^2 = a \cdot a.$

Then $$a^5 \div a^2 = \frac{\cancel{a} \cdot \cancel{a} \cdot a \cdot a \cdot a}{\cancel{a} \cdot \cancel{a}} = a^3, \text{ or } a^{5-2}.$$

Similarly $$2^6 \div 2^3 = \frac{\cancel{2} \times \cancel{2} \times \cancel{2} \times 2 \times 2 \times 2}{\cancel{2} \times \cancel{2} \times \cancel{2}} = 2^3 = 2^{6-3},$$

and $$ax^3 \div x^2 = \frac{a \cdot x \cdot \cancel{x} \cdot \cancel{x}}{\cancel{x} \cdot \cancel{x}} = ax, \text{ or } ax^{3-2}.$$

In like manner, $6\,by^5 \div 2\,y^3 = 3\,by^2$, or $3\,b \cdot y^{5-3}.$

These examples illustrate the

PRINCIPLE. *The exponent of any letter in the quotient is equal to its exponent in the dividend minus its exponent in the divisor.*

The foregoing principle expressed in general terms is:

$$n^a \div n^b = n^{a-b}.$$

What this equation means when $b = a$ and when b is greater than a will be explained later.

The law of signs in division may be indicated as follows:

$$+ ab \div (+ a) = + b.$$
$$+ ab \div (- a) = - b.$$
$$- ab \div (+ a) = - b.$$
$$- ab \div (- a) = + b.$$

From what precedes we see that $ax^2 \div x^2 = \dfrac{a \cdot \not{x} \cdot \not{x}}{\not{x} \cdot \not{x}} = a.$

Hence a letter which has the same exponent in divisor and dividend should not appear in the quotient.

Therefore for the division of monomials we have the

RULE. *Divide the numerical coefficient of the dividend by the numerical coefficient of the divisor, keeping in mind the rule of signs for division.*

Write after this quotient all the letters of the dividend except those having the same exponent in divisor and dividend, giving to each letter an exponent equal to its exponent in the dividend minus its exponent in the divisor.

If there are any letters in the divisor unlike those in the dividend, write them under the preceding result as a denominator.

ORAL EXERCISES

Perform the indicated division:

1. $-10 \div 2.$ **3.** $-16 \div (-4).$ **5.** $-4 a^6 \div 2 a^2.$

2. $12 \div (-3).$ **4.** $8 a^3 \div a^2.$ **6.** $6 x^2 \div (-3 x).$

    7. $-18 x^7 \div (-6 x^4).$ **8.** $-25 ax^3 \div 5 ax.$

9. $12\,ax^3 \div (-3\,bx^3)$. **13.** $-36\,x^6y^6 \div (-6\,x^2y^8)$.

10. $-28\,ay^4 \div (-7\,cy^3)$. **14.** $63\,c^8d^5 \div (-9\,bcd^3)$.

11. $70\,x^4y^9 \div (-10\,x^2y^8)$. **15.** $64\,a^5b^7 \div (-16\,ab^7)$.

12. $48\,ax^5 \div (-16\,bx^4)$. **16.** $-28\,a^6b^{12} \div (-7\,a^4b^8)$.

17. $\dfrac{15\,x^2y^4z^5}{75\,xy^4z}$. **21.** $\dfrac{-17\,a^9b^8c^7}{51\,a^7b^8c}$. **25.** $\dfrac{x^{a+b}}{x^b}$.

18. $\dfrac{42\,x^{24}y^{56}}{-6\,x^8y^7}$. **22.** $\dfrac{39\,x^{18}y^{26}z^{39}}{-13\,x^{18}y^{18}z^{13}}$. **26.** $\dfrac{x^c}{x}$.

19. $\dfrac{x^a}{x^2}$. **23.** $\dfrac{-11\,a^2b^{11}c^{13}}{66\,ac^{12}}$. **27.** $\dfrac{3\,a^3x^{3a}}{a^2x^a}$.

20. $\dfrac{-x^{3a}}{x^a}$. **24.** $\dfrac{-121\,a^{11}b^{22}c^{33}}{-11\,a^{11}b^{11}c^{11}}$. **28.** $\dfrac{6\,x^{2a+3}}{-2\,x^4}$.

38. Division of a polynomial by a monomial. The division of the binomial $(18 - 12)$ by 3 can be performed in two ways:

Thus $\qquad (18 - 12) \div 3 = 6 \div 3 = 2,$

or $\qquad (18 - 12) \div 3 = \frac{18}{3} - \frac{12}{3} = 6 - 4 = 2.$

Similarly $\quad (ax + bx) \div x = \dfrac{ax}{x} + \dfrac{bx}{x} = a + b.$

Therefore, for the division of a polynomial by a monomial we have the

RULE. *Divide each term of the polynomial by the monomial and write the partial quotients in succession.*

EXERCISES

Perform the indicated division:

1. $\dfrac{6\,x^2 - 4\,x}{2\,x}$. **3.** $\dfrac{4\,xy - 12\,x^2}{-4\,x}$. **5.** $\dfrac{25\,x^2y + 30\,xy^5}{-5\,xy}$.

2. $\dfrac{9\,x - 18\,x^4}{-3\,x}$. **4.** $\dfrac{9\,ax^3 - 12\,x^5}{-3\,ax^2}$. **6.** $\dfrac{16\,bx^4 - 36\,x^2}{4\,bx^2}$.

7. $\dfrac{14\,x^3y^4 - 28\,x^5y^6}{7\,x^2y^3}$. **8.** $\dfrac{4\,x^4y - 8\,x^6y^2 + 12\,x^8y^4}{4\,x^4y}$.

9. $\dfrac{a^3cd^2 - a^2c^3}{a^2cd}$.

10. $\dfrac{ax^4 - bx^3 + cx^2}{-x^2}$.

11. $\dfrac{15\,a^2b^2 + 9\,a^4b^2 - 30\,a^6b^2}{-3\,a^2b^2}$.

12. $\dfrac{16\,a^4b^5c^6 - 24\,a^5b^6c^7 - 48\,a^6b^7c^8}{8\,a^3b^2c}$.

13. $\dfrac{85\,xyz - 51\,x^2yz^2 + 102\,x^3yz^3 - 170\,x^5y^5z}{-17\,xyz}$.

14. $\dfrac{4\,(x-3) + a\,(x-3)}{x-3}$.

15. $\dfrac{3\,x\,(3\,x+4) - 4\,y\,(3\,x+4)}{3\,x+4}$,

16. $\dfrac{5\,a\,(2\,x^2-y) - 3\,b\,(2\,x^2-y)}{2\,x^2-y}$.

17. $\dfrac{(a+b)^4 - 3\,(a+b)^3}{(a+b)^2}$.

18. $\dfrac{21\,(x-y)^7 - 35\,(x-y)^5}{-7\,(x-y)^5}$.

19. $\dfrac{16\,(3\,x-4)^4 - 24\,(3\,x-4)^5 - 48\,(3\,x-4)^7}{-8\,(3\,x-4)^4}$.

20. $\dfrac{-5\,(ac^2-2\,d)^3 + x\,(ac^2-2\,d)}{5\,(ac^2-2\,d)}$.

21. $\dfrac{4\,x^4 - 8\,x^{3a} - 6\,x^{2a-2}}{2\,x^3}$.

22. $\dfrac{3\,x^a - 2\,x^{a+1} - x^{a+2} + x^2}{x^2}$.

23. $\dfrac{6\,x^{2a-3} - 12\,x^{4a+4} - 18\,x^{3a+5}}{-3\,x^{2a}}$.

39. Division of one polynomial by another. Division is the reverse of multiplication, and the process of dividing one polynomial by another will be best understood by finding the product of two polynomials and then dividing it by one of them; the other, of course, will be the quotient. A close inspection of the steps in the multiplication (A) which follows will make clear the necessity for each step in the division (B).

$$4 x^2 - 5 x + 6$$
$$\underline{2 x - 3}$$
$$\overline{8 x^3 - 10 x^2 + 12 x}$$
$$\underline{\quad\quad - 12 x^2 + 15 x - 18}$$ (A)
$$\overline{8 x^3 - 22 x^2 + 27 x - 18}$$

Now let $8 x^3 - 22 x^2 + 27 x - 18$ be the dividend and $4 x^2 - 5 x + 6$ the divisor. Then the quotient must be $2 x - 3$.

Dividend, $\quad 8 x^3 - 22 x^2 + 27 x - 18 \, | \, 4 x^2 - 5 x + 6$, Divisor
$(4 x^2 - 5 x + 6) 2 x, \; \underline{8 x^3 - 10 x^2 + 12 x} \qquad | \, 2 x - 3$, Quotient
$\qquad\qquad\qquad - 12 x^2 + 15 x - 18$ (B)
$(4 x^2 - 5 x + 6)(-3), \; \underline{- 12 x^2 + 15 x - 18}$

The term having the highest power of x in the dividend, $8 x^3$, was obtained by multiplying the term having the highest power of x in the multiplicand by $2 x$. If the multiplication were not before us, we could obtain the $2 x$ by dividing $8 x^3$ by $4 x^2$; that is, by dividing the term of highest degree in the dividend by the term of highest degree in the divisor. Multiplying the entire divisor by $2 x$, we get the first partial product of the multiplication (A). Subtracting, we get $- 12 x^2 + 15 x - 18$. If the multiplication (A) did not tell us that the second term of the quotient was $- 3$, we could obtain it by dividing $- 12 x^2$ by $4 x^2$; that is, by dividing the term of highest degree in the remainder by the term of highest degree in the divisor. Multiplying the entire divisor by $- 3$ and writing the product under the remainder, we get $(4 x^2 - 5 x + 6)(- 3)$, or $- 12 x^2 + 15 x - 18$, for the second partial product of the multiplication (A). As there is no final remainder the division is said to be exact.

The process of dividing one polynomial by another is expressed in the

RULE. *Arrange the dividend and the divisor according to the descending (or ascending) powers of some common letter, called the letter of arrangement.*

Divide the first term of the dividend by the first term of the divisor and write the result for the first term of the quotient.

Multiply the entire divisor by the first term of the quotient, write the result under the dividend, and subtract, being careful

to write the terms of the remainder in the same order as those of the divisor.

Divide the first term of the remainder by the first term of the divisor for the second term of the quotient and proceed as before until there is no remainder, or until the remainder is of lower degree in the letter of arrangement than the divisor.

If there is no remainder, the result of division may be expressed as follows:

$$\frac{\text{Dividend}}{\text{Divisor}} = \text{Quotient}.$$

If there is a remainder, the result is expressed as follows:

$$\frac{\text{Dividend}}{\text{Divisor}} = \text{Partial Quotient} + \frac{\text{Remainder}}{\text{Divisor}}.$$

This last corresponds to what is done in arithmetic in dividing 17 by 5, which is written $\frac{17}{5} = 3\frac{2}{5}$. This means that $\frac{17}{5} = 3 + \frac{2}{5}$, the plus being understood.

Note. We saw on page 1 that it is customary to represent the product of two letters by placing one after the other with no sign between them. Thus ab means a times b. But addition, not multiplication, is implied by placing the fraction $\frac{2}{5}$ after the number 3. This practice comes down to us from the Arabs, who denoted all additions by placing the number symbols in succession without any sign of operation. The later Greeks also had the same notation.

EXAMPLES

1. Divide $38\,x + 2\,x^4 - 7\,x^2 - 24 - 7\,x^3$ by $6 + x^2 - 5\,x$.

Solution: Arranging terms and dividing,

Dividend, $2\,x^4 - 7\,x^3 - 7\,x^2 + 38\,x - 24 \mid x^2 - 5\,x + 6$, Divisor

$\underline{2\,x^4 - 10\,x^3 + 12\,x^2} \qquad \mid \overline{2\,x^2 + 3\,x - 4}$, Quotient

$\qquad 3\,x^3 - 19\,x^2 + 38\,x$

$\qquad \underline{3\,x^3 - 15\,x^2 + 18\,x}$

$\qquad\qquad -\,4\,x^2 + 20\,x - 24$

$\qquad\qquad \underline{-\,4\,x^2 + 20\,x - 24}$

Check: Let $x = 1$. Then the dividend = 2, the divisor = 2, and the quotient = 1; and $2 \div 2 = 1$.

The student must avoid checking by any number which makes the divisor zero.

2. Divide $8\,xy^2 + 8\,x^3 - 7\,y^3 - 12\,x^2y$ by $4\,x^2 + y^2 - 4\,xy$.

Solution: Arranging terms and dividing,

$$
\begin{array}{l}
\text{Dividend, } 8\,x^3 - 12\,x^2y + 8\,xy^2 - 7\,y^3 \,\Big|\, \underline{4\,x^2 - 4\,xy + y^2},\ \text{Divisor}\\
\quad\ \ \underline{8\,x^3 -\ \ 8\,x^2y + 2\,xy^2} \qquad\quad\ \ \underline{2\,x - y},\ \text{Partial Quotient}\\
\quad\ \ \ -\ 4\,x^2y + 6\,xy^2 - 7\,y^3\\
\quad\ \ \ \underline{-\ 4\,x^2y + 4\,xy^2 -\ \ y^3}\\
\qquad\qquad\ \ \ 2\,xy^2 - 6\,y^3,\ \text{Remainder}
\end{array}
$$

The total quotient is $2\,x - y + \dfrac{2\,xy^2 - 6\,y^3}{4\,x^2 - 4\,xy + y^2}$.

Check: Let $x = y = 1$. Then the dividend $= -3$, the divisor $= 1$, and the quotient $= -3$; and $-3 \div 1 = -3$.

GENERAL CHECK FOR DIVISION. (*a*) When the division is exact. Multiply the divisor by the quotient. The product should be the dividend.

(*b*) When there is a remainder. Multiply the divisor by partial quotient and add in the remainder. The result should be the dividend.

EXERCISES

Divide:

    1. $x^2 + 7\,x + 12$ by $x + 3$.

    2. $x^2 - 2\,x - 15$ by $x - 5$.

    3. $x^2 + 5\,x + 6$ by $x + 3$.

    4. $-7\,x + 6 + x^2$ by $x - 1$.

    5. $6\,x^2 - 13\,x + 6$ by $2\,x - 3$.

    6. $25\,x^4 + 30\,x^2 - 7$ by $7 + 5\,x^2$.

    7. $12\,a^2 - 21 + 19\,a$ by $4\,a - 3$.

    8. $-8 + x^3 + 4\,x - 2\,x^2$ by $x - 2$.

    9. $a^3 + 3\,a^2b + 3\,ab^2 + b^3$ by $a + b$.

    10. $x^3 - 15\,x^2 + 65\,x - 63$ by $x - 7$.

    11. $5\,x^2 + 5\,x - 25\,x^3 - 1$ by $5\,x^2 - 1$.

    12. $2\,x^3 - 14\,x^2 + 14\,x + 12$ by $2\,x - 4$.

13. $3\,a^3 + 28\,a^2 + 89\,a - 140$ by $3\,a - 5$.

14. $37\,x + 6\,x^3 - 24 - 23\,x^2$ by $2\,x - 3$.

15. $53\,a + 8 - 53\,a^2 + 12\,a^3$ by $4\,a^2 - 7\,a - 1$.

16. $15\,a^3 - 56\,a^2 + 99\,a - 70$ by $3\,a^2 - 7\,a + 10$.

17. $23\,a^2 + a^4 - 55\,a + 11\,a^3 - 140$ by $a^2 - 5$.

18. $4\,a^3 + 1 + a^4 + 4\,a + 6\,a^2$ by $1 + a^2 + 2\,a$.

19. $a^4 - 8\,a^3 + 24\,a^2 - 32\,a + 16$ by $a^2 - 4\,a + 4$.

20. $40\,x - 31\,x^2 + 21 + x^4 + 4\,x^3$ by $x^2 - 3 - 7\,x$.

21. $11\,x - 42\,x^2 + 10\,x^4 - 27\,x^3 - 36$ by $9 + 2\,x^2 - 5\,x$.

22. $x^4 - 3\,a^2x^2 + a^4$ by $x^2 - ax + a^2$.

23. $a^4 + 4\,b^4 + 3\,a^2b^2$ by $2\,b^2 + a^2 - ab$.

24. $16\,x^4 - 60\,x^2y^2 + 25\,y^4$ by $4\,x^2 - 10\,xy - 5\,y^2$.

25. $9\,a^4 + 49\,b^4 + 26\,a^2b^2$ by $7\,b^2 + 3\,a^2 + 4\,ab$.

26. $4\,a^8 - 44\,a^4b^4 + 100\,b^8$ by $2\,a^4 - 10\,b^4 + 2\,a^2b^2$.

27. $25\,x^3 - 10\,x^2 + 40\,x - 18$ by $5\,x - 6$.

28. $x^3 - y^3$ by $x - y$.   **34.** $x^4 + y^4$ by $x + y$.

29. $a^3 - 125\,b^3$ by $a - 5\,b$.   **35.** $x^4 - y^4$ by $x + y$.

30. $a^6 + 343\,b^3$ by $a^2 + 7\,b$.   **36.** $x^4 - y^4$ by $x - y$.

31. $x^4 - 16$ by $x + 2$.   **37.** $x^5 + y^5$ by $x + y$.

32. $y^5 - 5\,y^2 - 3000$ by $y - 5$.   **38.** $x^5 + y^5$ by $x - y$.

33. $x^4 + y^4$ by $x - y$.   **39.** $x^5 - y^5$ by $x + y$.

40. $x^5 - y^5$ by $x - y$.

41. $x^{2a} - 5\,x^a + 6$ by $x^a - 3$.

42. $x^{6a} - 7\,x^{3a} + 12$ by $x^{3a} - 4$.

43. $x^{2a} + 2\,x^{a+1} + 3\,x^a + 3\,x$ by $x^a + 2\,x$.

CHAPTER XI

EQUATIONS AND PROBLEMS

40. Equations involving literal coefficients. The most general form of a simple equation in one unknown is one in which the unknown occurs with literal coefficients. The solution of such an equation frequently involves division of polynomials.

EXAMPLE

Find the value of x in $ax + 4a = a^2 + 2x + 4$ and check the result.

Solution: $\qquad ax + 4a = a^2 + 2x + 4.$

Transposing, $\qquad ax - 2x = a^2 - 4a + 4.$

Writing the coefficients of x as a binomial,

$$(a - 2)x = a^2 - 4a + 4.$$

Dividing both members by the coefficient of x,

$$x = \frac{a^2 - 4a + 4}{a - 2} = a - 2.$$

Check: Substituting $a - 2$ for x in the original equation, it becomes

$$a(a - 2) + 4a = a^2 + 2(a - 2) + 4.$$

Simplifying, $\quad a^2 - 2a + 4a = a^2 + 2a - 4 + 4.$

Combining, $\qquad a^2 + 2a = a^2 + 2a.$

EXERCISES

Solve for x and check:

1. $x + 2a = 6a.$

2. $x + a = b.$

3. $bx + b = 4b.$

4. $cx + c^2 = 6c^3.$

5. $5(b - x) = 10b.$

6. $bx - (b + c) = 5b - c.$

7. $3ax - ab = 2ax - ac.$

8. $4bx - 7a^2b = 6ab^2 + 3bx.$

82

9. $ax + bx = ac + bc.$

10. $a^2x + 1 - a^4 - x = 0.$

11. $ax + 2\,ab = 2\,a^2 + bx.$

12. $ax - a^3 - 4 = 3\,a - x.$

13. $4\,b^2c^2 + (a + bx)\,c = (a - bx)\,c.$

14. $ax - ac + bc = 2\,ac - 5\,bc + 2\,bx.$

15. $(x + a)\,(x + b) = x^2 + 2\,a^2 + 3\,ab.$

16. $15\,(x - a) - 6\,(x + a) = 3\,(5\,a - 3\,x).$

17. $4\,x - cx - 8 + 2\,a + 6\,c = 6\,a - 3\,ac + 2\,cx.$

18. $9\,ab + (x - 3\,a)\,(x - 3\,b) = (x + 3\,a)\,(x - 3\,a) - 9\,a^2.$

19. $(5\,a - 4\,b)\,x - 5\,(b^2 + 4\,a^2 + 6\,ab) =$
$$10\,b^2 - 3\,(2\,a^2 + 3\,bx) - a\,(2\,x - b).$$

20. $a^2x + 3\,ax + 10\,a = a^3 + x + 3.$

41. Uniform motion. If a train travels for 8 hours at an average rate of 40 miles an hour, the total distance traversed is 8×40, or 320 miles. This illustrates **uniform** motion involving:

1. Time measured in seconds, minutes, hours, etc.

2. Rate (velocity), or the distance traveled in a unit of time, one second, one hour, or one day.

3. Distance (total) measured in standard units of length as feet, or inches, or meters, or kilometers, etc.

Time (t), rate (r), and distance (d) are connected by the relation

$$d = r \times t.$$

On this simple equation a large number of problems in algebra and in physics are based.

Biographical note. Sir Isaac Newton. Sir Isaac Newton (1642–1727) was probably the keenest mathematical thinker who ever lived. He was the son of a farmer of slender means, and as a boy was rather lazy. It is said, however, that his complete victory over a larger boy in a fight at school led him to feel that perhaps he could be equally successful in his studies if he really tried. His ambition and interest being once roused, he never ceased to apply himself during the rest of his long life.

His most important scientific achievement was the discovery and verification of the laws of motion. In his great work called the "Principia" * he showed by mathematical reasoning that all bodies, great and small, — the planet revolving around the sun, as well as the apple falling from the tree, — follow the same laws. His greatest discovery in pure mathematics was that of a method called the calculus, which is the basis of most of the advances in mathematics and in theoretical physics made since his time.

But important as was Newton's mathematical work, his most significant contribution to mankind was an idea, — the idea that the world in which we live is not independent of the rest of the universe, but that every smallest particle of matter is connected with the most remote planet and star; that we cannot think of ourselves as the center of all things, but that we merely occupy our place in a system of universal law.

EXAMPLE

A pedestrian traveling 4 miles per hour is overtaken 14 hours after leaving a certain point by a horseman who left the same starting point 8 hours after the pedestrian. Find the rate of the horseman.

Solution: This is a problem in uniform motion, involving the distance, the rate, and the time of a pedestrian and a horseman respectively. By a careful reading of the problem one discovers that the time for each was a different number of hours, that each went at a different rate, but that each traveled the same distance. Hence the equation will be formed by expressing d in terms of r and t for both the pedestrian and the horseman and then equating the two expressions for d.

By the conditions:

	t, or time in hours	r, or rate in miles per hour	Distance, $d = r \times t$
Pedestrian	14	4	$56 = 4 \times 14$
Horseman	6	x	$6 \cdot x$

Hence $6x = 56,$
and $x = 9\frac{1}{3}.$
Check: $4 \cdot 14 = 56; \ 9\frac{1}{3} \cdot 6 = 56.$

* A copy of this book, presented to the College by Newton himself, may be seen in the library of Yale University.

SIR ISAAC NEWTON

PROBLEMS

A and B start from the same place at the same time and travel in opposite directions:

1. A goes 8 miles per hour and B 10 miles per hour. In how many hours will they be 120 miles apart? 180 miles apart?

2. A travels twice as fast as B. In 5 hours they are 135 miles apart. Find the rate of each.

3. A travels 2 miles per hour more than B. After 8 hours they are 96 miles apart. Find the rate of each.

4. A goes 4 miles per hour more than B. After 6 hours the distance between them is 168 miles. Find the rate of each.

5. B goes 3 miles per hour less than A, and travels $\frac{3}{4}$ as fast as A. Find the rate of each. After how many hours will the distance between them be 168 miles?

6. A travels 3 hours and stops, and B travels 5 hours. Then they are 77 miles apart. A's rate is twice B's. Find their rates and the distance each has traveled.

7. B travels 9 hours at a rate of 4 miles per hour less than A. A travels an equal distance in 3 hours less time, and then stops. How far are they apart at the end of 9 hours?

A and B start at the same time from two points 144 miles apart and travel toward each other until they meet. Find the rate of each:

8. If they travel at the same rate and meet in 8 hours.

9. If A travels 2 miles per hour less than B and they meet in 9 hours.

10. If B travels three times as fast as A and they meet in 12 hours.

11. If they meet in 6 hours and B travels 24 miles more than A.

12. If they meet in 8 hours and B goes 2 miles per hour more than A.

13. If they meet in 9 hours and A travels 4 miles per hour more than B.

Find the number of hours from the start until the time of meeting:

14. If B goes 6 miles per hour more than A and travels twice as far as A.

15. If A travels 6 miles per hour and B 9 miles per hour, but B is delayed 4 hours on the way.

16. If A is delayed 3 hours and B is delayed 5 hours, and their rates are 7 miles and 9 miles per hour respectively.

17. A and B start from the same place at the same time and travel in opposite directions. A travels 3 miles per hour and B 4 miles per hour. In how many hours will they be 42 miles apart?

18. A and B start at the same time from two points 72 miles apart and travel toward each other. A travels 8 miles per hour and B 10 miles per hour. In how many hours will they meet?

19. The distance from Kansas City to St. Louis is 285 miles. A train running 37 miles per hour leaves Kansas City for St. Louis at the same time a train running 38 miles per hour leaves St. Louis for Kansas City. In how many hours will they meet?

20. A starts from a certain place and travels 8 miles per hour. Four hours later B starts from the same place and travels in the same direction at the rate of 10 miles per hour. How many hours does B travel before overtaking A?

21. Two bicyclists 108 miles apart start at the same time and travel toward each other. One travels 10 miles per hour, the other 12 miles per hour. The latter is delayed 2 hours on the way. In how many hours will they meet, and how far has each traveled?

22. A passenger train starts 2 hours later than a freight train, from the same station but in an opposite direction. The rate of the passenger train is 42 miles per hour and the rate of the freight train is 24 miles per hour. In how many hours after the passenger train starts will the two trains be 246 miles apart?

23. A messenger going at the rate of 8 miles per hour has journeyed 2 hours when it is found necessary to change the message. At what rate must a second messenger then travel to overtake the first in 6 hours?

24. A passenger train and a freight train start together from the same station and move in the same direction on parallel tracks at the rate of 45 miles and 18 miles per hour respectively. How much time will have elapsed before the passenger train will be 144 miles ahead of the freight train?

(Problems 25–32 may be solved without using equations.)

The distance from P to Q is 108 miles. A and B leave P at the same time and travel at different rates toward Q. The one who reaches Q first at once returns. Find the distance each has traveled when they meet:

25. If A's rate is 9 miles per hour and B's is 15.

26. If B travels five times as fast as A.

27. If A travels 56 miles more than B.

28. If they meet 24 miles from Q and B travels faster than A.

Find the rate of each if A travels faster than B:

29. If they meet in 6 hours halfway between P and Q.

30. If they meet in 6 hours ⅔ of the way from P to Q.

31. If they meet in 6 hours 12 miles from Q.

32. If they meet in 6 hours 96 miles from P.

33. If A travels 4 miles per hour more than B and meets B in 12 hours.

Find the distance each travels:

34. If they meet in 6 hours and A travels 2 miles per hour more than B.

35. If A travels 4 miles per hour more than B and they meet in 9 hours.

The velocity of a bullet continually decreases from the instant it leaves the gun. This is due to the resistance of the air. In the following problems consider the velocity of sound as 1100 feet per second.

36. Two and one-half seconds after a marksman fires his rifle he hears the bullet strike the target which is 550 yards distant. Find the average velocity of the bullet.

37. One and three-fourths seconds after a marksman fires his revolver he hears the bullet strike the target 50 rods distant. Find the average velocity of the bullet.

38. A marksman fires at a target 1000 yards distant. The bullet passes over a boy, who hears the sound of it striking the target and the report of the gun at the same instant. The velocity (average) of the bullet is 1650 feet per second. Find the distance of the boy from the target.

REVIEW EXERCISES AND PROBLEMS

1. Simplify $5\,a - 7\,x + 3\,b - 10\,c - 14\,a + 12\,y - 8\,x + 12\,a - 11\,x + 9\,b$.

2. Simplify $2\,cd - a^2b + 7\,cd^2 - 12\,ab + 17\,ad - cd + 4\,c^2d$.

3. Add $10\,x - 9 + 4\,ax - 2\,cd$, $-6\,ax - 15\,x + 12\,cd$, $10 - ax + 5\,cd$, and $-6\,cd + 11\,x - 19 - 7\,ax$.

4. Add $a^3 - 3 + 4\,a^2 - a$, $-a + 3\,a^2 - 5\,a^3$, $-3\,a^2 + 6\,a^3 - 2\,a + 8$, $-a - 5\,a^2 - 2\,a^3 + 5$, and $2\,a^3 - 3\,a^2 + 4\,a - 5$.

5. Add $Ax^3 + Bx^2 + Cx$ and $Ax^2 + Bx + C$.

6. Add $7\,(a - b) - 10\,(c - d) + 8\,(x - y)$, $-6\,(c - d) - 4\,(a - b) - 7\,(x - y)$, and $12\,(x - y) - 15\,(c - d) + 7\,(a - b)$.

7. Add $-2\,(x + y) + 3\,(x - y) - 4\,(a + b)$, $8\,(x - y) - 9\,(x + y) + 4\,(a - b)$, and $-(a + b) + (x - y) - 10\,(x + y)$.

8. Add $\frac{1}{3}\,ax + \frac{2}{3}\,ax^2 - \frac{5}{6}\,a^2x^2 + a$, $\frac{1}{6}\,ax^2 - ax - 9\,a + 2\,a^2x^2$, and $a^2x^2 + \frac{1}{2}\,ax^2 - \frac{1}{4}\,a$.

9. What must be added to $2\,x^2 - 3\,xy + y^2 - 1$ to give $x^2 + 10\,xy - 9 - 5\,y^2$?

10. What must be added to $3\,a^2y - 7\,ay^2 + z - 5\,ay$ to give $-a^2y + 12\,ay^2 - ay - 15$?

11. What must be added to $-17\,a^2bcd^2 - 4\,ab^2c^2d^3 + 3\,abcd + ax$ to give $3\,ab^2c^2d^3 - 12$?

12. What must be added to $27xy + 13\,z - 12 + ab$ to give 0?

Remove the parentheses and collect terms:

13. $(a + b) - (a - b) + 4\,a - (a + 3\,b) + c.$

14. $15\,x - 2\,(12\,x - 16\,y) + xy + 3\,(3\,x - 4\,xy) - x.$

15. $ab - (7\,x + 4\,y - 2\,z) + 42 + 5\,(5\,ab - x - y).$

16. $[x - (-4\,x + 8\,y + 2\,z) + b - 4\,(3\,x - z)] - 5\,b.$

17. $[ab - \{-5\,ac + 7\,(d - a) + 4\,ca + 7\,d\} - 6\,ba] + 13\,a.$

18. $\{5\,x^2 - 2\,[-4 - (2\,x^2 - 3\,x)] + 5\} - (x^2 + 4\,x - 2).$

Perform the indicated multiplication:

19. $(x^4 - 4\,x^2y^2 + 4\,y^4)\,(x^4 + 4\,x^2y^2 + 4\,y^4).$

20. $(4\,x^4 - x^2 + 5)\,(3\,x^3 - x + 7).$

21. $(a + b + c)\,(a^2 + b^2 + c^2 - ab - ac - bc).$

22. $(x + y)\,(x^6 - x^5y + x^4y^2 - x^3y^3 + x^2y^4 - xy^5 + y^6).$

23. $(5\,x - 9\,x^5 + x^2 - 4\,x^4 - 3\,x^3 + 10)\,(-x^3 + 3\,x - x^2 + 2\,x^4).$

24. $(3\,x^2 - 4\,y)\,(9\,x^4 + 16\,y^2)\,(3\,x^2 + 4\,y).$

25. $(a - 3\,b + 2\,c)^2.$ **27.** $(x^a - y^b)\,(x^a + y^b).$

26. $(x - y + z)^3.$ **28.** $(x^a + 2\,y^b + 3\,z^c)\,(x^a - 3\,y^b).$

Divide:

29. $6\,a^5 - 13\,a^4 + 4\,a^3 + 3\,a^2$ by $2\,a^2 - 3\,a^2 + a.$

30. $-30\,a^4 - 11\,a^3 + 82\,a^2 + 12\,a - 48$ by $3\,a^2 + 2\,a - 4.$

31. $10\,x^2 + 20\,x^3 - 11\,x^5 + 10\,x^6 - 3\,x^4 + 2$ by $-3\,x^2 - 2 + 2\,x + 5\,x^3.$

32. $a^8 - 3\,a^6 + a^4 - 7\,a^2 + 3$ by $(a^2 - 1)^2.$

33. $a^5 - 5\,a^4b + 10\,a^3b^2 - 10\,a^2b^3 + 7\,ab^4 - b^5$ by $(a - b)^2.$

34. $(6\,a^2 + 5\,a - 6)\,(2\,a^2 - 13\,a + 20)$ by $(3\,a - 2)\,(2\,a - 5).$

35. $x^3 - 27\,y^3 + 64 + 36\,xy$ by $x - 3\,y + 4.$

Find the value of y in the following equations:

36. $6y - 20 + 5y - 18 = 36y - 4 - 40y + 9$.

37. $4y - 3(6 - y) + 2 = 6(y - 2) - 13y + 24$.

38. $6y - 4(1 - 2y) + 10 = 4(2y - 5) - 4y + 1$.

39. $(y + 7)(y - 11) = (y + 8)(y - 5) - 2$.

40. $(y - 3)^3 = (y^2 - 6y + 9)(5 + y) - 8y^2$.

41. $y^2 + a^2 - (y + 1)^2 - (a + 1)^2 = 0$.

42. $3ay + 6ac + 4b^2 = 3ab + 4by + 8bc$.

Find the value of x, if $x = \dfrac{-b + \sqrt{b^2 - 4ac}}{2a}$:

43. When $a = 1$, $b = +10$, and $c = -11$.

44. When $a = 5$, $b = -6$, and $c = -8$.

Find the value of x, if $x = \dfrac{-b - \sqrt{b^2 - 4ac}}{2a}$:

45. When $a = 3$, $b = 5$, and $c = -8$.

46. When $a = 2$, $b = 7$, and $c = -22$.

47. If $f = 12$, $m = 18$, and $v = 20$, find the value of s in the equation $fs = \frac{1}{2}mv^2$.

48. If $a = 32.2$, $m = 7$, $t = 40$, find the value of e in the equation $e = \frac{1}{2}m(at)^2$.

49. If $s = \dfrac{a + b + c}{2}$, find the value of $\sqrt{s(s - a)(s - b)(s - c)}$ when $a = 3$, $b = 4$, and $c = 5$.

50. If the square of a certain number is increased by 38, the result is equal to the product of the next two consecutive numbers. Find the numbers.

51. The square of a certain odd number is 98 less than the product of the next two consecutive odd numbers. Find the numbers.

52. If the square of a certain odd number is increased by 47, the result is equal to the product of the next two consecutive even numbers. Find the numbers.

53. The product of two consecutive numbers is 42 less than the product of the next two consecutive numbers. Find the numbers.

54. The ages of two persons are respectively 42 years and 15 years. In how many years will the elder be twice as old as the younger?

55. The ages of two persons are respectively 36 years and 16 years. How many years ago was the older person three times as old as the younger?

56. The ages of two men are respectively 52 years and 21 years. How many years hence will the older man be twice as old as the younger?

57. The ages of two persons are 87 years and 42 years respectively. How many years ago was the elder four times as old as the younger?

58. A collection of quarters, dimes, and nickels, containing 32 coins, is worth $3.60. There being twice as many nickels as quarters, find the number of each.

59. A bullet is fired from a rifle at a speed which would average 1280 feet per second. Six seconds later the marksman hears it strike the target. The velocity of sound is 1120 feet per second. Find the distance to the target.

60. The leader in some games proposed to tell the age of the others thus: each was to add 12 years to his age, to multiply the sum by 3, to subtract 36 from the product, and then to add his age. Each in turn announced his final result and the leader at once gave the correct age. What did he do to each result to obtain the proper age?

61. The per cent of the population of the United States under 20 years exceeds by 5% the population between 20 years and 60 years. The per cent between 20 years and 60 years is nine times the per cent above 60 years. Find the per cent of the population under 20 years, between 20 years and 60 years, and over 60 years.

62. The length of the St. Gothard tunnel exceeds that of Mount Cenis (Italy) by 9000 feet. The length of the St. Gothard tunnel is 1320 feet less than twice the length of the tunnel at Hoosac, Massachusetts. If the sum of the lengths of these tunnels is 113,760 feet, find the length of each.

63. The height of the first cascade of the Yosemite waterfall exceeds that of Staubbach Falls by 520 feet and is 60 feet more than four times the height of the falls of the Zambezi. The height of the latter is 32 feet more than twice the height of Niagara Falls. The sum of the four heights is 3004 feet. Find each.

64. The combined weight of a cubic foot of mercury, a cubic foot of water, and a cubic foot of alcohol is 962.2 pounds. Alcohol weighs 11.5 pounds per cubic foot less than water, while a cubic foot of mercury weighs 32.7 pounds more than sixteen cubic feet of alcohol. Find the weight of each per cubic foot.

65. If the average annual rainfall at Boston were 3 inches less, it would be one third the rainfall of Neahbay, Washington. The annual rainfall of Boston is 1 inch greater than that of St. Louis and 1 inch less than five times that of San Diego, California. If these places together have a total annual rainfall of 219 inches, find the rainfall at each place.

66. From tables which have been compiled it is found that a person 10 years old may expect to live 5.39 years longer than one 21 years old and 15.31 years longer than one 45 years old; and a person 45 years old may expect to live .94 of a year less than twice as long as one 65 years old. If four people (one at each of these ages) may expect to live a total of 109.42 years, how many years may each expect to live?

CHAPTER XII

IMPORTANT SPECIAL PRODUCTS

42. The square of a binomial. The multiplication

$$
\begin{aligned}
&a + b \\
&a + b \\
\hline
&a^2 + \quad ab \\
&\quad\quad ab + b^2 \\
\hline
&a^2 + 2\,ab + b^2
\end{aligned}
$$

gives the formula

$$(a + b)^2 = a^2 + 2\,ab + b^2.$$

This may be expressed in words as follows:

I. *The square of the sum of two terms is the sum of the squares of the terms plus twice their product.*

Similarly

$$(a - b)^2 = a^2 - 2\,ab + b^2,$$

which may be expressed in words as follows:

II. *The square of the difference of two terms is the sum of their squares minus twice their product.*

EXERCISES

Square the following either by I or II:

1. 16.

Solution: $16^2 = (10 + 6)^2 = 100 + 36 + 2 \cdot 10 \cdot 6 = 256.$

2. 49.

Solution: $49^2 = (40 + 9)^2$ or $(50 - 1)^2.$
Using the latter, $(50 - 1)^2 = 2500 + 1 - 2 \cdot 50 \cdot 1 = 2401.$

3. 15.	**6.** 19.	**9.** $x + 1.$
4. 17.	**7.** $x + y.$	**10.** $a + 2.$
5. 18.	**8.** $x - c.$	**11.** $b^2 + 3.$

12. $c - 4$.

13. $2 c^2 + d$.

14. $3 x - y$.

15. $x + 2 y$.

16. $a - 4 b$.

17. $y^5 - 2$.

18. $2 a + 1$.

19. $3 a^2 + 2$.

20. $4 a + 3$.

21. $2 a^2 - 3 b$.

22. $3 c^2 - 4 a^2$.

23. $2 x^3 - 6$.

24. $3 xy + y^2$.

25. $7 x^2 - 3 y^4$.

26. $8 y^3 + 2 bx$.

27. $6 xy - 2 a^2$.

28. $4 xy - 2 x^2$.

29. $3 x^4 - 5 x^6$.

30. $2 x^2 - 6 x^3 y$.

31. 41.

32. 92.

33. 101.

34. 202.

35. 1001.

Perform mentally the indicated division :

36. $\dfrac{a^2 + 2 ab + b^2}{a + b}$.

37. $\dfrac{a^2 - 2 ac + c^2}{a - c}$.

38. $\dfrac{a^2 - 4 a + 4}{a - 2}$.

39. $\dfrac{9 x^2 - 6 x + 1}{3 x - 1}$.

40. $\dfrac{y^2 + 40 y + 400}{20 + y}$.

41. $\dfrac{9 x^2 - 12 xy + 4 y^2}{2 y - 3 x}$.

42. $\dfrac{4 a^2 - 20 a + 25}{- 5 + 2 a}$.

43. $\dfrac{4 x^2 - 12 xy + 9 y^2}{3 y - 2 x}$.

Find a binomial divisor for each of the following trinomials:

44. $x^2 - 2 xy + y^2$.

45. $a^2 + 2 a + 1$.

46. $a^2 + 4 a + 4$.

47. $4 x^2 + 4 x + 1$.

48. $16 x^2 - 8 x + 1$.

49. $16 x^2 - 8 xy + y^2$.

50. $9 x^4 - 6 x^2 + 1$.

51. $16 y^6 - 40 y^3 + 25$.

State the two binomials whose product is :

52. $c^2 + 2 cd + d^2$.

53. $a^2 - 2 a + 1$.

54. $x^2 - 10 x + 25$.

55. $4 a^2 - 4 a + 1$.

56. $4 x^2 + 12 x + 9$.

57. $9 a^2 b^2 - 6 ab + 1$.

58. $16 x^4 y^2 - 24 x^2 ya + 9 a^2$.

59. $25 a^4 b^6 - 60 a^2 b^3 c^2 + 36 c^4$.

It is often convenient to use the word *term* in a broader sense than that in which it has been used in the work thus far.

For example, in the expression $(a + b) - 3(a + 2b) + 4(a + 3b)$ the binomials $(a + b)$, $-3(a + 2b)$, and $4(a + 3b)$ are often spoken of as terms, and the entire expression is then called a trinomial.

If in $(a + b)(a + b) = a^2 + 2ab + b^2$ we substitute $x + y$ for a, we get $[(x + y) + b][(x + y) + b] = (x + y)^2 + 2(x + y)b + b^2$. Expanding $(x + y)^2$ by the formula, and expanding $2b(x + y)$ also, we obtain $x^2 + 2xy + y^2 + 2bx + 2by + b^2$.

This means that if we regard $(x + y)$ as a term and apply the formula for squaring the sum of *two* terms, we can square the trinomial $x + y + b$ mentally.

Similarly
$$(x + y - b)^2 = [(x + y) - b][(x + y) - b]$$
$$= (x + y)^2 - 2b(x + y) + b^2$$
$$= x^2 + 2xy + y^2 - 2bx - 2by + b^2.$$

EXERCISES

Using one of the formulæ on page 93, square the following trinomials:

1. $a + b + c$.
2. $a + b - c$.
3. $a + b - 1$.
4. $a + b + 1$.

5. $a - b + c$.
6. $a - b - c$.
7. $a + 2b - 3$.
8. $a - 2b + c$.

9. $2a + b - 4c$.
10. $3a - 2b + 5c$.
11. $2a - 3b - 4c$.
12. $4c - 1 + 2ab$.

43. The product of the sum and the difference of two terms. The multiplication

$$\begin{array}{r} a + b \\ a - b \\ \hline a^2 + ab \\ - ab - b^2 \\ \hline a^2 \qquad - b^2 \end{array}$$

gives the formula

$$(a + b)(a - b) = a^2 - b^2.$$

This may be expressed in words as follows:

III. *The product of the sum and the difference of two terms equals the difference of their squares taken in the same order as the difference of the terms.*

EXERCISES

Expand by the preceding formula:

1. $(6 + 3)(6 - 3)$.   **4.** $(10 - 4)(10 + 4)$.

2. $(8 + 4)(8 - 4)$.   **5.** $(7 + 2)(7 - 2)$.

3. $(9 - 2)(9 + 2)$.   **6.** $(12 - 3)(12 + 3)$.

7. $22 \cdot 18$.

Solution: $22 \cdot 18 = (20 + 2)(20 - 2) = 400 - 4 = 396$.

8. $35 \cdot 25$.   **11.** $35 \cdot 45$.   **14.** $72 \cdot 68$.

9. $33 \cdot 27$.   **12.** $52 \cdot 48$.   **15.** $75 \cdot 85$.

10. $36 \cdot 44$.   **13.** $65 \cdot 75$.   **16.** $97 \cdot 103$.

17. $(x + 3)(x - 3)$.   **26.** $(4 + y^2)(4 - y^2)$.

18. $(a + 5)(a - 5)$.   **27.** $(4 - x)(x + 4)$.

19. $(2x + 4)(2x - 4)$.   **28.** $(2c + a)(2c - a)$.

20. $(3n + 5)(3n - 5)$.   **29.** $(3a + b)(b - 3a)$.

21. $(x + y)(x - y)$.   **30.** $(4b + 2c)(4b - 2c)$.

22. $(x - a)(x + a)$.   **31.** $(3xy - 2)(3xy + 2)$.

23. $(x - 1)(x + 1)$.   **32.** $(4ab - 3)(4ab + 3)$.

24. $(a + 2)(a - 2)$.   **33.** $(a^4 - b^3)(a^4 + b^3)$.

25. $(a^2 + 3)(a^2 - 3)$.   **34.** $(a^6 + a^3)(- a^3 + a^6)$.

35. $(x^3 - 2y)(x^3 + 2y)$.

36. $(4ab - a^2)(4ab + a^2)$.

37. $(3cd^2 + 2d)(- 2d + 3cd^2)$.

38. $(6cd + 3)(- 3 + 6cd)$.

39. $(4xy + 2y)(2y - 4xy)$.

40. $(3abc - 2bc)(2bc + 3abc)$.

Perform the indicated division:

41. $(a^2 - b^2) \div (a + b)$.   **44.** $(36 - a^2) \div (6 - a)$.

42. $(c^2 - d^2) \div (c - d)$.   **45.** $(9x^2 - 16) \div (4 + 3x)$.

43. $(9 - b^2) \div (3 + b)$.   **46.** $(x^4 - 1) \div (x^2 - 1)$.

Find a binomial divisor for each of the following binomials:

47. $x^2 - y^2$. **49.** $4x^2 - 9$. **51.** $16 - x^8$.

48. $x^2 - 1$. **50.** $25 - 16x^2$. **52.** $y^6 - 4$.

State the two binomials whose product is:

53. $c^2 - d^2$. **55.** $n^2 - 16$. **57.** $36b^2 - 1$.

54. $n^2 - 4$. **56.** $9 - 4a^2$. **58.** $a^2 - 9$.

59. $25 - 4n^2$. **60.** $100 - 9x^2$.

If in $(a+b)(a-b) = a^2 - b^2$ we replace a by $x + y$, we get $[(x+y)+b][(x+y)-b] = (x+y)^2 - b^2$; which, when $(x+y)^2$ is expanded, becomes $x^2 + 2xy + y^2 - b^2$.

Similarly, replacing b by $(x + y)$, we get

$[a+(x+y)][a-(x+y)] = a^2 - (x+y)^2$.

Expanding, $\qquad = a^2 - (x^2 + 2xy + y^2)$.

Removing the parenthesis, $\quad = a^2 - x^2 - 2xy - y^2$.

Perform the indicated multiplication:

61. $[(x+y)+1][(x+y)-1]$.

62. $(x+a+3)(x+a-3)$.

63. $[(x-a)+3][(x-a)-3]$.

64. $(x+4+c)(x+4-c)$.

65. $(2a-b+c)(2a-b-c)$.

66. $[x+(b+c)][x-(b+c)]$.

67. $[x+(b-c)][x-(b-c)]$.

68. $[3+(x-y)][3-(x-y)]$.

69. $[4x+(2y-x)][4x-(2y-x)]$.

70. $[10-(a-5)][10+(a-5)]$.

State the two binomials whose product is:

71. $49x^2 - 1$. **76.** $(3y-z)^2 - b^2$.

72. $64x^2 - 25$. **77.** $b^2 - (x+y)^2$.

73. $(a+b)^2 - 1$. **78.** $b^2 - (x-y)^2$.

74. $(x-y)^2 - 4$. **79.** $c^2 - (x+c)^2$.

75. $(2x-1)^2 - a^2$. **80.** $4 - (x-2)^2$.

44. The product of two binomials having a common term. The multiplication

$$x + a$$
$$x + b$$
$$\overline{x^2 + ax}$$
$$ + bx + ab$$
$$\overline{x^2 + (a + b)x + ab}$$

gives the formula

$$(x + a)(x + b) = x^2 + (a + b)x + ab.$$

This may be expressed in words as follows:

IV. *The product of two binomials having a common term equals the square of the common term, plus the algebraic sum of the unlike terms multiplied by the common term, plus the algebraic product of the unlike terms.*

EXERCISES

Expand by the preceding formula:

1. $(x + 1)(x + 2)$.
2. $(x + 2)(x + 3)$.
3. $(x + 3)(x + 4)$.
4. $(x + 4)(x + 5)$.
5. $(x + 5)(x + 6)$.

6. $(n + 1)(n - 2)$.
7. $(n - 2)(n + 3)$.
8. $(n - 3)(n + 4)$.
9. $(n - 4)(n + 5)$.
10. $(n - 5)(n + 6)$.

11. $(a - 1)(a - 2)$.
12. $(a - 2)(a - 3)$.
13. $(a - 3)(a - 4)$.
14. $(a - 4)(a - 5)$.
15. $(a - 4)(a - 6)$.

16. $(2y + 3)(2y + 4)$.
17. $(2y + 2)(2y + 3)$.
18. $(3a + 1)(3a + 4)$.
19. $(2n + 3)(2n + 5)$.
20. $(2n + 3)(2n - 5)$.
21. $(2n + 3)(2n - 4)$.
22. $(2a + 1)(2a - 5)$.

23. $(3a - 5)(3a + 1)$.
24. $(4a + 3)(4a - 5)$.
25. $(4a - 5)(4a - 6)$.
26. $(4ab + 1)(4ab - 6)$.
27. $(3x - 2)(3x + 5)$.
28. $(4a - 3b)(4a + 5b)$.
29. $(5a - 6b)(5a - 7b)$.

Perform mentally the indicated division:

30. $\dfrac{x^2 + 3x + 2}{x + 1}$.
31. $\dfrac{x^2 + 5x + 6}{x + 2}$.
32. $\dfrac{x^2 + 4x + 3}{x + 3}$.

33. $\dfrac{x^2 + 6x + 5}{x + 1}$.   **35.** $\dfrac{x^2 - 7x + 12}{x - 3}$.   **37.** $\dfrac{x^2 - 5x + 4}{x - 1}$.

34. $\dfrac{x^2 + 7x + 12}{x + 3}$.   **36.** $\dfrac{x^2 - 5x + 6}{x - 3}$.   **38.** $\dfrac{x^2 - 6x + 5}{x - 5}$.

39. $\dfrac{x^2 - 7x + 6}{x - 6}$.   **40.** $\dfrac{x^2 - 7x + 12}{x - 4}$.

Find an exact binomial divisor for each of the following trinomials:

41. $x^2 + 3x + 2$.   **45.** $x^2 + 7x + 10$.   **49.** $x^2 - 6x + 8$.
42. $x^2 + 5x + 6$.   **46.** $x^2 + 8x + 15$.   **50.** $x^2 - 8x + 15$.
43. $x^2 + 7x + 12$.   **47.** $x^2 - 3x + 2$.   **51.** $x^2 - 8x + 12$.
44. $x^2 + 6x + 8$.   **48.** $x^2 - 5x + 6$.   **52.** $x^2 - 9x + 14$.

State the two binomials whose product is:

53. $x^2 + 8x + 7$.   **56.** $x^2 - 11x + 10$.   **59.** $x^2 + 9x + 20$.
54. $x^2 + 9x + 8$.   **57.** $x^2 - 10x + 16$.   **60.** $x^2 - 9x + 18$.
55. $x^2 - 10x + 9$.   **58.** $x^2 + 10x + 21$.   **61.** $x^2 + 9x + 14$.

62. $x^2 - 12x + 32$.   **63.** $x^2 + 11x + 10$.

45. The square of any polynomial. The multiplication

$$
\begin{array}{l}
a + b - c \\
a + b - c \\
\hline
a^2 + \quad ab - \quad ac \\
\qquad ab \qquad\quad + b^2 - \quad bc \\
\qquad\quad - \quad ac \qquad\quad - \quad bc + c^2 \\
\hline
a^2 + 2\,ab - 2\,ac + b^2 - 2\,bc + c^2
\end{array}
$$

gives the formula

$$(a + b - c)^2 = a^2 + b^2 + c^2 + 2\,ab - 2\,ac - 2\,bc.$$

This may be expressed in words as follows:

V. *The square of any polynomial is equal to the sum of the squares of the terms, plus twice the algebraic product of each term by each term that follows it in the polynomial.*

Expand by the preceding formula:

1. $(a + b + c)^2$.   **5.** $(a - b - c)^2$.   **9.** $(3a - 3b + 1)^2$.

2. $(a + b + 1)^2$.   **6.** $(2x + y - 1)^2$.   **10.** $(a - b + c - d)^2$.

3. $(a + b + 2)^2$.   **7.** $(4x + y - 2)^2$.   **11.** $(x + y - a + 1)^2$.

4. $(2a + b - c)^2$.   **8.** $(a - bc + d)^2$.   **12.** $(a - y + b - 3)^2$.

46. The cube of a binomial. The multiplication

$$
\begin{array}{l}
a + b \\
a + b \\
\hline
a^2 + ab \\
ab + b^2 \\
\hline
a^2 + 2ab + b^2 \\
a + b \\
\hline
a^3 + 2a^2b + ab^2 \\
a^2b + 2ab^2 + b^3 \\
\hline
a^3 + 3a^2b + 3ab^2 + b^3
\end{array}
$$

gives the formula $(a + b)^3 = a^3 + 3a^2b + 3ab^2 + b^3$.

Similarly $(a - b)^3 = a^3 - 3a^2b + 3ab^2 - b^3$.

Expand by the preceding formula:

1. $(x + y)^3$.   **6.** $(x - 2)^3$.   **11.** $(2x - 1)^3$.

2. $(x - y)^3$.   **7.** $(x - 3)^3$.   **12.** $(3x + 2)^3$.

3. $(x + 1)^3$.   **8.** $(x + 3)^3$.   **13.** $(3x - 2y)^3$.

4. $(x - 1)^3$.   **9.** $(2x + y)^3$.   **14.** $(4x + 3y)^3$.

5. $(x + 2)^3$.   **10.** $(x - 2y)^3$.   **15.** $(5x - 2y)^3$.

16. Express in words the formula for the cube of the binomial $a + b$.

17. Express in words the formula for the cube of the binomial $a - b$.

CHAPTER XIII

FACTORING

47. Definition. Factoring is the process of finding the two or more expressions whose product is equal to a given expression.

The subject of factoring is very extensive. In this chapter we shall consider only the more common forms of factorable expressions and only such factors as do not contain irrational numbers and fractional terms (see § 91).

Thus fractional expressions like $\frac{1}{9} - a^2$, $\frac{1}{a^2} - 4$, etc., will be regarded as prime,* though the student can readily prove that $\left(\frac{1}{3} + a\right)\left(\frac{1}{3} - a\right) = \frac{1}{9} - a^2$, and that $\left(\frac{1}{a} + 2\right)\left(\frac{1}{a} - 2\right) = \frac{1}{a^2} - 4$. Possibly he can see that $(\sqrt{3} + a)(\sqrt{3} - a) = 3 - a^2$, and perhaps that $(x + \sqrt{2}\,y)(x - \sqrt{2}\,y) = x^2 - 2\,y^2$. But here also $3 - a^2$ and $x^2 - 2\,y^2$ are considered prime because their factors contain the irrational numbers $\sqrt{3}$ and $\sqrt{2}$.

48. Roots of monomials. In factoring it is often necessary to find the square root, the cube root, and other roots of various monomials.

The **square root** of a monomial is one of the two equal factors whose product is the monomial.

Since $+2 \cdot +2 = 4$ and $-2 \cdot -2 = 4$, the square root of 4 is ± 2, which means plus 2 or minus 2.

Similarly the square root of 9 is ± 3 and the square root of a^2 is $\pm a$.

That is, *Every positive number or algebraic expression has two square roots which have the same absolute value but opposite signs.*

It is customary to speak of the positive square root of a number as the **principal square root,** and if no sign precedes

---

*An integral expression is here regarded as *prime* when no two rational integral expressions (see page 122) can be found (except the expression itself and 1) whose product is the given expression.

the radical the principal root is understood. When both the positive and the negative square roots are considered, both signs must precede the radical.

Thus $\sqrt{4} = 2$, not -2; $-\sqrt{4} = -2$, not $+2$.

Since $a^5 \cdot a^5 = (-a^5)(-a^5) = a^{10}$, $\pm\sqrt{a^{10}} = \pm a^5$.

Similarly $a^6b^3 \cdot a^6b^3 = a^{12}b^6$, and $\pm\sqrt{a^{12}b^6} = \pm a^6b^3$.

That is, *The exponent of any letter in the square root of a monomial is one half the exponent of that letter in the monomial.*

Hence for extracting the square root of a monomial we have the

RULE. *Write the square root of the numerical coefficient preceded by the double sign $\pm$ and followed by all the letters of the monomial, giving to each letter an exponent equal to one half its exponent in the monomial.*

A rule much like the preceding one holds for fourth root, sixth root, and other even roots.

Thus $\pm\sqrt[4]{81\,a^4} = \pm 3\,a$, and $\pm\sqrt[6]{x^{12}} = \pm x^2$.

In the chapters on Factoring and Fractions where square roots arise only the *positive* square root will be considered.

According to the definition of square root the two factors of a term, either of which is its square root, *must be equal.* Consequently they must have the same sign. Since the product of two terms having like signs cannot be negative, we cannot extract the square root of a negative term. Hence we do not consider the square root of such terms as -4, $-9\,a^2$, and $-16\,x^2y^4$ in this chapter.

The **cube root** of a monomial is one of the three equal factors whose product is the monomial.

In this chapter only a single cube root of a number is considered; that is, the **principal cube root**.

Since $3 \cdot 3 \cdot 3 = 27$, $\sqrt[3]{27} = 3$.

And as $-3 \cdot -3 \cdot -3 = -27$, $\sqrt[3]{-27} = -3$.

That is, *The cube root of a monomial has the same sign as the monomial.*

Since $a^4 \cdot a^4 \cdot a^4 = a^{12}$, $\sqrt[3]{a^{12}} = a^4$.

Similarly $a^2b^3 \cdot a^2b^3 \cdot a^2b^3 = a^6b^9$, and $\sqrt[3]{a^6b^9} = a^2b^3$.

That is, *The exponent of any letter in the cube root of a term is one third of the exponent of that letter in the term.*

Hence for extracting the cube root of a monomial we have the

RULE. *Write the cube root of the numerical coefficient preceded by the sign of the monomial and followed by all the letters of the monomial, giving to each letter an exponent equal to one third of its exponent in the monomial.*

A rule much like the preceding one holds for fifth root, seventh root, and other odd roots.

Thus $\sqrt[3]{-8} = -2$, $\sqrt[5]{x^{10}} = x^2$, and $\sqrt[7]{128\,x^{21}} = 2\,x^\circ$.

EXERCISES

Find the value of the following:

1. $\sqrt{4\,a^2}$.

2. $\sqrt{9\,a^4}$.

3. $\sqrt{25\,a^6x^4}$.

4. $\sqrt{4\,x^4}$.

5. $\sqrt{9\,x^6}$.

6. $\sqrt{16\,x^{16}}$.

7. $\sqrt{49\,x^{14}y^{10}}$.

8. $\sqrt{81\,x^{12}d^{20}}$.

9. $\sqrt{121\,c^{22}d^6}$.

10. $\sqrt{169\,x^6}$.

11. $\sqrt{196\,y^{10}}$.

12. $\sqrt{225\,y^4z^6}$.

13. $\sqrt{256\,c^{12}}$.

14. $\sqrt{400\,a^2b^2c^4}$.

15. $\sqrt{324\,b^8}$.

16. $\sqrt{625\,b^2y^{18}z^6}$.

17. $\sqrt{x^{2n}}$.

18. $\sqrt{x^{4n}}$.

19. $\sqrt{x^{6n}}$.

20. $\sqrt{a^{4n}b^{8n}}$.

21. $\sqrt[3]{8}$.

22. $\sqrt[3]{-8\,a^3}$.

23. $\sqrt[3]{27}$.

24. $\sqrt[3]{64}$.

25. $\sqrt[3]{-125}$.

26. $\sqrt[3]{216}$.

27. $\sqrt[3]{-a^3}$.

28. $\sqrt[3]{-a^6}$.

29. $\sqrt[3]{a^9b^3}$.

30. $\sqrt[3]{343\,y^3}$.

31. $\sqrt[3]{512\,x^{15}}$.

32. $\sqrt[3]{-729\,a^3b^9}$.

33. $\sqrt[3]{1000\,a^6b^{12}}$.

34. $\sqrt[3]{-27\,a^3b^6c^{12}}$.

35. $\sqrt[3]{8\,a^{12}b^3c^9}$.

36. $\sqrt[3]{-125\,a^6b^6z^6}$.

37. $\sqrt[3]{x^{3n}}$.

38. $\sqrt[3]{x^{6n}}$.

39. $\sqrt[3]{-x^{9n}}$.

40. $\sqrt[3]{x^{12n}y^{6n}}$.

41. $\sqrt[5]{x^{15}}$.

42. $\sqrt[5]{32\,x^{10}}$.

49. Polynomials with a common monomial factor. The type form is

$$ab + ac - ad.$$

Plainly $ab + ac - ad = a(b + c - d).$

This gives, for factoring expressions having a common monomial factor, the

RULE. *Determine by inspection the greatest monomial factor which occurs in each term of the polynomial.*

Divide the polynomial by this monomial factor.

Write the quotient in a parenthesis preceded by the monomial factor.

Example. Factor $9\,x^2y - 36\,y^2$.

Solution: By inspection the greatest monomial factor of each term is $9\,y$. Dividing the binomial by $9\,y$, the quotient is $x^2 - 4\,y$.

Therefore $9\,x^2y - 36\,y^2 = 9\,y(x^2 - 4\,y).$

EXERCISES

Factor the following:

1. $3\,x + 6.$ $3(x+2)$
2. $x^3 - x^2.$ $x^2(x-1)$
3. $8\,x - 2\,x^4.$ $2x(4-x^3)$
4. $xy + y^2.$
5. $5\,b^3 - 15\,b^6.$
6. $c^3 - c^2y.$
7. $x^3 - x + x^2.$
8. $c^5 - c^3 + c^2.$
9. $3\,y - 9\,y^4 + 12.$
10. $c^2 + 2\,bc - c.$
11. $3\,y^2 - 15\,y + 6\,y^3.$
12. $10\,ab - 14\,bc - 8\,b^2.$
13. $y^5 + 3\,y^4z + 6\,y^3z^2.$
14. $4\,a^2x^2 - 6\,a^3y^3 + 12\,a^4x^2y^2.$
15. $12\,z^3 + 30\,a^4z^7 - 18\,c^3z^5.$
16. $6\,c^6 + 10\,c^{10} - 20\,c^2.$
17. $8\,y^8 - 4\,y^4 - 12\,y^{12}.$
18. $x^4 + x^3 - x^2 + x.$
19. $-8\,y^6 - 4\,y^6 + 12\,y^3 + 6\,y^5.$
20. $14\,b^5 - 49\,b^7 + 21\,b^2 - 7\,b^3.$
21. $-a^2x^2y^3 - 3\,a^4x^3y^2 - 2\,a^3x^5y^6z^3 + 5\,a^4x^4y^4z.$
22. $-18\,a^8b^3c^4 - 45\,a^4cy^2 - 36\,a^3c^2xz - 63\,a^4cxy.$
23. $32\,c^7x^2 + 80\,c^{10}bx - 112\,c^6b + 48\,c^{12}x.$
24. $56\,a^4b^3x^2 - 28\,a^3x + 112\,a^5x^2y^2 - 196\,a^6x^3.$

a(x + y) + b(x + y)
(a + b)(x + y)

50. Polynomials which may be factored by grouping terms.
The type form is
$$ax + ay + bx + by.$$

Plainly $ax + ay + bx + by = a(x + y) + b(x + y)$.

Dividing both terms of $a(x + y) + b(x + y)$ by $(x + y)$, the quotient is $a + b$.

Therefore $ax + ay + bx + by = (x + y)(a + b)$.

The preceding example illustrates the

RULE. *Arrange the terms of the polynomial to be factored, in groups of two or more terms each, such that in each group a monomial factor may be written outside a parenthesis, which in each case contains the same expression.*

Then divide by the expression in parenthesis and write the divisor as one factor and the quotient as the other.

Polynomials which may be factored by grouping terms, according to the foregoing rule, usually contain either four, six, or eight terms.

It is important to note that one can obtain two apparently different sets of factors for a given expression. Thus
$$(a - 3b)(c - d) = (3b - a)(d - c) = ac - 3bc - ad + 3bd.$$
But the difference between the first pair of binomials and the second pair is only one of sign, and it is customary in this and in similar cases to regard either pair of binomials as a different form of the other pair.

The relation that the process of factoring bears to the processes of multiplication and division of polynomials should be constantly kept in mind. In multiplication we have two factors given and are required to find their product. In division we have the product and one factor given and are required to find the other factor. In factoring, however, the problem is a little more difficult, for we have only the product given, and our experience is supposed to enable us to determine the factors. For this reason a very careful study of several forms of products is necessary.

There is no simple operation the performance of which makes us sure that we have found the *prime* factors of a given expression. Only insight and experience enable us to find prime factors with certainty.

A partial check, however, that may be applied to all the exercises in factoring consists in actually multiplying together the factors that have been found. The result should be the original expression.

EXERCISES

Factor the following (see Exercises 23–31, p. 32):

    1. $2(x + y) + a(x + y)$. $(x+y)(2+a)$

    2. $b(x + 2y) + (x + 2y)$. $(b+1)(x+2y)$

    3. $c(c - a) - a(c - a)$. $(c-a)(c-a)$

    4. $2c(3b - d) + 3a(3b - d)$.

    5. $6d(c + x) - (c + x) + 4k(c + x)$.

    6. $-5(2a - 3b) + 7a(2a - 3b) - 3b(2a - 3b)$.

    7. $k(a - b) + 3(b - a)$.

This can be written $k(a - b) - 3(a - b)$.

    8. $h(x - y) + k(y - x)$.

    9. $5x(c - 2d) - 6(2d - c)$.

    10. $3y(k - 4h) + (4h - k)$. $(3y-1)(k-4h)$

    11. $2c(4k - 3c) - 5h(3c - 4k)$. $(2c+5h)(4k-3c)$

    12. $3y(5x - b) - 7(b - 5x) + 6z(5x - b)$.

13. $ab + bx + ac + cx$.

Solution : $ab + bx + ac + cx = (ab + bx) + (ac + cx)$
$$= b(a + x) + c(a + x)$$
$$= (a + x)(b + c).$$

14. $ax - bx + a - b$.

Solution : $ax - bx + a - b = (ax - bx) + (a - b)$
$$= x(a - b) + 1(a - b)$$
$$= (a - b)(x + 1).$$

✗15. $4\,x^3 - 3\,xy - 8\,x^2y + 6\,y^2.$

Solution: $4\,x^3 - 3\,xy - 8\,x^2y + 6\,y^2$

$\qquad = (4\,x^3 - 3\,xy) + (-8\,x^2y + 6\,y^2)$

$\qquad = x\,(4\,x^2 - 3\,y) + 2\,y\,(-4\,x^2 + 3\,y)$

$\qquad = x\,(4\,x^2 - 3\,y) - 2\,y\,(4\,x^2 - 3\,y)$

$\qquad = (4\,x^2 - 3\,y)\,(x - 2\,y).$

Expressions similar to 13, 14, and 15 may be grouped in more than one way. For example, the terms of 15 can be grouped thus:

$\qquad (4\,x^3 - 8\,x^2y) + (-3\,xy + 6\,y^2)$

$\qquad = 4\,x^2\,(x - 2\,y) + 3\,y\,(-x + 2\,y)$

$\qquad = 4\,x^2\,(x - 2\,y) - 3\,y\,(x - 2\,y)$

$\qquad = (x - 2\,y)\,(4\,x^2 - 3\,y). \quad \longleftarrow$

✗16. $ax + bx + ay + by.$ $\quad (a+b)(x+y)$

17. $ch + h^2 + cx + hx.$

18. $bh - ch + bk - ck.$ $\quad (b-c)(h+k)$

19. $bx + xz - ab - az.$

✗20. $ax + 3\,a - bx - 3\,b.$ $\quad (a-b)(x+3)$

21. $2\,x^2 + 10\,xy - 4\,x - 20\,y.$

22. $6\,ab - 2\,ac + 3\,b - c.$

✗23. $36\,ax + 45\,ac - 4\,x - 5\,c.$

24. $6\,a^3 + 14\,ab - 15\,a^2y - 35\,by.$

✗25. $3\,ax - ay - 6\,bx + 2\,by.$ $\quad (3\,x - y)(a - 2\,b)$

✗26. $12\,ax - 6\,ay - 50\,cx + 25\,cy.$ $\quad (6\,a - 25\,c)(2\,x - y)$

✗27. $2\,h^3 - 3\,h^2k - 10\,h + 15\,k.$ $\quad (2\,h - 3\,k)(h^2 - 5)$

✗28. $10\,dh - 45\,hk - 22\,cd + 99\,ck.$ $\quad (2\,d - 9\,k)(5\,h - 11\,c)$

✗29. $28\,hx + 9\,ky - 21\,hy - 12\,kx.$ $\quad (4\,x - 3\,y)(7\,h - 3\,k)$

30. $-2\,ax + 7\,a^2 + 16\,bx - 56\,ab.$

31. $6\,hk + 15\,xy - 10\,ky - 9\,hx.$

32. $-21\,ax + 12\,cx - 4\,cd + 7\,ad.$

33. $7\,gy - 77\,hy - cg + 11\,ch.$

34. $5\,a^3 + 10\,a - 5\,a^2 - 10.$

35. $3\,a - 5\,ax^3 - 6\,ax + 10\,ax^4.$

36. $4\,abxy - 24\,dxy - 3\,abgh + 18\,dgh.$

37. $8\,acxy - 20\,bx^2y - 6\,abc^2 + 15\,b^2cx.$

38. $ax + bx + cx + ay + by + cy.$

39. $cg + 2\,ch + ck - gx - 2\,hx - kx.$

Handwritten margin note near 23: $x\,(9a-1) + 5c\,(9a-\ )$

40. $3\,ab - bx + 2\,by - 3\,ac + cx - 2\,cy.$

41. $4\,ax - ac + 2\,ay + 12\,bx - 3\,bc + 6\,by.$

42. $ax - 6\,cy - 2\,bx + 4\,by + 3\,cx - 2\,ay.$

43. $-2\,xz + 6\,ay + cz + 4\,xy - 3\,az - 2\,cy.$

51. Trinomials which are perfect squares. The type form is

$$a^2 \pm 2\,ab + b^2.$$

This, by § 42, gives us the two expressions:

$$a^2 + 2\,ab + b^2 = (a + b)^2,$$
$$a^2 - 2\,ab + b^2 = (a - b)^2.$$

If an algebraic expression is the product of two equal factors, it is said to be a **perfect square**.

A trinomial, arranged according to the descending powers of one letter, *is a perfect square if the absolute value of the middle term is twice the product of the absolute values of the square roots of the other two terms.*

Thus in the type form above, $2\,ab = 2 \cdot \sqrt{a^2} \cdot \sqrt{b^2}$.

Similarly the trinomial $4\,x^2 - 20\,xy^2 + 25\,y^4$ is a perfect square, since $20\,xy^2 = 2 \cdot \sqrt{4\,x^2} \cdot \sqrt{25\,y^4} = 2 \cdot 2\,x \cdot 5\,y^2$.

EXERCISES

Form perfect trinomial squares of the following by supplying the missing term:

1. $c^2 + (?) + d^2.$ **3.** $4\,a^2 + (?) + 1.$ **5.** $4\,x^2 + (?) + 25.$

2. $a^2 + (?) + 4.$ **4.** $x^6 + (?) + 9.$ **6.** $9\,x^6 + (?) + 4\,y^2.$

7. $100\,x^2 + (?) + 36\,y^2.$ **14.** $121\,y^6 - 88\,y^3z + (?).$

8. $49 + (?) + 64\,y^8.$ **15.** $100\,a^8 + 240\,a^4x^5 + (?).$

9. $x^2 + 2\,x + (?).$ **16.** $(?) - 6\,y^2 + 9.$

10. $y^2 - 6\,y + (?).$ **17.** $(?) - 10\,y^4 + 25.$

11. $4\,y^2 - 40\,y + (?).$ **18.** $(?) + 16\,k^2 + 4.$

12. $9\,y^2 + 36\,y + (?).$ **19.** $(?) - 80\,k^2h^2 + 64\,h^4.$

13. $16\,z^4 - 16\,xz^2 + (?).$ **20.** $(?) + 104\,a^8k + 169\,k^2.$

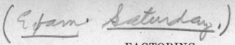

For obtaining *one* of the two equal factors of a perfect trinomial square, we have the

RULE. *Arrange the terms of the trinomial according to the descending powers of some letter in it.* (Dead)

Extract the square root of the first and third terms and connect the results by the ~~sign~~ of the middle term.

EXERCISES

Factor the following:

1. $c^2 + 2cd + d^2$.   4. $a^2 - 10a + 25$.   7. $9 - 6x + x^2$.

2. $x^2 + 2xy + y^2$.   5. $a^2 + 8a + 16$.   8. $16k^2 + 1 - 8k$.

3. $x^2 + 2x + 1$.   6. $4h^2 + 4h + 1$.   9. $4h^2 - 12h + 9$.

10. $x^4 + 1 + 2x^2$.   16. $c^6d^{10} + 2c^3d^5 + 1$.

11. $x^6 - 6x^3 + 9$.   17. $24x^2y^2 + 16y^4 + 9x^4$.

12. $25h^2 + 4k^2 - 20hk$.   18. $x^4 + 4y^4 + 4x^2y^2$.

13. $9h^2 - 24hk + 16k^2$.   19. $4x^2y^8 - 4xy^4 + 1$.

14. $x^2 - 24xz^2 + 144z^4$.   20. $25h^6k^2 - 30h^3kz + 9z^2$.

15. $12x^4z^3 + 9z^6 + 4x^8$.   21. $121c^6d^4 - 220c^3d^2g^2 + 100g^4$.

22. $169a^4 - 156a^2x^4y^3 + 36x^8y^6$.

It is only in the beginning of factoring that polynomials are classified for the student. In the practical work of handling fractions and solving equations he must determine for himself the type of the polynomial to be factored. It is therefore very important that he fix in mind the various types and the manner of factoring each. Moreover, he should remember that the polynomials which arise in practice often have three or more factors. Miscellaneous review exercises afford excellent practice in recognizing types and in determining all the prime factors.

The suggestions given on page 120 will prove helpful, though only the first three of the types there given have as yet been considered.

REVIEW EXERCISES

Separate into prime factors:

1. $x^3 + 2x^2 + x$.

2. $x^5 - 4x^4 + 4x^3$.

3. $2a^4 + 12a^2 + 18$.

4. $3a^2 + 18a + 27$.

5. $x^6 - 20x^4 + 100x^2$.

6. $5cx^6 - 70cx^3 + 245c$.

7. $16x^8 - 24x^6 + 9x^4$.

8. $28x^2 - 28x^3 + 7x^4$.

9. $3ax + 3ay + 3bx + 3by$.

10. $4cx - 4cy + 4dx - 4dy$.

11. $ax - a + x - 1$.

12. $63xy - 84y^2 + 98yz$.

13. $30ax - 34bx - 15a + 17b$.

14. $ax - bx + cx + ay - by + cy$.

15. $14anx - 21bny - 7n$.

16. $3ax - 5by - 5ay + 3bx$.

17. $56a^2 - 40ab + 63ac - 45bc$.

52. The quadratic trinomial. The type form is *(Factoring by trial)*

$$x^2 + bx + c.$$

Suppose $(x + h)(x + k) \equiv x^2 + bx + c$.

Then $x^2 + (h + k)x + hk \equiv x^2 + bx + c$.

Since this is an *identity* we may assume that the corresponding terms in each member are equal.

That is, $(h + k)x = bx$,

or $h + k = b$;

and $hk = c$.

Therefore, if two numbers exist whose sum is b and whose product is c, the trinomial $x^2 + bx + c$ can be factored; if such numbers do not exist, the trinomial cannot be factored. Many trinomials of the form $x^2 + bx + c$ are prime; for factoring such as are not we have the

RULE. *Find two numbers whose algebraic product is c and whose algebraic sum is b.*

Write for the factors the two binomials which have x for the common term and the numbers just obtained for the unlike terms.

EXAMPLES

1. Factor $x^2 + 7x + 12$.

Solution: Here it is necessary to find two numbers whose product is $+12$ and whose sum is $+7$. Now $12 = 1 \cdot 12$, or $2 \cdot 6$, or $3 \cdot 4$. Obviously only the last pair gives 7 for a sum.

Therefore $\qquad x^2 + 7x + 12 = (x + 3)(x + 4)$.

2. Factor $x^2 - 12x + 32$.

Solution: Since 32 is positive its two factors must have the same sign; since -12 is negative both factors must be negative. Now $32 = 1 \cdot 32$, or $2 \cdot 16$, or $4 \cdot 8$. By inspection of these products, -4 and -8 are found to be the required numbers.

Therefore $\qquad x^2 - 12x + 32 = (x - 4)(x - 8)$.

3. Factor $x^2 - 6x - 40$.

Solution: The product, -40, is negative; hence the required factors have *unlike* signs. The sum, -6, being negative, the negative factor of -40 must have the greater absolute value. Now $40 = 1 \cdot 40$, or $2 \cdot 20$, or $4 \cdot 10$, or $5 \cdot 8$. We see that $4 + (-10) = -6$.

Therefore $\qquad x^2 - 6x - 40 = (x + 4)(x - 10)$.

4. Factor $x^2 + 13x - 48$.

Solution: The product is negative; hence the required factors have unlike signs. The sum being positive, the positive factor of 48 must have the greater absolute value. Now $48 = 1 \cdot 48 = 2 \cdot 24 = 3 \cdot 16 = 4 \cdot 12 = 6 \cdot 8$. We observe that $16 + (-3) = 13$.

Therefore $\qquad x^2 + 13x - 48 = (x - 3)(x + 16)$.

EXERCISES

Factor:

1. $x^2 + 5x + 6$.   **5.** $x^2 + 19x + 18$.   **9.** $x^2 + x - 30$.

2. $x^2 + 9x + 20$.   **6.** $x^2 + 18x + 17$.   **10.** $x^2 - 2x - 35$.

3. $x^2 - 7x + 12$.   **7.** $x^2 - x - 6$.   **11.** $x^2 + 11x - 42$.

4. $x^2 - 9x + 14$.   **8.** $x^2 - 3x - 40$.   **12.** $6 - 5x - x^2$.

Solution: Arranging the terms, this becomes $-x^2 - 5x + 6$. The minus sign in the term $-x^2$ prevents our obtaining its square root. Taking out the common factor -1, and factoring as usual,

$$-x^2 - 5x + 6 = (-1)(x^2 + 5x - 6) = (-1)(x - 1)(x + 6)$$
$$= (-x + 1)(x + 6) = (1 - x)(x + 6).$$

13. $14 - 5x - x^2$.

14. $21 + 4x - x^2$.

15. $24 + 10a - a^2$.

16. $10 + 3x - x^2$.

17. $72 + c - c^2$.

18. $x^2 + x - 90$.

19. $28 + x^2 - 11x$.

20. $27 - 12x + x^2$.

21. $8x + x^2 - 48$.

22. $x^2 - x - 90$.

23. $x^2 - 5ax + 6a^2$.

24. $x^2 + 7ax + 12a^2$.

25. $a^2x^2 - 2ax - 15$.

26. $h^2k^2 - 9hk + 20$.

27. $x^4 - 5x^2 - 14$.

28. $x^2 + x^4 - 110$.

29. $x^6 - 11x^3 + 18$.

30. $b^2x^2 - 3bxy - 28y^2$.

31. $h^2k^2 - 5hkx - 36x^2$.

32. $a^6b^2 - 5a^3bx - 24x^2$.

33. $h^4d^2 + 10h^2dg^3 - 24g^6$.

34. $9k^2x^4y^6 + k^4x^8 - 22y^{12}$.

REVIEW EXERCISES

Factor:

1. $x^4 + 6x^3 + 9x^2$.

2. $x^3 - 5x^2 + 6x$.

3. $3b^2 - 9b - 30$.

4. $3ax^3 - 3ax^2 - 6ax$.

5. $4x^5 - 4x^3 - 360x$.

6. $3x^4 - 21x^3 - 54x^2$.

7. $4a^6y^4 - 64a^4y^2 + 256a^2$.

8. $3x - 3ax - 18a^2x$.

9. $56x + x^2 - x^3$.

10. $140h^2 + 23h^3 - h^4$.

11. $3x^3 - 3x^4 + 60x^2$.

12. $32a^2x^2 + 2a^2 - 16a^2x$.

13. $4ay^2x^2 - 40ay^2x + 100ay^2$.

14. $3x^4 - 3x^3 + 3x^2 - 3x$.

15. $2ax^3 - 4ax^2 - 12ax + 24a$.

16. $5xyz - 15yz + 10xz - 30z$.

53. The general quadratic trinomial. The type form is

$$ax^2 + bx + c.$$

A trinomial of this type can always be factored by grouping, if two numbers can be found whose product is *ac* and whose algebraic sum is *b*. If such numbers do not exist, the trinomial is prime.

1. Factor $6x^2 + 17x + 7$.

Solution: Here $b = 17$ and $ac = 6 \cdot 7 = 42$. Now $42 = 1 \cdot 42 = 2 \cdot 21 = 3 \cdot 14 = 6 \cdot 7$. Obviously the only pair of factors whose sum is 17 is 3 and 14.

Therefore we write $6x^2 + 17x + 7 = 6x^2 + 3x + 14x + 7$
$$= 3x(2x + 1) + 7(2x + 1)$$
$$= (2x + 1)(3x + 7).$$

2. Factor $3x^2 + 10x - 8$.

Solution: Here $b = 10$ and $ac = 3(-8) = -24$. Now $24 = 1 \cdot 24 = 2 \cdot 12 = 3 \cdot 8 = 4 \cdot 6$. Since the product, -24, is negative the parts into which $+10$ is to be separated must have opposite signs. Obviously $+12$ and -2 are the required numbers.

Therefore we write $3x^2 + 10x - 8 = 3x^2 + 12x - 2x - 8$
$$= 3x(x + 4) - 2(x + 4)$$
$$= (x + 4)(3x - 2).$$

For factoring a trinomial of the form $ax^2 + bx + c$ the preceding examples illustrate the

RULE. *Find two numbers whose product is* **ac** *and whose algebraic sum is* **b**.

Replace **bx** *by two terms in* **x** *whose respective coefficients are the numbers just found, and factor by grouping terms.*

A perfect trinomial square and a trinomial of the form $x^2 + bx + c$ are special forms of $ax^2 + bx + c$. Therefore the exercises on page 109 and those on pages 111–112 could be factored by the rule just given.

Factor:

1. $2x^2 + 5x + 3$.

2. $3x^2 + 5x + 2$.

3. $2x^2 - 7x + 3$.

4. $x^2 + 6x + 9$.

5. $3x^2 + 8x + 4$.

6. $5x^2 - 8x + 3$.

7. $9x^2 + 18x + 8$.

8. $7x^2 + 9ax + 2a^2$.

9. $4x^2 + 16x + 15$.

10. $2x^2 - 3x - 2$.

11. $2x^2 - x - 3$.

12. $4x^2 - 7x - 15$.

13. $3 x^4 + 7 x^2 - 6.$

14. $3 x^2 + 5 xy - 2 y^2.$

15. $3 x^2 - x - 2.$

16. $2 x^2 - 5 x - 3.$

17. $2 x^2 + xz - 3 z^2.$

18. $6 x^2 - x - 2.$

19. $25 x^2 - 20 x + 3.$

20. $49 x^2 - 21 x + 2.$

21. $36 x^2 - 36 x + 5.$

22. $6 x^4 + 13 x^2 + 6.$

23. $9 x^6 - 6 x^3 - 8.$

24. $5 x^2 + 2 x - 16.$

25. $3 x^2 - 11 x - 20.$

26. $5 x^4 + 18 x^2 y + 16 y^2.$

27. $6 x^2 + 23 x - 55.$

28. $6 x^6 + 23 x^3 + 21.$

29. $10 x^2 - 7 x - 12.$

30. $4 c^2 + 11 cg - 3 g^2.$

31. $8 x^2 + 26 xy + 15 y^2.$

32. $35 x^2 + 22 x + 3.$

33. $14 x^2 - x - 3.$

34. $21 x^4 - x^2 - 2.$

35. $22 x^2 - 3 x - 7.$

36. $18 x^2 + 65 x + 7.$

37. $26 x^2 + 9 x - 2.$

38. $14 x^2 - 39 x + 10.$

39. $35 x^2 - 39 x - 36.$

40. $42 x^2 - 9 x - 6.$

REVIEW EXERCISES

Factor:

1. $4 ax^2 + 8 ax + 3 a.$

2. $2 c^2 x^2 + c^2 x - 3 c^2.$

3. $48 ax^4 - 120 ax^2 + 75 a.$

4. $18 c^2 d - 30 cd - 28 d.$

5. $x^4 + x^3 - 110 x^2.$

6. $75 x^3 + 60 x^2 + 12 x.$

7. $4 x^2 y^2 - 4 xy^2 - 120 y^2.$

8. $70 x^3 - 85 x^2 y - 30 xy^2.$

9. $18 x^3 - 39 x^2 + 18 x.$

10. $36 x^4 - 6 x^3 - 12 x^2.$

11. $4 x^4 - 20 x^3 - 24 x^2.$

12. $5 ax^2 + 5 ax + 5 a.$

54. A binomial the difference of two squares. The type form is

$$a^2 - b^2.$$

By § 43 $a^2 - b^2 = (a + b)(a - b).$

•Hence the

RULE. *Regarding each term of the binomial as positive, extract its square root.*

Add the two square roots for one factor, and subtract the second from the first for the other.

EXAMPLES

1. Factor $x^8 - y^4$.

Solution: $x^8 - y^4 = (x^4 + y^2)(x^4 - y^2)$, by application of the rule.
$$= (x^4 + y^2)(x^2 + y)(x^2 - y), \text{ by application of the}$$
rule to $x^4 - y^2$.

2. Factor $256\,x^{16} - y^8$.

Solution: $256\,x^{16} - y^8 = (16\,x^8 + y^4)(16\,x^8 - y^4)$
$$= (16\,x^8 + y^4)(4\,x^4 + y^2)(4\,x^4 - y^2)$$
$$= (16\,x^8 + y^4)(4\,x^4 + y^2)(2\,x^2 + y)(2\,x^2 - y).$$

EXERCISES

Factor:

1. $k^2 - h^2$.

2. $h^2 - 1$.

3. $k^2 - 4$.

4. $a^4 - x^2$.

5. $1 - a^2$.

6. $1 - 4\,a^2$.

7. $4\,a^2 - 9$.

8. $25 - x^2$.

9. $h^4 - 81$.

10. $16\,x^4 - 25$.

11. $36\,c^8 - 49\,d^8$.

12. $a^2b^4 - 121$.

13. $100 - z^8$.

14. $x^4 - y^4$.

15. $64\,h^6 - 169$.

16. $a^8 - b^8$.

17. $1 - 16\,x^4$.

18. $16\,x^4 - y^8$.

19. $x^{16} - y^{16}$.

20. $x^{16} - 4\,y^{16}$.

21. $144\,a^2b^4 - 9$.

22. $196 - x^4y^6$.

23. $225\,a^4 - 16\,b^8c^{12}$.

24. $x^{2n} - y^2$.

25. $x^2 - y^{4n}$.

26. $a^{4n} - b^2$.

27. $a^{6n} - b^{2n}$.

28. $a^{4n} - b^{6n}$.

29. $4\,x^{2n} - y^{4n}$.

30. $9\,x^{2n} - 4\,y^{6n}$.

31. $(a + b)^2 - 4$.

32. $(x - y)^2 - 4\,c^2$.

33. $(a - 2\,b)^2 - 9\,x^2$.

34. $4\,(x + y)^2 - 1$. **35.** $25\,(3\,b - c)^2 - 64$.

36. $4 - (a + b)^2$.

Solution: $4 - (a + b)^2 = [2 + (a + b)][2 - (a + b)]$
$$= (2 + a + b)(2 - a - b).$$

37. $81 - (x - y)^2$. **38.** $4\,a^2 - (2\,x + y)^2$.

Some polynomials of four or six terms may be arranged as the difference of two squares and factored as in the preceding exercises.

EXAMPLES

1. Factor: $a^2 + 2ab + b^2 - c^2$.

Solution: $a^2 + 2ab + b^2 - c^2 = (a+b)^2 - c^2$
$$= (a+b+c)(a+b-c).$$

2. Factor: $a^2 + 2ab + b^2 - c^2 - 2cd - d^2$.

Solution: $a^2 + 2ab + b^2 - c^2 - 2cd - d^2$
$$= a^2 + 2ab + b^2 - (c^2 + 2cd + d^2)$$
$$= (a+b)^2 - (c+d)^2$$
$$= (a+b+c+d)(a+b-c-d).$$

EXERCISES

Factor:

1. $(a-b)^2 - 9x^2$.

2. $16y^2 - (h+2k)^2$.

3. $25a^4 - (2b-3c)^2$.

4. $49x^6 - (7c-2d)^2$.

5. $1 - (5h-3k)^2$.

6. $(5x+2y)^2 - (3x-7y)^2$

Solution: $(5x+2y)^2 - (3x-7y)^2$
$$= [(5x+2y)+(3x-7y)][(5x+2y)-(3x-7y)]$$
$$= (5x+2y+3x-7y)(5x+2y-3x+7y)$$
$$= (8x-5y)(2x+9y).$$

7. $(a-b)^2 - (a+b)^2$.

8. $(a-b)^2 - (x+y)^2$.

9. $(a+2b)^2 - (a-3b)^2$.

10. $(2a-3b)^2 - (3a-2b)^2$.

11. $(5h+3k)^2 - (2c-9d)^2$.

12. $(4b-a)^2 - (7a-6b)^2$.

13. $4(a-2b)^2 - (2x-y)^2$.

14. $9(a+b)^2 - (2a-5b)^2$.

15. $(a-2b)^2 - 4(a+b)^2$.

16. $y^2 - c^2 + x^2 - 2xy$.

Solution: $y^2 - c^2 + x^2 - 2xy = x^2 - 2xy + y^2 - c^2$
$$= (x-y)^2 - c^2$$
$$= (x-y+c)(x-y-c).$$

17. $x^2 + 2ax + a^2 - y^2$.

18. $x^2 + 2x + 1 - 4z^2$.

19. $c^2 - 2cd + d^2 - 16a^2$.

20. $4x^2 - 12cx + 9c^2 - 25y^2$.

21. $x^2 - y^2 - 2ax + a^2$.

22. $k^2 - g^4 - 4kh + 4h^2$.

23. $6xy - c^2 + 9x^2 + y^2$.

24. $12ab - 4h^2 + 4b^2 + 9a^2$.

25. $1 - 4ax + 4a^2x^2 - x^2$.

26. $4c^2 - 20cd + 25d^2 - 9d^4$.

27. $9\,d^2 - 25\,a^2 - 6\,cd + c^2$.   **28.** $12\,ab + x^2 - 4\,a^2 - 9\,b^2$.

Solution: $12\,ab + x^2 - 4\,a^2 - 9\,b^2$
$$= x^2 - 4\,a^2 + 12\,ab - 9\,b^2$$
$$= x^2 - (4\,a^2 - 12\,ab + 9\,b^2)$$
$$= x^2 - (2\,a - 3\,b)^2$$
$$= (x + 2\,a - 3\,b)(x - 2\,a + 3\,b).$$

29. $a^2 - b^2 - 2\,bc - c^2$.   **33.** $9\,x^2 - 4\,y^2 - a^2 - 4\,ay$.

30. $x^2 - a^2 - 2\,ac - c^2$.   **34.** $6\,x + 9\,y^2 - 9 - x^2$.

31. $y^2 - b^2 + 4\,bc - 4\,c^2$.   **35.** $4\,bc + 1 - 4\,c^2 - b^2$.

32. $2\,bc - c^2 - b^2 + a^4$.   **36.** $4\,bc - 4\,b^2 + 4\,x^6 - c^2$.

37. $x^2 - a^2 + y^2 - 4 - 2\,xy + 4\,a$.

Solution: $x^2 - a^2 + y^2 - 4 - 2\,xy + 4\,a$
$$= x^2 - 2\,xy + y^2 - a^2 + 4\,a - 4$$
$$= (x^2 - 2\,xy + y^2) - (a^2 - 4\,a + 4)$$
$$= (x - y)^2 - (a - 2)^2$$
$$= (x - y + a - 2)(x - y - a + 2).$$

38. $a^2 + 2\,ab + b^2 - c^2 - 2\,cd - d^2$.

39. $9\,k^2 - 6\,hk + h^2 - 4\,c^2 - 4\,cd - d^2$.

40. $x^2 - 1 + y^2 - a^2 + 2\,xy + 2\,a$.

41. $1 + 2\,bc + 2\,a - c^2 - b^2 + a^2$.

REVIEW EXERCISES

Factor:

1. $x^3 - x$.   **3.** $x^8 - 2\,x^4 + 1$.   **5.** $x^5 - x$.

2. $x^4 - 2\,x^2 + 1$.   **4.** $x^5 - 8\,x^3 + 16\,x$.   **6.** $x^{10} - x^2$.

7. $x^4 - 10\,x^2 + 9$.   **13.** $4\,n^6 + 48\,n^2 - 28\,n^4$.

8. $x^4 - 13\,x^2 + 36$.   **14.** $16\,x^4 + 8\,x^2 - 3$.

9. $3\,a^2x^4 - 12\,a^4x^2 + 12\,a^6$.   **15.** $a^3 - a + a^2b - b$.

10. $18\,a^2x^2 - 24\,a^2x - 10\,a^2$.   **16.** $x^3 - x^2 - 4\,x + 4$.

11. $3\,x^4 - 15\,x^2 + 12$.   **17.** $3\,a^3 + 3\,a^2 - 27\,a - 27$.

12. $12\,a - 39\,ay - 51\,ay^2$.   **18.** $2\,a^3b + 3\,a^2b - 8\,ab - 12\,b$.

19. $4\,a^2 - a^4 + 81 + 10\,a^2x - 36\,a - 25\,x^2$.

20. $12\,cd^3 - 6\,a^3x - a^6 + 4\,c^2 + 9\,d^6 - 9\,x^2$.

55. A binomial the sum or the difference of two cubes. The type form is

$$a^3 \pm b^3.$$

$a^3 + b^3$ divided by $(a + b)$ gives the quotient $a^2 - ab + b^2$, and $a^3 - b^3$ divided by $(a - b)$ gives the quotient $a^2 + ab + b^2$.

Therefore $a^3 + b^3 = (a + b)(a^2 - ab + b^2)$,
and $a^3 - b^3 = (a - b)(a^2 + ab + b^2)$.

EXAMPLES

1. Factor $x^3 + 8$.

Solution: $x^3 + 8 = x^3 + 2^3 = (x + 2)(x^2 - x \cdot 2 + 2^2)$
$= (x + 2)(x^2 - 2x + 4)$.

2. Factor $27 x^3 - 1$.

Solution: $27 x^3 - 1 = (3x)^3 - 1^3 = (3x - 1)[(3x)^2 + 3x \cdot 1 + 1^2]$
$= (3x - 1)(9x^2 + 3x + 1)$.

3. Factor $64 x^3 + 125 y^6$.

Solution: $64 x^3 + 125 y^6 = (4x)^3 + (5y^2)^3$
$= (4x + 5y^2)[(4x)^2 - (4x)(5y^2) + (5y^2)^2]$
$= (4x + 5y^2)(16x^2 - 20xy^2 + 25y^4)$.

EXERCISES

Factor:

1. $x^3 + 1$.   **6.** $x^3 - y^6$.   **11.** $125 y^3 + 8 x^3$.

2. $x^3 - 1$.   **7.** $x^3 + 8 y^3$.   **12.** $216 - 27 x^3$.

3. $a^3 - 8$.   **8.** $x^3 + y^9$.   **13.** $x^6 + y^9$.

4. $27 + b^3$.   **9.** $8 x^3 - 27 y^3$.   **14.** $a^6 + b^6$.

5. $64 x^3 - 1$.   **10.** $27 a^3 + 64 b^3$.   **15.** $a^6 - b^6$.

HINT. This expression may be regarded as the difference of two cubes, $(a^2)^3 - (b^2)^3$, or as the difference of two squares, $(a^3)^2 - (b^3)^2$. *Whenever an expression may be regarded in both these ways the latter is always preferable.* Thus $a^6 - b^6 = (a^3 + b^3)(a^3 - b^3)$, etc.

16. $x^6 - 64$.   **20.** $x^{12} + y^{12}$.   **24.** $x^{3a} - y^{3a}$.

17. $64 x^6 + 1$.   **21.** $27 x^{27} - 1$.   **25.** $x^{3a} + y^{6a}$.

18. $1 - 64 x^6$.   **22.** $k^{12} - y^6$.   **26.** $8 x^{6a} - y^{9a}$.

19. $a^6 b^6 - 64$.   **23.** $x^{3a} + 1$.   **27.** $27 x^{3m} - 64$.

REVIEW EXERCISES

Factor:

1. $x^6 + 2x^3 + 1$.

2. $x^6 - 2x^3y^3 + y^6$.

3. $x^4 + x$.

4. $x^5 - x^2$.

5. $8x^3 - 64$.

6. $8x^6 + 216x^3$.

7. $x^5 - x^3y^2 - x^2y^3 + y^5$.

8. $x^5 + x^3 + 8x^2 + 8$.

9. $x^7 - x^4 - 16x^3 + 16$.

10. $x^6 - 7x^3 - 8$.

11. $8x^6 - 3 - 23x^3$.

12. $x^4 + x^3 - x - 1$.

13. $x^6 - x^2y^2$.

14. $x^8 + 64x^2$.

15. $1 + 3x + 3x^2 + x^3$.

Solution:
$$\begin{aligned}
1 + 3x + 3x^2 + x^3 &= (1 + x^3) + (3x + 3x^2) \\
&= (1 + x)(1 - x + x^2) + 3x(1 + x) \\
&= (1 + x)(1 - x + x^2 + 3x) \\
&= (1 + x)(1 + 2x + x^2) \\
&= (1 + x)(1 + x)(1 + x).
\end{aligned}$$

16. $1 - 3x + 3x^2 - x^3$.

17. $x^3 + 3x^2y + 3xy^2 + y^3$.

18. $x^3 - 3x^2y + 3xy^2 - y^3$.

19. $x^3 + 2x^2 + 4x + 8$.

20. $8 - 4x + 2x^2 - x^3$.

21. $x^3 + 9x^2 + 27x + 27$.

22. $x^3 - 9x^2 + 27x - 27$.

23. $x^3 + 12x^2 + 48x + 64$.

24. $64 - 48x + 12x^2 - x^3$.

25. $8x^3 - 12x^2 + 6x - 1$.

26. $x^4 + x^3 + x^2 - 1$.

27. $x^3 + a^3 + x^2 - a^2$.

56. General directions for factoring. Since the various methods of factoring cannot be stated in a few simple rules, they must be learned by means of such type forms and typical solutions as are given in the preceding pages. When once these have been thoroughly mastered, readiness in factoring becomes a matter of experience. Usually a student finds it comparatively easy to factor a list of exercises classified under a particular type form, yet a list of miscellaneous exercises he finds difficult. This often indicates inability to determine the type of an expression by its *form*. Until the student, by careful study of the type forms, has acquired the ability to do this, he will make little progress.

The following suggestions will prove helpful:

I. *First look for a common monomial factor, and if there is one (other than 1), separate the expression into its greatest monomial factor and the corresponding polynomial factor.*

II. *Then by the form of the polynomial factor determine with which of the following types it should be classed and use the methods of factoring applicable to that type.*

1. $ax + ay + bx + by$.
2. $a^2 \pm 2ab + b^2$.
3. $x^2 + bx + c$.
4. $ax^2 + bx + c$.
5. $\begin{cases} a^2 - b^2. \\ a^2 + 2ab + b^2 - c^2. \\ a^2 + 2ab + b^2 - c^2 - 2cd - d^2. \end{cases}$
6. $a^3 \pm b^3$.

III. *Proceed again as in II with each polynomial factor obtained until the original expression has been separated into its prime factors.*

MISCELLANEOUS EXERCISES

Factor:

1. $x^4 + 64y^4 + 16x^2y^2$.
2. $4a^2x^4 + 4a^2x^2 - 120a^2$.
3. $9x^2 + 27x + 14$.
4. $3x^4 + x^2 - 2$.
5. $3x^3 - 75x$.
6. $x^2 + 2a^2x^2 + x^2a^4$.
7. $x^3 - 27$.
8. $x^2 - xz + 2xy - 2yz$.
9. $2ac - bc + 6ad - 3bd$.
10. $25x^2y^2 + 16x^4 - 40x^3y$.
11. $x^4 - 15x^3 + 56x^2$.

12. $9x^6 - 6x^3 - 35$.
13. $a^6 - 4096$.
14. $a^{2x+2} - 1$.
15. $4x^4 - 13x^2y^2 + 9y^4$.
16. $216 + x^3$.
17. $x^9 - 512$.
18. $x^2 - 4y^2 + 9 - 6x$.
19. $ah - 2ak + 2bh - 4bk$.
20. $4x^4 - 25y^8$.
21. $a^2 - 25c^2 + 10ab + 25b^2$.
22. $y^6 - 343$.

23. $9x^4 - 9x^2 - 28$.

24. $9x^2y^2 + 39xy^2 - 30y^2$.

25. $3x^6y^2 + 63x^3y^2 - 300y^2$.

26. $12 - 15a + 16x - 20ax$.

27. $2cx + 3dx - 2cy - 3dy$.

28. $y^4 + z^8 - 2y^2z^4$.

29. $81c^{10} - 64d^{10}$.

30. $100x^8 - 220x^4y^2 + 121y^4$.

31. $27y^3 - 512$.

32. $81 - 16x^8$.

33. $25x^4 - 3025x^8$.

34. $16c^7 - 4c^5 - 72c^3$.

35. $c^3 + c^2d + 3cd^2 + 3d^3$.

36. $1 + 81x^8 - 18x^4$.

37. $x^4 + 12x^2 - 64$.

38. $c^9 - 512c^{12}$.

39. $h^{6a} - k^{8a}$.

40. $a^2 - b^4 - 12ab + 36b^2$.

41. $5h^2 + 21hk - 20k^2$.

42. $x^6 - x^3 - 2$.

43. $2x^2y^2 - y^4 - x^4$.

44. $5h^3 - 9h^2k - 9k^3 + 5hk^2$.

45. $3x^2 - 17x + 10$.

46. $9x^{5n} - x^{3n}$.

47. $27a - 18ab^2 - 3a^9 + 3ab^4$.

48. $1 + 2x^2 - 3x^4$.

49. $x^4 - x^2 - 12$.

50. $16x^4 + 8x^2 - 3$.

51. $1024 - 64h^3 + h^6$.

52. $h^2k^2 - h^2 - k^2 + 1$.

53. $12 - 2h - 4h^2$.

54. $3 - y^2 + 3y^3 - y^5$.

CHAPTER XIV

· SOLUTION OF EQUATIONS BY FACTORING

57. Definitions. A term is **rational** if it may be obtained from unity and the letters involved by means of the four fundamental operations without the extraction of any root.

Thus $15\,x$, $\dfrac{a-b}{2}$, $\dfrac{8\,y}{3}$, and $\sqrt{4\,a^2}$ are rational, while $\sqrt{2\,x}$, $\sqrt{a-b}$, and $\sqrt{x^3}$ are irrational.

An algebraic expression is rational if its terms are rational.

An irrational term or an irrational expression may be rational with respect to a certain letter or letters.

Thus $4\,x^2 - \sqrt{a}\,x + 2\,a$ is rational with respect to x. The equation $4\,x^2 - \sqrt{a}\,x + 2\,a = 0$ is an equation rational in x.

A term is **integral** if it has no literal denominator and the exponents of the letters are *positive integers*.

Thus $\dfrac{3\,x^4}{5}$ and $4\,ax^2$ are integral terms.

(It will be seen later what x^{-2} and $x^{\frac{3}{2}}$ mean, and why they are not integral terms.)

An expression is integral if its terms are integral.

A nonintegral term or expression may be integral with respect to a certain letter, if that letter does not occur in any denominator.

Thus the left member of $x^3 - \dfrac{3\,x}{a} - \dfrac{b}{a^2} = 0$ is integral with respect to x and the equation itself is integral in x.

The *degree* of a rational integral equation in one unknown is the same as the highest power of the unknown in it.

An equation of the second degree is called a **quadratic** equation.

The equations $x^2 - 6\,x = 18$ and $ax^2 + bx + c = 0$ are quadratic.

122

An equation of the third degree is called a **cubic**.

For example, $x^3 = 1$, $x^3 - 5x^2 + 6x + 2 = 0$, and $ax^3 + bx^2 + cx + d = 0$ are cubic equations.

An equation of the fourth degree is called a **biquadratic**.

Thus $x^4 = 16$, $x^4 + 3x^2 = 4$, and $ax^4 + bx^3 + cx^2 + dx + e = 0$ are biquadratic equations.

One important application of factoring is determining the roots of equations of the second or a higher degree.

In the solution of equations by factoring use is made of the following

PRINCIPLE. *If the product of two or more factors is zero, one of the factors must be zero.*

Two or more, or even all of the factors *may* be zero, but the vanishing of one is *sufficient* to make a product zero.

EXAMPLES

1. Solve the quadratic equation $x^2 + 5x = 6$.

Solution : Transposing, $x^2 + 5x - 6 = 0$.
Factoring, $(x - 1)(x + 6) = 0$.

Suppose the first factor, $x - 1$, has the value zero. Then its product with the second factor is zero, no matter what value $x + 6$ may have. Hence the value of x which makes $x - 1$ equal to zero is a root of the quadratic.

Setting $x - 1 = 0$, we obtain $x = 1$.
Then $(x - 1)(x + 6) = (1 - 1)(1 + 6)$
$= (0) \cdot (7)$
$= 0$.

Similarly if the second factor, $x + 6$, has the value zero, its product with the first factor is zero, no matter what value $x - 1$ may have.

Setting $x + 6 = 0$, we obtain $x = -6$.
Then $(x - 1)(x + 6) = (-6 - 1)(-6 + 6)$
$= (-7) \cdot (0)$
$= 0$.

Check : Substituting 1 for x in $x^2 + 5x = 6$, $1 + 5 = 6$.
Substituting -6 for x in $x^2 + 5x = 6$, $36 - 30 = 6$.

2. Solve the cubic equation $x^3 + x^2 = 4x + 4$.

Solution: Transposing, $x^3 + x^2 - 4x - 4 = 0$.

Grouping,
$$(x^3 + x^2) + (-4x - 4) = 0.$$
$$x^2(x + 1) - 4(x + 1) = 0.$$
$$(x + 1)(x^2 - 4) = 0.$$
$$(x + 1)(x + 2)(x - 2) = 0.$$

Setting each factor equal to zero,

$$x + 2 = 0, \quad \text{whence} \quad x = -2;$$
$$x - 2 = 0, \quad \text{whence} \quad x = +2;$$
$$x + 1 = 0, \quad \text{whence} \quad x = -1.$$

Therefore -2, $+2$, and -1 are the roots of the equation $x^3 + x^2 = 4x + 4$.

Check:
$$\begin{cases} \text{When } x = -2, & -8 + 4 = -8 + 4. \\ \text{When } x = 2, & 8 + 4 = 8 + 4. \\ \text{When } x = -1, & -1 + 1 = -4 + 4. \end{cases}$$

For solving an equation in one unknown by factoring we have the

RULE. *Transpose the terms so that the right member is zero. Then factor the left member, set each factor which contains an unknown equal to zero, and solve the resulting equations.*

It must be kept in mind that a *root* of an equation is a number which satisfies the equation.

Thus the equation $x^2 + 3x + 2 = 0$ has the two roots -2 and -1, since each of these numbers, if put for x, reduces the equation to an identity.

The two preceding examples indicate that in solving equations by factoring, two factors will arise for a quadratic, three for a cubic, four for a biquadratic, etc. Further, if the factors of a given equation are unlike, each will yield a different root. Some of the factors, however, may be alike. Thus $x^2 - 6x + 9 = 0$ can be written $(x - 3)(x - 3) = 0$. Here each factor gives the same root, 3, and though this equation is of the *second* degree, it has only one number, 3, for a root. Therefore, *an equation usually has the same number of distinct roots as the number representing its degree, but never more than that number.*

One should never divide each member of an equation by an expression containing the unknown, for in this manner roots may be lost.

EXERCISES

Find the roots of the following quadratic equations:

1. $x^2 - 9 = 0.$ **5.** $x^2 - 7x = -12.$ **9.** $8 - 9x = -x^2.$

2. $x^2 = 16.$ **6.** $x^2 - x = 20.$ **10.** $12x - 28 = -x^2.$

3. $x^2 - 3x = 0.$ **7.** $3x^2 - 15x = 0.$ **11.** $4x^2 = 16x.$

4. $x^2 = 7x.$ **8.** $5x^2 + 35x = 0.$ **12.** $x^2 - a^2 = 0.$

13. $x^2 = 9b^2.$ **20.** $9x^2 = 3x + 2.$

14. $x^2 - 2ax + a^2 = 0.$ **21.** $16x^2 - 12x = 10.$

15. $x^2 + 4b^2 = 4bx.$ **22.** $50x + 24 = 25x^2.$

16. $x^2 + ax + 3x + 3a = 0.$ **23.** $x^2 + bx = 0.$

17. $x^2 + bx = 4x + 4b.$ **24.** $x^2 - ax - bx = 0.$

18. $x^2 + ax + bx + ab = 0.$ **25.** $x^2 + 3x = ax.$

19. $4x^2 + 8x + 3 = 0.$ **26.** $4x = x^2 + 4.$

Solve the following cubics:

27. $x^3 - 9x = 0.$ **29.** $x^3 - 5x^2 + 6x = 0.$

28. $x^3 + x^2 = 4x + 4.$ **30.** $2x^3 - x^2 = 32x - 16.$

31. $5x^2 + x^3 = 45 + 9x.$

Find the roots of the following biquadratics:

32. $x^4 - 5x^2 + 4 = 0.$ **34.** $x^4 - 36x^2 = 0.$

33. $9 + x^4 = 10x^2.$ **35.** $x^4 + 15x^2 = 8x^3.$

36. $x^4 - 2x^2 + 1 = 0.$

37. Point out the error in the following:

Let	$x = 1.$
Then	$x^2 = x.$
Subtracting 1,	$x^2 - 1 = x - 1.$
Factoring,	$(x - 1)(x + 1) = x - 1.$
Dividing by $x - 1$,	$x + 1 = 1.$
Therefore	$1 + 1 = 1,$
or	$2 = 1.$

PROBLEMS

1. The square of a certain number plus the number itself is 90. Find the number.

2. If from the square of a certain number twice the number be taken, the remainder will be 35. Find the number.

3. If to the square of a certain number the sum of twice the number and 5 be added, the result will be 148. Find the number.

4. Four times the square of a certain number is equal to seven times the number. What is the number?

5. A certain number is added to 20, and the same number is also added to 21; the product of the two sums is 930. What is the number?

6. A certain number is subtracted from 17, and the same number is also subtracted from 23; the product of the remainders is 216. Find the number.

7. From 27 a certain number is subtracted, and the same number is added to 21; the product of the results thus obtained is 540. Find the number.

8. If a certain number be added to 15, and the same number be subtracted from 22, the product of the sum and difference thus obtained will be 70 more than 23 times the number. Find the number.

9. The difference of two numbers is 6, and the difference of their squares is 120. Find the numbers.

10. If from the square of three times a certain number, five times the number be taken, the result will be eight times the square of the number. Find the number.

11. The depth of a certain lot whose area is 2500 square feet is four times its frontage. Find its dimensions.

12. The area of the floor of a certain room is 24 square yards. The length is 6 feet more than the breadth. What are the dimensions of the floor?

13. The area of a rectangular field is 216 square rods. The field is 6 rods longer than it is wide. Find its dimensions.

14. The sum of the squares of two consecutive numbers is 145. Find the numbers.

15. The sum of the squares of two consecutive odd numbers is 290. Find the numbers.

16. The sum of the squares of three consecutive odd numbers is 251. Find the numbers.

17. An uncovered square box 8 inches deep has 185 square inches of inside surface. Find the other inside dimensions.

18. Remembering that the faces of a cube are squares, find the edge of a cubical box whose entire outer surface is 294 square inches.

19. A rectangular box is four times as long and three times as wide as it is deep. There are 608 square feet in its entire outer surface. Find its dimensions.

20. A box is 3 inches longer and 1 inch wider than it is deep. There are 62 square inches in its entire outer surface. Find its dimensions.

The *altitude* of a triangle is the length of a perpendicular from any vertex to the side opposite. This side is called the *base*.

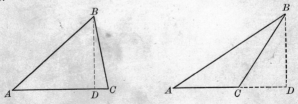

In the adjacent figures BD is the altitude and AC is the base of each triangle.

If a is the altitude of a triangle and b its base, the area of the triangle is $\dfrac{ab}{2}$.

21. The area of a triangle is 30 square feet; its altitude is 6 feet. Find the base.

22. The altitude of a triangle is three times the base and the area is 54 square feet. Find the base and the altitude.

23. The base of a triangle is five times the altitude and the area is 40 square feet. Find the base and the altitude.

24. The area of a triangle is 75 square meters; the base is six times the altitude. Find the altitude and the base.

25. The area of a triangle is 24 square feet; the altitude is 2 feet longer than the base. Find the altitude and the base.

HINT. Let $\qquad\qquad x =$ the base in feet.

Then $\qquad\qquad x + 2 =$ the altitude in feet,

and $\qquad \dfrac{x(x+2)}{2}$, or $\dfrac{x^2 + 2x}{2} =$ the area.

Therefore $\qquad\qquad \dfrac{x^2 + 2x}{2} = 24.$

Multiplying each member by 2, this equation becomes
$$x^2 + 2x = 48.$$

26. The altitude of a triangle is 3 feet longer than the base and the area is 6 square yards. Find the base and the altitude.

27. One leg of a right triangle is 2 feet longer than the other and the area is 24 square feet. Find the legs.

28. The area of a right triangle is 30 square feet and one leg is 7 feet longer than the other. Find the legs.

29. The area of a triangle is $2\frac{5}{8}$ square feet and the base is 6 inches longer than twice the altitude. Find the base and altitude.

30. The area of a triangle is 4 square yards and the altitude is 6 feet more than three times the base. Find the base and the altitude.

31. The area of a triangle is .015 square meters. The altitude 5 centimeters shorter than the base. Find the dimensions.

A *trapezoid* is a four-sided figure, two of whose sides are unequal and parallel.

The bases of the adjacent trapezoid are the two parallel sides b and c.

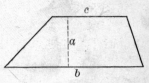

The altitude, a, of the trapezoid is the perpendicular distance between the bases.

The area of a trapezoid is $\dfrac{a(b+c)}{2}$.

32. Find the area of a trapezoid whose bases are 10 and 18 and whose altitude is 12.

33. The altitude of a trapezoid is 8 inches, its area is 96 square inches, and one base is 4 inches longer than the other. Find each base.

HINT. Let $\qquad\qquad x =$ the length of one base in inches.
Then $\qquad\qquad\qquad x + 4 =$ the length of the other base in inches,
and $\dfrac{8(x+x+4)}{2}$, or $8x + 16 =$ area of the trapezoid.

Therefore $\qquad\qquad 8x + 16 = 96$.

34. One base of a trapezoid is 12 feet, the other base is twice the altitude, and the area is 112 square feet. Find the altitude.

35. The altitude of a trapezoid is $\frac{1}{2}$ the shorter base and the latter is $\frac{2}{3}$ of the other base. The area is 360 square feet. Find the bases and the altitude.

36. One base of a trapezoid is 4 feet longer than the altitude, the other base is 6 feet longer than the altitude, and the area is 66 square feet. Find the bases and the altitude.

37. The bases of a trapezoid are respectively 8 feet and 12 feet longer than the altitude, and the area is 16 square yards. Find the bases and the altitude.

38. One base of a trapezoid is 4 feet longer than the other, the altitude is $\frac{1}{2}$ the sum of the bases, and the area is 4 square yards. Find the bases and the altitude.

39. The area of a trapezoid is 10 square yards, the altitude equals one base, and the other base exceeds the altitude by 2 feet. Find the bases and the altitude.

40. One base of a trapezoid exceeds the other by 10 feet, the altitude is 2 feet longer than five times the shorter base, and the area is 22 square yards. Find the altitude and the two bases.

41. The area of a trapezoid is .09 square meters. One base is twice the other and the altitude 10 centimeters less than the longer base. Find the bases and the altitude.

CHAPTER XV

HIGHEST COMMON FACTOR AND LOWEST COMMON MULTIPLE

58. Highest common factor. The degree of a rational, integral monomial is determined by the sum of the exponents of the letters in it.

Thus ax^3 is of the fourth degree, and $4\,a^3x^3y^2$ is of the eighth degree.

The degree of a rational, integral polynomial is the same as that of its term of highest degree.

Thus $6\,axy^2 + 4\,a^3x^4 - 3\,ax^2yz$ is of the seventh degree.

The **highest common factor** (H.C.F.) of two or more rational, integral expressions is the rational, integral expression of highest degree with the greatest numerical coefficient which is an exact divisor of each.

Thus the H.C.F. of $36\,a^2b^2$ and $48\,a^3b$ is $12\,a^2b$. The H.C.F. of $x^3 - 4\,x$ and $x^3 - 5\,x^2 + 6\,x$ is $x^2 - 2\,x$.

The problem of finding the H.C.F. of polynomials which cannot be factored by inspection will not be considered here, as it is not necessary to find the H.C.F. of such expressions in elementary work.

EXAMPLES

1. Find the H.C.F. of $24\,x^3y^2z$, $48\,x^4y^6z^3$, and $72\,x^5y^5z^2$.

Solution: Factoring, we have
$$24\,x^3y^2z = 2^3 \cdot 3\;x^3y^2z,$$
$$48\,x^4y^6z^3 = 2^4 \cdot 3\;x^4y^6z^3,$$
$$72\,x^5y^5z^2 = 2^3 \cdot 3^2x^5y^5z^2.$$

Here the highest power of 2 common to each expression is the third, of 3 the first, of x the third, of y the second, and of z the first. Therefore the H.C.F. of the three expressions is $2^3 \cdot 3 \cdot x^3y^2z$, which equals $24\,x^3y^2z$.

2. Find the H.C.F. of $2x^4 - 12x^3 + 18x^2$ and $4x^5 - 36x^3$.

Solution: Factoring, we have

$$2x^4 - 12x^3 + 18x^2 = 2x^2(x-3)^2,$$
$$4x^5 - 36x^3 = 2^2x^3(x-3)(x+3).$$

Therefore the H.C.F. is $2x^2(x-3)$, which equals $2x^3 - 6x^2$.

The method of the preceding solutions for finding the H.C.F. of two or more rational, integral expressions is stated in the

RULE. *Separate each expression into its prime factors. Then find the product of such factors as occur in each expression, using each the least number of times it occurs in any one expression.*

EXERCISES

Find the H.C.F. of the following:

1. 12, 18.   **3.** 96, 144.   **5.** 125, 225.

2. 24, 56.   **4.** 84, 196.   **6.** 64, 96, 256.

7. 90, 108, 324.

8. $12x^4$ and $18x^3$.

9. $16x^2y^4$ and $24x^3y^5$.

10. $27c^2d$ and $21cd^4$.

11. $32a^3bc^4$ and $48a^2b^2d$.

12. $125m^7n^5p$ and $100ng^4$.

13. $18h^2k^2$, $36h^4k$, and $24h^3k^3$.

14. $9xy^4$, $54x^5y$, and $15x^4y^5$.

15. $27a^4b^5c^2$, $54a^3b^2d$, and $81a^2b^2e^3$.

16. $x^2 - 9$ and $x^2 - 5x + 6$.

17. $x^2 + 3x - 10$ and $x^2 + 6x + 5$.

18. $x^3 - 4x$ and $x^3 - 8x^2 + 12x$.

19. $2c^3 + 12c^2 + 18c$ and $c^3 - 2c^2 - 15c$.

20. $8 + y^3$ and $y^2 + 4y + 4$.

21. $x^4 - 2x^2 + 1$ and $x^2 - 2x + 1$.

22. $ab + 3b + ac + 3c$ and $2ab + 6b - 2ac - 6c$.

23. $c^2 + 3cd + 2d^2$, $c^2 + 5cd + 6d^2$, and $c^2 + cd - 2d^2$.

59. Lowest common multiple. The **lowest common multiple** (L.C.M.) of two or more rational, integral expressions is the rational, integral expression of lowest degree which will exactly contain each.

EXAMPLES

1. Find the L.C.M. of $24\ x^3y^2$, $36\ x^4y$, and $54\ x^2y^2z$.

Solution:
$$24\ x^3y^2 = 2^3 \cdot 3 \cdot x^3y^2,$$
$$36\ x^4y = 2^2 \cdot 3^2 \cdot x^4y,$$
$$54\ x^2y^2z = 2^1 \cdot 3^3 \cdot x^2y^2z.$$

Since the L.C.M. must contain each of the expressions, it must have 2^3 as a factor. If the L.C.M. has 2^3 as a factor, it will contain 2^2 and 2^1 which occur in the second and third monomials respectively. Similarly, the L.C.M. must contain as factors 3^3, x^4, y^2, and z. Therefore the L.C.M. is $2^3 \cdot 3^3 \cdot x^4y^2z$, which equals $216\ x^4y^2z$.

2. Find the L.C.M. of $9\ a^2y + 18\ aby + 9\ b^2y$, $15\ ax^2 - 15\ bx^2$, and $2\ a^2 - 4\ ab + 2\ b^2$.

Solution:
$$9\ a^2y + 18\ aby + 9\ b^2y = 3^2y\,(a+b)^2,$$
$$15\ ax^2 - 15\ bx^2 = 3 \cdot 5\ x^2\,(a-b),$$
$$2\ a^2 - 4\ ab + 2\ b^2 = 2\,(a-b)^2.$$

In order that the L.C.M. may exactly contain each of the three expressions, it must have 2^1, 3^2, 5^1, x^2, y, $(a+b)^2$, and $(a-b)^2$ as factors. Hence the L.C.M. is $2 \cdot 3^2 \cdot 5^1\ x^2y\,(a+b)^2\,(a-b)^2$, which equals $90\ a^4x^2y - 180\ a^2b^2x^2y + 90\ b^4x^2y$.

The method of finding the L.C.M. of two or more rational, integral expressions is stated in the following

RULE. *Separate each expression into its prime factors. Then find the product of all the different prime factors, using each factor the greatest number of times it occurs in any one expression.*

EXERCISES

Find the L.C.M. of :

1. 12, 18.
2. 32, 48.
3. 20, 28.
4. 96, 144.
5. 64, 120, 216.
6. 128, 160, 200.

7. x^2y, xy^2, xy^3.

8. $6\ cd^3$, $4\ c^5de$, $10c^2d^2e^3$.

9. $8\ abc$, $3\ b^2c$, $12\ c^2$.

10. $18\ m^2$, $15\ mn^2p$, $20\ m^3p^2$.

11. 20, $18\ xy^4$, $27\ ax^3y$.

12. $36\ ab^2$, $42\ abc$, $63\ b^2c$.

13. $4\ a$, $a^2 - ab$.

14. $12\ ax$, $3\ a^3x^2 - 3\ ax^3$.

15. $cx + cy$, $dy + dx$.

16. $3\ x + 3\ z$, $6\ a^2x + 6\ a^2z$.

17. $x^2 - xy,\ ax + ay.$

18. $x^2 - 9,\ x^2 - 5x + 6.$

19. $c^2 - 4,\ c^2 - 8c - 20.$

20. $4ax,\ 4x^2 - 1,$ and $4x^2 + 4x + 1.$

21. $x^2 + 1,\ x^4 - 1,$ and $x^4 - 2x^2 + 1.$

22. $4 - c^2,\ c^3 + 8,$ and $c^2 + 6c + 8.$

23. $ac - 2bd + 2ad - bc,\ a^2 + ab - 2b^2.$

24. $x^2 - y^2,\ x^3 - y^3,$ and $x^2 + 2xy + y^2.$

25. $ax^2 + bxy,\ 2ax + 2by,$ and $a^2x^2 - b^2y^2.$

26. $2x^3 - 2x,\ 3x^4 + 15x^3 - 18x^2,$ and $x^2 - 36.$

27. $8 - y^3,\ y^2 - 4,$ and $4y^2 + 2y^3 + y^4.$

28. $2x^3 - 6x^2 + 4x^2y$ and $x^2 - 4y^2 - 6x + 9.$

CHAPTER XVI

FRACTIONS

60. Algebraic fractions. The expression $\dfrac{a}{b}$, in which a and b represent numbers or polynomials, is an **algebraic** fraction. It is read "a divided by b," or "a over b." A fraction is an indicated quotient in which the dividend is called the numerator and the divisor the denominator. The numerator and denominator are often called the *terms* of a fraction.

As division by zero has no meaning, **the denominator of a fraction can never be zero.**

The reduction of a fraction to lower or to higher terms, the addition of fractions, and the subtraction of fractions in both arithmetic and algebra depend on the

PRINCIPLE. *The numerator and the denominator of a fraction may be multiplied by the same expression or divided by the same expression without changing the value of the fraction.*

Thus $\qquad \dfrac{3}{4} = \dfrac{3 \cdot 4}{4 \cdot 4} = \dfrac{12}{16}$, and $\dfrac{18}{30} = \dfrac{18 \div 6}{30 \div 6} = \dfrac{3}{5}$.

Similarly $\qquad \dfrac{a}{b} = \dfrac{a \cdot n}{b \cdot n} = \dfrac{an}{bn}$, and $\dfrac{a}{b} = \dfrac{a \div n}{b \div n} = \dfrac{a/n}{b/n}$.

Since $\dfrac{4}{4}$, $\dfrac{6}{6}$, and $\dfrac{n}{n}$ are each equal to 1, each of the four preceding illustrations is really a multiplication or a division of a fraction by 1. This produces no change in the numerical value of *any* fraction, though it may change its form.

61. Reduction of fractions to lowest terms. A rational fraction is in its **lowest terms** when no rational factor except 1 is common to both numerator and denominator.

Cancellation is the process of dividing the numerator and the denominator of a fraction by a factor common to both.

EXAMPLES

Reduce to lowest terms:

1. $\dfrac{72\,a^3x^2y^5}{108\,a^2x^4y^2}$.

Solution: $\dfrac{72\,a^3x^2y^5}{108\,a^2x^4y^2} = \dfrac{\overset{2}{2^3}\cdot 3^2 \cdot \overset{a}{a^3} \cdot x^2 \cdot \overset{y^3}{y^5}}{\underset{3}{2^2}\cdot 3^3 \cdot a^2 \cdot \underset{x^2}{x^4} \cdot y^2} = \dfrac{2\,ay^3}{3\,x^2}$.

2. $\dfrac{2\,c^5 - 32\,c}{4\,c^6 + 16\,c^4 - 128\,c^2}$

Solution: $\dfrac{2\,c^5-32\,c}{4\,c^6+16\,c^4-128\,c^2} = \dfrac{2\,c(c^2+4)(c+2)(c-2)}{\underset{2\,c}{4\,c^2}(c^2+8)(c+2)(c-2)} = \dfrac{c^2+4}{2\,c^3+16\,c}$

For reducing a fraction to its lowest terms the preceding examples illustrate the

RULE. *Separate the numerator and the denominator into their prime factors and cancel the factors common to both.*

Cancellation as used in the rule means an actual division of the numerator and the denominator by the same expression. Therefore *only **factors** which are common to the numerator and the denominator can be cancelled.*

The terms (the parts connected by plus or minus signs) in polynomial numerators and denominators, even if alike, can never be cancelled. For example, $\dfrac{5+2}{6+2} = \dfrac{7}{8}$. Here it would be incorrect to "cancel" thus: $\dfrac{5+\cancel{2}}{6+\cancel{2}}$, as the resulting fraction would be $\frac{5}{6}$. Similarly, in the fraction $\dfrac{x+a+4\,c^2}{y+a+8\,c^2}$ no cancellation is possible.

We have seen that we may multiply or divide both numerator and denominator of a fraction by the same number without affecting the value of the fraction. But we should never forget that adding the same number to or subtracting the same number from both numerator and denominator changes the value of the fraction. Also squaring both numerator and denominator leads to a different value. Compare this statement with the operations that may be performed on each member of an equation as given on page 33.

EXERCISES

Reduce to lowest terms :

1. $\dfrac{a^3 b}{a^2 b^4}$.

2. $\dfrac{12\,x^2 y^6}{18\,xy^7}$.

3. $\dfrac{32\,a^4 b^4 c}{48\,a^3 b^6 c^2}$.

4. $\dfrac{45\,cd^5 e^2}{20\,c^5 d^3}$.

5. $\dfrac{36\,a^2 b^2}{54\,a^5 bc^3}$.

6. $\dfrac{2\,a}{2\,a + 2}$.

7. $\dfrac{3\,xy + 3\,y^2}{3\,y^4}$.

8. $\dfrac{21\,d^2 + 14\,c}{14\,c}$. (take out)

9. $\dfrac{a^2 - 1}{a^2 - 2\,a + 1}$.

10. $\dfrac{4\,x^2 + 4\,x + 1}{4\,x^2 - 1}$.

11. $\dfrac{2\,a^2 - 2\,b^2}{4\,a^2 - 8\,ab + 4\,b^2}$.

12. $\dfrac{18\,ax^3 + 9\,ay}{12\,bx^3 + 6\,by}$.

13. $\dfrac{x^2 - 25}{x^2 - x - 30}$.

14. $\dfrac{c^2 - 5\,cd + 4\,d^2}{c^2 - 16\,d^2}$.

15. $\dfrac{2\,x^2 - 2\,x - 180}{2\,x^2 - 162}$.

16. $\dfrac{21 + 10\,x + x^2}{x^2 - 9}$.

17. $\dfrac{4\,c^3 - 5\,c^2 - 4\,c + 5}{8\,c^4 - 10\,c^3 + 12\,c - 15}$.

18. $\dfrac{x^2 - y^2}{(x - y)^2}$.

19. $\dfrac{a^2 - b^2}{(a - b)^3}$.

20. $\dfrac{c^2 - d^2}{c^3 - d^3}$.

21. $\dfrac{y^3 - z^3}{(y - z)^3}$.

22. $\dfrac{x^3 - 8}{x^2 - 4}$.

23. $\dfrac{x^6 - 1}{x^2 - 1}$.

24. $\dfrac{x^4 - y^4}{x^6 - y^6}$.

25. $\dfrac{64\,x^3 + 1}{1 + 8\,x + 16\,x^2}$.

62. Changes of sign in a fraction. The *sign of a fraction* is the plus or minus sign placed before the line separating the numerator from the denominator. Hence there are in a fraction three signs to consider, — the sign of the fraction, the sign of the numerator, and the sign of the denominator.

Now in division the quotient of two expressions having like signs is positive, and the quotient of two expressions having unlike signs is negative.

Therefore $+\dfrac{+8}{+2}=+4$; $+\dfrac{-8}{-2}=+4$;

$$-\dfrac{-8}{+2}=-(-4)=+4\,;\quad -\dfrac{+8}{-2}=-(-4)=+4.$$

Or, in general terms, $+\dfrac{+a}{+b}=+\dfrac{-a}{-b}=-\dfrac{-a}{+b}=-\dfrac{+a}{-b}$.

These examples illustrate the

PRINCIPLE. *In a fraction the signs of both numerator and denominator, or the sign of the numerator and the sign before the fraction, or the sign of the denominator and the sign before the fraction may be changed without altering the value of the fraction.*

Hence any fraction may be written in at least four ways, if proper changes of sign are made.

Thus $+\dfrac{2\,a}{x-3}=+\dfrac{-2\,a}{-x+3}=-\dfrac{-2\,a}{x-3}=-\dfrac{+2\,a}{-x+3}$.

Similarly

$$+\dfrac{2\,x-5}{x-2\,y+4}=+\dfrac{-2\,x+5}{-x+2\,y-4}=-\dfrac{-2\,x+5}{x-2\,y+4}=-\dfrac{2\,x-5}{-x+2\,y-4}.$$

EXERCISES

Write in three other ways each of the following:

1. $\dfrac{-x}{y}$.

2. $\dfrac{x}{-y}$.

3. $\dfrac{a}{a-b}$.

4. $\dfrac{x-3}{2\,x+4}$.

5. $-\dfrac{c^2-d}{-2\,c+d}$.

6. $-\dfrac{x-y}{x+y-3}$.

7. $\dfrac{x^2-5\,x+6}{x^2-7\,x+12}$.

8. $-\dfrac{-x+x^2-2}{x^3-x^2y-1}$.

63. **Equivalent fractions.** Two fractions are **equivalent** when one can be obtained from the other by multiplying or by dividing both of its terms by the same expression.

For example, $\dfrac{2}{3}$ and $\dfrac{8}{12}$ are equivalent fractions; also $\dfrac{a^2}{ab}$ and $\dfrac{a}{b}$.

The lowest common denominator (L.C.D.) of two or more fractions is the L.C.M. of their denominators.

EXAMPLES

Reduce to equivalent fractions having the lowest common denominator:

1. $\dfrac{5\,a}{6\,b^2c}$ and $\dfrac{3\,b}{4\,ac^2}$.

Solution: The L.C.M. of the denominators is $12\,ab^2c^2$. Multiplying both numerator and denominator of the first fraction by the factor $2\,ac$, which is found in the L.C.M. but not in the denominator of the fraction, gives $\dfrac{10\,a^2c}{12\,ab^2c^2}$. Multiplying both numerator and denominator of the second fraction by the factor $3\,b^2$, which is found in the L.C.M. but not in the denominator of this fraction, gives $\dfrac{9\,b^3}{12\,ab^2c^2}$. Hence the required fractions are $\dfrac{10\,a^2c}{12\,ab^2c^2}$ and $\dfrac{9\,b^3}{12\,ab^2c^2}$.

2. $\dfrac{3\,x-1}{2\,x^3-18\,x}$ and $\dfrac{5}{x^2-5\,x+6}$.

Solution: Factoring the denominators and rewriting gives

$$\frac{3\,x-1}{2\,x\,(x+3)\,(x-3)} \text{ and } \frac{5}{(x-3)\,(x-2)}.$$

By inspection the L.C.D. is seen to be $2\,x\,(x+3)\,(x-3)\,(x-2)$. Multiplying both terms of the first fraction by the factor $x-2$, which is found in the L.C.D. but not in the denominator of the fraction, gives $\dfrac{(3\,x-1)\,(x-2)}{2\,x\,(x+3)\,(x-3)\,(x-2)}$, or $\dfrac{3\,x^2-7\,x+2}{2\,x^4-4\,x^3-18\,x^2+36\,x}$. Multiplying both terms of the second fraction by $2\,x\,(x+3)$, found in the L.C.D. but not in the denominator of the fraction, gives $\dfrac{5 \cdot 2\,x\,(x+3)}{(x-3)\,(x-2)\,2\,x\,(x+3)}$, or $\dfrac{10\,x^2+30\,x}{2\,x^4-4\,x^3-18\,x^2+36\,x}$.

Therefore, to change two or more fractions (in their lowest terms) to equivalent fractions having the L.C.D., we have the

RULE. *Rewrite the fractions with their denominators in factored form.*

Find the L.C.M. of the denominators of the fractions.

Multiply the numerator and the denominator of each fraction by those factors of this L.C.M. which are not found in the denominator of the fraction.

EXERCISES

Change the following fractions to equivalent fractions having the lowest common denominator:

1. $\dfrac{1}{2}$, $\dfrac{1}{3}$, $\dfrac{1}{6}$.

10. $\dfrac{x+y}{3\,xy^2}$, $\dfrac{x-2\,y}{2\,x^2y}$.

2. $\dfrac{5}{24}$, $\dfrac{7}{32}$.

11. $\dfrac{2+m^2}{2\,m}$, $\dfrac{4+m^2}{4\,n}$.

3. $\dfrac{4}{3\,d}$, $\dfrac{2\,c}{5\,d}$.

12. $\dfrac{2}{x+2}$, $\dfrac{4}{3\,x+6}$.

4. $\dfrac{3\,a+b}{12}$, $\dfrac{3\,a}{16}$.

13. $\dfrac{4}{x+1}$, $\dfrac{5}{x-1}$.

5. $\dfrac{5\,x+y}{21}$, $\dfrac{4\,x+3\,y}{35}$.

14. $\dfrac{3\,c}{c^2-d^2}$, $\dfrac{4}{c+d}$.

6. $\dfrac{4}{5\,a^2b}$, $\dfrac{3}{abc}$.

15. $\dfrac{3\,x}{x+3}$, $\dfrac{5}{x^2+5\,x+6}$.

7. $\dfrac{5\,c}{3\,mn^3}$, $\dfrac{12\,d}{11\,m^2n^2}$.

16. $\dfrac{2\,x}{x^2-xy}$, $\dfrac{3\,y}{x^2-2\,xy+y^2}$.

8. $\dfrac{3\,a}{2\,b^2c}$, $\dfrac{2\,b}{3\,a^2c}$, and $\dfrac{c}{6\,ab}$.

17. $\dfrac{3\,c+2}{c^2-d^2}$, $\dfrac{4-c}{c^2-7\,cd+6\,d^2}$.

9. $\dfrac{3\,b}{2\,cd^3}$, $\dfrac{9\,a}{4\,cde}$, and $\dfrac{7\,ab}{5\,cde^2}$.

18. $\dfrac{2\,x+5}{x^2-1}$, $\dfrac{2\,x-4}{x^3-3\,x^2+2\,x}$.

Note. The problem of operating with fractions presented great difficulties to all the early races. The Egyptians and the Greeks, even down to the sixth century of our era, always reduced their fractions to the sum of several fractions, each of which had 1 for a numerator. For instance, $\frac{5}{8}$ would be expressed as $\frac{1}{2}+\frac{1}{8}$. The Romans usually expressed all the fractions of a sum in terms of fractions with the common denominator 12. The Babylonians resorted to a similar device, but used 60 for the denominator. In some way they all attempted to evade the difficulty of considering changes in both numerator and denominator. The Hindus seem to have been the first to reduce fractions to a common denominator, though Euclid (300 B.C.) was familiar with the method of finding the least common multiple of two or more numbers.

64. Addition and subtraction of fractions. If two or more fractions have the same denominator, their sum is the fraction obtained by adding their numerators and writing the result over their common denominator.

For example, $\dfrac{1}{9} + \dfrac{2}{9} + \dfrac{4}{9} = \dfrac{7}{9}$, and $\dfrac{a}{b} + \dfrac{2a}{b} + \dfrac{3a}{b} = \dfrac{6a}{b}$.

If two fractions have the same denominator, their difference is the fraction obtained by subtracting the numerator of the subtrahend from the numerator of the minuend and writing the result over their common denominator.

For example, $\dfrac{5}{7} - \dfrac{2}{7} = \dfrac{3}{7}$, and $\dfrac{a}{c} - \dfrac{b}{c} = \dfrac{a-b}{c}$.

If it is required to add or to subtract two fractions having unlike denominators, the fractions must be changed to equivalent fractions having a common denominator; then their sum or their difference is obtained as above.

For example, to find the sum of $\frac{1}{6} + \frac{3}{4} + \frac{2}{3}$, we reduce the fractions to equivalent fractions having a common denominator by multiplying both terms of $\frac{1}{6}$ by 2, of $\frac{3}{4}$ by 3, and of $\frac{2}{3}$ by 4. The fractions become $\frac{2}{12}$, $\frac{9}{12}$, and $\frac{8}{12}$ respectively, and their sum is $\frac{19}{12}$.

In adding unlike algebraic fractions, as $\dfrac{a}{b}$ and $\dfrac{c}{d}$, we treat them in a similar way. Multiply both terms of $\dfrac{a}{b}$ by d, and both terms of $\dfrac{c}{d}$ by b. The fractions become $\dfrac{ad}{bd}$ and $\dfrac{bc}{bd}$ respectively, whose sum is $\dfrac{ad+bc}{bd}$. Similarly $\dfrac{a}{b} - \dfrac{c}{d} = \dfrac{ad}{bd} - \dfrac{bc}{bd}$, which equals $\dfrac{ad-bc}{bd}$.

EXAMPLES

1. Simplify $\dfrac{6x+1}{3x^2} + \dfrac{3x-5y}{4xy}$.

Solution: The L.C.D. is $12x^2y$. The work of reducing the two fractions to equivalent fractions whose denominator is $12x^2y$, and of adding the resulting fractions, follows.

$$\frac{6x+1}{3x^2} + \frac{3x-5y}{4xy} = \frac{(6x+1)4y}{3x^2 \cdot 4y} + \frac{(3x-5y)3x}{4xy \cdot 3x}$$

$$\frac{6\,x+1}{3\,x^2} + \frac{3\,x-5\,y}{4\,xy} = \frac{24\,xy+4\,y}{12\,x^2y} + \frac{9\,x^2-15\,xy}{12\,x^2y}$$

$$= \frac{24\,xy+4\,y+9\,x^2-15\,xy}{12\,x^2y} = \frac{9\,xy+4\,y+9\,x^2}{12\,x^2y}.$$

Check : Setting the original expression equal to the final result and substituting 1 for both x and y we obtain :

$$\frac{6\,x+1}{3\,x^2} + \frac{3\,x-5\,y}{4\,xy} = \frac{9\,xy+4\,y+9\,x^2}{12\,x^2y}.$$

$$\frac{6+1}{3} + \frac{3-5}{4} = \frac{9+4+9}{12}.$$

$$\frac{7}{3} + \frac{-2}{4} = \frac{22}{12}, \text{ or } \frac{22}{12} = \frac{22}{12}.$$

At this point the student should read the rule on page 143 and then solve Exercises 1–20, p. 144.

2. Find the algebraic sum of $\dfrac{2x-3}{x^2-9} - \dfrac{3x-4}{x^2-5x+6} + \dfrac{-2}{x+3}.$

Solution : Rewriting the fractions with their denominators in the factored form, we get $\dfrac{2\,x-3}{(x+3)\,(x-3)} - \dfrac{3\,x-4}{(x-3)\,(x-2)} + \dfrac{-2}{x+3}.$ The L.C.D. is $(x+3)\,(x-3)\,(x-2)$. The work of reducing these fractions to equivalent fractions and finding their algebraic sum follows.

$$\frac{2\,x-3}{(x+3)\,(x-3)} - \frac{3\,x-4}{(x-3)\,(x-2)} + \frac{-2}{x+3}$$

$$= \frac{(2\,x-3)\,(x-2)}{(x+3)\,(x-3)\,(x-2)} - \frac{(3\,x-4)\,(x+3)}{(x-3)\,(x-2)\,(x+3)} + \frac{-2\,(x-3)\,(x-2)}{(x+3)\,(x-3)\,(x-2)}$$

$$= \frac{2\,x^2-7\,x+6 - (3\,x^2+5\,x-12) + (-2\,x^2+10\,x-12)}{(x+3)\,(x-3)\,(x-2)}$$

$$= \frac{2\,x^2-7\,x+6 - 3\,x^2-5\,x+12 - 2\,x^2+10\,x-12}{(x+3)\,(x-3)\,(x-2)}$$

$$= \frac{-3\,x^2-2\,x+6}{(x+3)\,(x-3)\,(x-2)}, \text{ or } \frac{-3\,x^2-2\,x+6}{x^3-2\,x^2-9\,x+18}.$$

Check : Proceed as in Example 1, substituting 1 for x.

$$\frac{2\,x-3}{x^2-9} - \frac{3\,x-4}{x^2-5\,x+6} + \frac{-2}{x+3} = \frac{-3\,x^2-2\,x+6}{x^3-2\,x^2-9\,x+18}.$$

$$\frac{2-3}{1-9} - \frac{3-4}{1-5+6} + \frac{-2}{1+3} = \frac{-3-2+6}{1-2-9+18}.$$

$$\frac{1}{8} + \frac{1}{2} - \frac{1}{2} = \frac{1}{8}.$$

In checking work in fractions, *such values must be chosen for the letters as will make no denominator zero.* This prevents the substitution of 2, 3, or − 3 for x in checking the foregoing example.

3. Simplify $3x - 4 - \dfrac{x^2 - 5x}{x + 2}$.

Solution: This may be written $\dfrac{3x - 4}{1} - \dfrac{x^2 - 5x}{x + 2}$.

The L.C.M. of the denominators is $x + 2$. Multiplying both terms of the first fraction by $x + 2$ and leaving the second unchanged, we get

$$3x - 4 - \frac{x^2 - 5x}{x + 2} = \frac{(3x - 4)(x + 2)}{1(x + 2)} - \frac{x^2 - 5x}{x + 2}$$

$$= \frac{3x^2 + 2x - 8 - (x^2 - 5x)}{x + 2}$$

$$= \frac{3x^2 + 2x - 8 - x^2 + 5x}{x + 2}$$

$$= \frac{2x^2 + 7x - 8}{x + 2}.$$

Check: Let $x = 2$.

$$3x - 4 - \frac{x^2 - 5x}{x + 2} = \frac{2x^2 + 7x - 8}{x + 2}.$$

$$6 - 4 - \frac{4 - 10}{2 + 2} = \frac{8 + 14 - 8}{2 + 2}.$$

$$2 - \frac{-6}{4} = \frac{14}{4}.$$

$$\tfrac{14}{4} = \tfrac{14}{4}.$$

Therefore, to find the algebraic sum of two or more fractions (in their lowest terms), we have the

RULE. *Reduce the fractions to equivalent fractions having the lowest common denominator. Write in succession over the lowest common denominator the numerators of the equivalent fractions, inclosing each numerator in a parenthesis preceded by the sign of the corresponding fraction.*

Rewrite the fraction just obtained, removing the parentheses in the numerator.

Then combine like terms in the numerator and, if necessary, reduce the resulting fraction to its lowest terms.

EXERCISES

Find the algebraic sum of:

1. $\dfrac{2x}{3} + \dfrac{3x}{5}$.

3. $\dfrac{3c}{7} + \dfrac{c}{21} - \dfrac{1}{3}$.

5. $\dfrac{x-3}{4} + \dfrac{2x-5}{6}$.

2. $\dfrac{2a}{3} - \dfrac{5a}{6} + \dfrac{a}{4}$.

4. $\dfrac{9a}{16} - \dfrac{12m}{8} - \dfrac{5m}{24}$.

6. $\dfrac{5a+7}{14} - \dfrac{9a+x}{21}$

7. $\dfrac{5c}{3} - \dfrac{3c-x}{5} + \dfrac{x-3c}{10}$.

8. $\dfrac{4m-3}{6} - \dfrac{7-9m}{9} - \dfrac{3a+5m-4}{27}$.

9. $\dfrac{2}{a} + \dfrac{3}{4a^2}$.

12. $\dfrac{a}{b} + \dfrac{b}{c} - \dfrac{c}{a}$.

10. $\dfrac{3}{x^2} + \dfrac{4}{x} - \dfrac{8}{3x^3}$.

13. $\dfrac{7}{m^2} - \dfrac{5}{mn} + \dfrac{6}{n^2}$.

11. $\dfrac{x}{y} - \dfrac{5}{2y^3} + \dfrac{a}{4}$.

14. $\dfrac{3}{xy} - \dfrac{5}{2x^2} - \dfrac{6}{5xy^3}$.

15. $\dfrac{3x-1}{6x^2} - \dfrac{7-2x^2}{4x^3} + \dfrac{5x^3-8}{9x^4}$.

16. $\dfrac{4c^2-9}{2cd} - \dfrac{6-c}{5e^2} - \dfrac{c^2-4}{cd^2}$.

17. $\dfrac{3+x}{x-3} + \dfrac{3}{4}$.

19. $\dfrac{5x}{x^2+xy} - \dfrac{7}{x}$.

18. $\dfrac{3}{x-5} - \dfrac{2}{x+5}$.

20. $\dfrac{3a-b}{a^2-b^2} + \dfrac{2}{a-b}$.

In the solution of exercises similar to 21–30 the student should follow the method of Example 2, p. 142.

21. $\dfrac{10}{25-m^2} - \dfrac{1}{m^2+16m+55}$.

22. $\dfrac{3}{a^2-16} + \dfrac{5}{a^2-6a+8}$.

24. $\dfrac{c-5}{c^2-6c} + \dfrac{2c-3}{c^2-8c+12}$.

23. $\dfrac{2x+1}{x^2-1} + \dfrac{4}{x^2-3x+2}$.

25. $\dfrac{x^2-3xy+y^2}{9-6x+x^2} - \dfrac{5x-3y}{9-3x}$.

26. $\dfrac{x+2}{x^2+x} + \dfrac{1}{x} + \dfrac{3-x}{x^2+2x+1}$.

27. $\dfrac{a+b}{a^2-ab} + \dfrac{a-2b}{a^2-2ab+b^2} - \dfrac{2a-b}{a^2-b^2}$.

28. $\dfrac{m-2n}{m^2+mn+n^2} - \dfrac{m^2-3n^2}{m^3-n^3} + \dfrac{3m-n}{m-n}$.

29. $\dfrac{c^2+cd+d^2}{c^2-cd+d^2} - \dfrac{c-d}{2c+2d} - \dfrac{2c^2+5cd}{c^3+d^3}$.

30. $\dfrac{x+y}{x^3-y^3} - \dfrac{x-2y}{(x-y)^3}$.

31. $R^2 + \dfrac{R^2}{4}$.

33. $\dfrac{m^2+n^2}{m-n} + n + m$.

34. $3a + b - \dfrac{a^2-3b^2}{3a-b}$. (on board)

HINT. See Example 3, p. 143.

32. $x - 3 - \dfrac{x+3}{5}$.

35. $x^2 + y^2 - \dfrac{3x^3-y^3}{x+y} - xy$.

36. $m^2 - \dfrac{m^4-2m^2}{m^2+m+1} + 1 - m$.

37. $\dfrac{m^3+8n^3}{m^2+2mn+4n^2} + m - 2n$.

38. $a^2 - \dfrac{a^4+2a^2b^2-b^4}{a^2+ab+b^2} - ab + b^2$.

39. $x^3 + x^2y - \dfrac{x^4+3y^4}{x-y} + xy^2 + y^3$.

40. $\dfrac{2c^2+d^2}{c^2-d^2} - \dfrac{c}{c+d} + 5$.

41. $6 + \dfrac{6r^2-s^2}{r^2-9rs+14s^2} - \dfrac{3r-5s}{r-7s} + 5$.

42. $\left(x - 3 - \dfrac{3}{x+3}\right) - \left(2x - 7 - \dfrac{4}{x+4}\right)$.

HINT. Removing parentheses, we get $x - 3 - \dfrac{3}{x+3} - 2x + 7 + \dfrac{4}{x+4}$.

Combining like terms, gives $-x + 4 - \dfrac{3}{x+3} + \dfrac{4}{x+4}$, etc.

43. $\left(5\,m + \dfrac{6\,m}{2\,n}\right) - \left(m - \dfrac{m - 3\,n}{n}\right)$.

44. $\left(7\,c - \dfrac{2\,d}{3\,de}\right) - \left(5\,c + \dfrac{c}{3\,de}\right)$.

45. $\left(\dfrac{2\,a}{a - b} - 5\,a\right) - \left(2\,a - \dfrac{4\,a}{a + b}\right)$.

46. $\left(2\,a - 3\,b + \dfrac{3\,a}{2\,a + b}\right) - \left(3\,a + 2\,b - \dfrac{5\,a}{2\,a - b}\right)$.

47. $\left(-\dfrac{4\,r^2}{2\,r + s} + 2\,r - s\right) - \left(-\dfrac{4\,s^2}{2\,s - 3\,r} + 2\,s + 3\,r\right)$.

$$\textbf{48.}\quad \frac{x - 1}{2 - x} + \frac{x^2 - 3}{x^2 - 4}.$$

HINT. These fractions may be written $\dfrac{x - 1}{2 - x} + \dfrac{x^2 - 3}{(x + 2)(x - 2)}$.
Apparently the L.C.M. of the denominators is $(2 - x)(x + 2)(x - 2)$,
but if both terms of the first fraction be multiplied by -1, we
obtain $\dfrac{1 - x}{x - 2}$. The L.C.M. of the denominators of the fractions
$\dfrac{1 - x}{x - 2}$ and $\dfrac{x^2 - 3}{x^2 - 4}$ is $(x + 2)(x - 2)$.

49. $\dfrac{5}{x - 3} + \dfrac{3}{3 - x}$.   **51.** $\dfrac{3\,a}{a^2 - 4} + \dfrac{2\,a - 1}{2 - a}$.

50. $\dfrac{6}{x^2 - 25} - \dfrac{3}{5 - x}$.   **52.** $\dfrac{3\,c}{9 - c^2} - \dfrac{4\,c - 2}{c - 3}$.

53. $\dfrac{x}{2\,x - 1} - \dfrac{x}{1 + 2\,x} - \dfrac{x}{1 - 4\,x^2}$.

54. $\dfrac{7}{x^2 - 13\,x + 42} + \dfrac{4\,x - 1}{7 - x} - \dfrac{2\,x + 3}{6 - x}$.

55. $\dfrac{3\,x - 1}{x^2 + 7\,x - 8} - \dfrac{4\,x - 1}{1 - x} + \dfrac{x + 2}{8 + x}$.

Multiplying one factor of an indicated product by -1
changes the sign of every term of the expanded product.

Thus $(x - 2)(x - 3) = x^2 - 5\,x + 6$. Multiplying the terms of the
factor $x - 2$ by -1, we have $(2 - x)(x - 3)$, or $-x^2 + 5\,x - 6$.

Multiplying the terms in two factors of an indicated product by -1 does not change the sign of the expanded product.

Thus $(x-2)(x-3) = x^2 - 5x + 6.$

But $(x-2)(-1)(x-3)(-1) = (2-x)(3-x)$
$$= x^2 - 5x + 6.$$

In general, changing the sign of an *odd* number of factors in an indicated product changes the sign of every term of the expanded product; but if an *even* number of factors are thus treated, the expanded product is unchanged.

56. $\dfrac{1}{(a-b)(a-c)} + \dfrac{1}{(b-c)(b-a)} - \dfrac{1}{(c-a)(c-b)}.$

HINT. Apparently $(a-b)(a-c)(b-c)(b-a)(c-a)(c-b)$ is the L.C.D.; multiplying both terms of the second fraction once by -1 and those of the third twice by -1 the three fractions become

$$\dfrac{1}{(a-b)(a-c)} + \dfrac{-1}{(b-c)(a-b)} - \dfrac{1}{(a-c)(b-c)},$$

of which the L.C.D. is $(a-b)(a-c)(b-c)$.

57. $\dfrac{2}{(x-y)(x-z)} - \dfrac{1}{(x-y)(z-x)}.$

58. $\dfrac{3a}{(a-3)(a-4)} - \dfrac{2a}{(3-a)(4-a)}.$

59. $\dfrac{2}{(m-n)(m+n)} + \dfrac{3}{(n-m)(m-7)} - \dfrac{4}{(n-m)(7-m)}.$

60. $\dfrac{c}{c^2 - 10c + 24} - \dfrac{1}{6c - c^2 - 8} + \dfrac{3}{(6-c)(2-c)}.$

65. Reduction of a fraction to a mixed expression. A mixed expression is an expression consisting of a rational, integral part and a rational, fractional part.

In arithmetic $4\frac{2}{3}$ means $4 + \frac{2}{3}$, while in algebra $a\dfrac{b}{c}$ means a times $\dfrac{b}{c}$, or $\dfrac{ab}{c}.$ Hence in algebraic mixed expressions the integral and fractional portions must be connected by a plus or a minus sign.

If the numerator of a fraction (in its lowest terms) is of the same degree as the denominator, or of a higher degree, the fraction may often be reduced to a mixed expression.

Obviously such fractions as $\dfrac{x^2}{a^2 + b^2}$, $\dfrac{xy}{x^2 + y^2}$, and $\dfrac{x^3 + y^3}{xy}$ cannot be reduced to mixed expressions.

Example: Reduce $\dfrac{4\,x^4 - 6\,x^3 - x^2 - 1}{x^3}$ to a fraction.

Solution: Dividing, $\dfrac{4\,x^4 - 6\,x^3 - x^2 - 1}{x^3} = 4\,x - 6 + \dfrac{-x^2 - 1}{x^3}$

$$= 4\,x - 6 - \dfrac{x^2 + 1}{x^3}.$$

To reduce a fraction (in its lowest terms) to a mixed expression we have the

RULE. *Perform the indicated division, thus obtaining a partial quotient, until the remainder is of lower degree than the divisor.*

Write the remainder over the divisor and connect the resulting fraction by a plus sign to the partial quotient, thus forming the complete quotient.

The reduction of a mixed expression to a fraction is performed as in Exercises 31–41, p. 145.

EXERCISES

Reduce to mixed expressions:

1. $\dfrac{15\,x^2 - 10\,x + 2}{5\,x}$.

2. $\dfrac{24\,a^3 - 6\,a^2 - 14}{6\,a}$.

3. $\dfrac{c}{c + 1}$.

7. $\dfrac{a^4 + a^2b^2 + b^4}{a^2 + ab - b^2}$.

11. $\dfrac{5\,a^3 + 3\,a^2 - 6}{5\,a^2 + 3\,a + 2}$.

4. $\dfrac{d^3 + 1}{d - 1}$.

8. $\dfrac{3\,y^3 - 11}{y + 3}$.

12. $\dfrac{x^6 + y^6}{x^2 - y^2}$.

5. $\dfrac{27\,x^3 - y^3}{3\,x + y}$.

9. $\dfrac{(a + b)^3}{a^3 + b^3}$.

13. $\dfrac{x^4}{x + 1}$.

6. $\dfrac{y^4 + y^2 + 1}{y^2 - y - 1}$.

10. $\dfrac{16\,a^4 + b^4}{2\,a - 1}$.

14. $\dfrac{(a^2 + b)^2}{a^2 + b^2}$.

66. Multiplication of fractions. In algebra as in arithmetic the product of two or more fractions is the product of their numerators divided by the product of their denominators.

Thus $\frac{3}{4} \cdot \frac{5}{7} = \frac{15}{28}$.

Similarly $\frac{a}{b} \cdot \frac{c}{d} = \frac{ac}{bd}$,

and $5 \cdot \frac{3}{7} = \frac{5}{1} \cdot \frac{3}{7} = \frac{15}{7}$.

In like manner $n \cdot \frac{a}{b} = \frac{n}{1} \cdot \frac{a}{b} = \frac{na}{b}$.

EXAMPLES

(on board)

1. Multiply $\frac{4\,a^2x^3}{5\,y^3}$ by $\frac{35\,y^5}{16\,a^3x^2}$.

Solution: Canceling common factors,

$$\frac{4\,a^2x^3}{5\,y^3} \cdot \frac{35\,y^5}{16\,a^3x^2} = \frac{\overset{x}{\cancel{4\,a^2x^3}}}{\cancel{5\,y^3}} \cdot \frac{\overset{7\,y^2}{\cancel{35\,y^5}}}{\underset{4\,a}{\cancel{16\,a^3x^2}}} = \frac{7\,xy^2}{4\,a}.$$

2. Simplify $\dfrac{x^2 - 4}{x^2 - 5x + 6} \cdot \dfrac{x + 2}{x + 3} \cdot \dfrac{2\,x^3 - 18\,x}{x^2 + 4x + 4}$.

Solution: Factoring and canceling common factors,

$$\frac{x^2 - 4}{x^2 - 5x + 6} \cdot \frac{x + 2}{x + 3} \cdot \frac{2\,x^3 - 18\,x}{x^2 + 4x + 4}$$
$$= \frac{(x+2)(x-2)}{(x-3)(x-2)} \cdot \frac{x+2}{x+3} \cdot \frac{2\,x\,(x+3)(x-3)}{(x+2)(x+2)}$$
$$= 2\,x.$$

Check: Let $x = 1$.

$$\frac{x^2 - 4}{x^2 - 5x + 6} \cdot \frac{x + 2}{x + 3} \cdot \frac{2\,x^3 - 18\,x}{x^2 + 4x + 4} = 2\,x.$$
$$\frac{1 - 4}{1 - 5 + 6} \cdot \frac{1 + 2}{1 + 3} \cdot \frac{2 - 18}{1 + 4 + 4} = 2.$$
$$\frac{-3}{2} \cdot \frac{3}{4} \cdot \frac{-16}{9} = 2.$$
$$2 = 2.$$

At this point the student should read the rule on page 150 and solve Exercises 1–16, p. 151. He should then study Example 3 and solve the remaining exercises.

3. Simplify

$$\left(3\,a - \frac{b^2 - 3\,ab^2}{3\,a - b^2}\right) \cdot \frac{8\,a^2y^3}{3\,ab^2 + 6\,a^2b - 9\,a^3} \cdot (a^2 - b^2) \cdot \frac{9\,bx}{16\,a^3y}.$$

Solution: Reducing the mixed expression to a fraction, this becomes

$$\frac{9\,a^2 - b^2}{3\,a - b^2} \cdot \frac{8\,a^2y^3}{3\,ab^2 + 6\,a^2b - 9\,a^3} \cdot (a^2 - b^2) \cdot \frac{9\,bx}{16\,a^3y}.$$

Factoring and canceling common factors,.

$$\frac{(3\,a + b)(3\,a - b)}{3\,a - b^2} \cdot \frac{2^3 \cdot a^2 \cdot y^3}{3\,a\,(b - a)(b + 3\,a)} \cdot \frac{(a + b)(a - b)}{1} \cdot \frac{3^2\,bx}{2^4\,a^3y}.$$

(Note that $(a - b)$ is contained in $(b - a)$, -1 times.)

We have left $\dfrac{(3\,a - b)\,y^2\,(a + b)}{(3\,a - b^2)\,(-1)(2\,a^2)}\,\dfrac{3\,bx}{} = \dfrac{9\,a^2bxy^2 + 6\,ab^2xy^2 - 3\,b^3xy^2}{-6\,a^3 + 2\,a^2b^2}.$

Check: Let $x = y = a = 2$, and $b = 3$.

$$\left(3\,a - \frac{b^2 - 3\,ab^2}{3\,a - b^2}\right) \cdot \frac{8\,a^2y^3}{3\,ab^2 + 6\,a^2b - 9\,a^3} \cdot (a^2 - b^2)\,\frac{9\,bx}{16\,a^3y}$$
$$= \frac{9\,a^2bxy^2 + 6\,ab^2xy^2 - 3\,b^3xy^2}{-6\,a^3 + 2\,a^2b^2}.$$

$$\left(6 - \frac{9 - 54}{6 - 9}\right) \cdot \frac{256}{54 + 72 - 72} \cdot (4 - 9) \cdot \frac{54}{256}$$
$$= \frac{864 + 864 - 648}{-48 + 72}.$$

$$(-9) \cdot \tfrac{256}{54} \cdot (-5) \cdot \tfrac{54}{256} = \tfrac{1080}{24}.$$
$$45 = 45.$$

To find the product of two or more fractions or mixed expressions we have the

RULE. *If there are integral or mixed expressions, reduce them to fractional form.*

Separate each numerator and each denominator into its prime factors.

Cancel the factors common to any numerator and any denominator.

Write the product of the factors remaining in the numerator over the product of the factors remaining in the denominator.

EXERCISES

Simplify:

1. $\dfrac{3\,x^2y^3}{4\,a^4}\cdot\dfrac{8\,a^3}{12\,xy}.$

2. $\dfrac{10\,a^3b^2}{15\,c^3}\cdot\dfrac{18\,c}{7\,a^2}.$

3. $\dfrac{3\,x}{8\,y}\cdot\dfrac{6\,ax}{9\,b}\cdot\dfrac{12\,b^2y}{16\,x}.$

4. $\dfrac{14\,m^2n^4}{5\,n}\cdot\dfrac{25\,n^3}{6\,m^2}\cdot\dfrac{4\,x}{7\,m}.$

5. $\left(\dfrac{2\,x}{3\,ay}\right)^2\cdot\dfrac{12\,a^3}{16\,b^2xy^3}\cdot 8\,b^4y^2.$

6. $\dfrac{a}{4\,c^2}\cdot\left(\dfrac{c}{2\,a}\right)^3\cdot 16.$

7. $\left(\dfrac{2\,a}{c}\right)^2\cdot\left(\dfrac{2\,c}{a}\right)^3\cdot\left(\dfrac{1}{4}\right)^2.$

8. $\left(\dfrac{-3\,a}{3}\right)^2\cdot\dfrac{c^5}{(2\,a)^5}\cdot\left(\dfrac{2}{3}\right)^2.$

9. $\dfrac{6\,c}{a}\cdot\left(\dfrac{9\,c^2}{4\,a}\right)^2\cdot\left(\dfrac{-2\,a}{3\,c}\right)^3.$

10. $\dfrac{(4\,ax)^2}{225\,c^4}\cdot\dfrac{(5\,ac^2)^3}{(2\,x^2)^3}\cdot\left(\dfrac{-x}{c}\right)^5.$

11. $\dfrac{2\,a+4\,x}{5\,y^2}\cdot\dfrac{15\,y}{a+2\,x}.$

12. $\dfrac{3\,c}{9-c^2}\cdot\dfrac{c^2+5\,c+6}{18\,cd}.$

13. $\dfrac{3\,a-6\,y}{4\,a+2\,y}\cdot\dfrac{8(2\,a+y)^2}{4\,a^2-24\,ay+24\,y^2}.$

14. $\dfrac{c^2+6\,ce+9\,e^2}{6\,(c+d)^2}\cdot\dfrac{3\,c^2e-12\,d^2e}{c^2-2\,cd+3\,ce-6\,de}.$

15. $\dfrac{a^2+4\,ab+4\,b^2}{9-a^2}\cdot\dfrac{a^2-5\,a+6}{a^2-4\,b^2}.$

16. $\dfrac{5\,c^2-20\,d^2}{c^3+8\,d^3}\cdot\dfrac{c^2-2\,cd+4\,d^2}{25\,cd^4}.$

17. $\dfrac{(x+2)^2}{3\,x^3+6\,x^2+12\,x}\cdot(15-9\,x^2)\cdot\dfrac{x^3-8}{4-x^2}.$

18. $\dfrac{8\,c-24\,d}{c^2-6\,cd+9\,d^2}\cdot\left(4\,c-\dfrac{d^2}{c}\right)\cdot\dfrac{4\,c^2+d^2}{64\,c^4-4\,d^4}.$

19. $\left(\dfrac{6\,m-9}{2\,m-3}+2\,m\right)\left(2\,m-9+\dfrac{36}{2\,m+3}\right).$

20. $\left(\dfrac{3}{2\,a}-1\right)^2\cdot\dfrac{8\,a^2x}{9-4\,a^2}\cdot\dfrac{3+2\,a}{2\,a-3}.$

21. $\left(1+\dfrac{2}{x}-\dfrac{3}{x^2}\right)\cdot\dfrac{9\,x^3}{3\,(x^2-18\,x+17)}.$

22. $\dfrac{x^3 - 8}{6\,xy} \cdot \left(3 - \dfrac{4}{2 - x}\right) \cdot \dfrac{18\,x^2 y^2}{x^2 + 2\,x + 4}.$

23. $\dfrac{a^3 - b^3}{(a - b)^3} \cdot \dfrac{6\,a + 6\,b}{2\,a^2 + 2\,ab + 2\,b^2} \cdot \dfrac{(a - b)^2}{a^2 - b^2}.$

24. $\left(4 - \dfrac{20 - 9x}{5 - x} - x\right)\left(\dfrac{1}{x} + \dfrac{1}{x^2} - \dfrac{30}{x^3}\right).$

25. $\left(x + 2\,y - \dfrac{5\,x + 10\,y}{x + y}\right)\left(\dfrac{y^2 + x^2 + 2\,yx}{x^2 - 3\,xy - 4\,y^2}\right) \cdot \dfrac{1}{x + 2\,y}.$

67. Division of fractions. In arithmetic $\frac{3}{4} \div \frac{5}{7} = \frac{3}{4} \cdot \frac{7}{5} = \frac{21}{20}$; and $\frac{3}{4} \div 11 = \frac{3}{4} \cdot \frac{1}{11} = \frac{3}{44}$. Also $\frac{3}{4} \div 1\frac{4}{7} = \frac{3}{4} \div \frac{11}{7} = \frac{3}{4} \cdot \frac{7}{11} = \frac{21}{44}$.

Similarly $\dfrac{a}{b} \div \dfrac{c}{d} = \dfrac{a}{b} \cdot \dfrac{d}{c} = \dfrac{ad}{bc}$; and $\dfrac{a}{b} \div n = \dfrac{a}{b} \cdot \dfrac{1}{n} = \dfrac{a}{bn}$.

Also $\dfrac{a}{b} \div \left(c + \dfrac{n}{d}\right) = \dfrac{a}{b} \div \left(\dfrac{cd + n}{d}\right) = \dfrac{a}{b} \cdot \dfrac{d}{cd + n} = \dfrac{ad}{bcd + bn}.$

For division of fractions we have the

RULE. *Reduce all integral or mixed expressions to fractional form.*

Then invert the divisor, or divisors, and proceed as in multiplication of fractions.

EXERCISES

Perform the indicated operations:

1. $\dfrac{6\,a}{3\,b} \div \dfrac{4\,a}{12\,b^2}.$

6. $\dfrac{5\,x}{5\,y} \div \dfrac{10\,x^2}{12\,y^3} \div \dfrac{4\,ax}{3\,by^2}.$

2. $\dfrac{9\,a^2}{6\,b^2} \div \dfrac{14\,ab}{8\,x}.$

7. $\dfrac{6}{(2\,x)^2} \div \dfrac{12}{(4\,x^2)^3} \cdot \left(\dfrac{2}{x}\right)^2.$

3. $\left(\dfrac{2\,ax}{3\,c}\right)^2 \div \dfrac{6\,ax^2}{9\,c^4}.$

8. $\dfrac{3\,m^2}{5\,n} \div \dfrac{21\,m^3}{10\,mn^2} \div 14\,m^4 n.$

4. $\dfrac{a}{b} \div \dfrac{c}{d} \div \dfrac{ad^2}{bc^2}.$

9. $\left(\dfrac{4\,x^2}{3\,a}\right)^2 \div \left(\dfrac{2\,x}{3\,a}\right)^3 \cdot \left(\dfrac{a}{x}\right)^2.$

5. $2\,a \cdot \left(\dfrac{2\,a^2}{3\,x}\right)^2 \div \dfrac{(4\,a^2)^2}{18\,x^2}.$

10. $\dfrac{6\,a - 3}{5\,x} \div \dfrac{2\,a - 1}{15\,bx^3}.$

11. $\dfrac{4 - x^2}{3\,x^2 + x^3} \div \dfrac{4 - 4\,x + x^2}{x^3 - x^2 - 12\,x}.$

12. $\dfrac{a^2 - 7a + 12}{a - 1} \div \dfrac{a^2 - 16}{1 - a^2}.$

13. $(-14 - 5c + c^2) \div \dfrac{ac^2 - 49a}{bc^2 + 9bc + 14b}.$

14. $\dfrac{4a^2 - 4ab - 3b^2}{8a^3x} \div \left(a - \dfrac{9b^2}{4a}\right).$

15. $\left(\dfrac{2a}{x}\right)^4 \div \left(\dfrac{-6a^2c}{5x}\right)^3 \cdot \left(\dfrac{3c^3}{10ax}\right)^2.$

16. $\left(\dfrac{-a^2}{x}\right) \div \left(\dfrac{-a}{x^2}\right)^5 \cdot \left(\dfrac{a}{x}\right)^3 \cdot \left(\dfrac{-1}{x^2}\right)^3.$

17. $\left(\dfrac{m^2}{n^2} - \dfrac{n^2}{m^2}\right) \div \left(\dfrac{m^4 + 2m^2n^2 + n^4}{m^2n - 4mn^2}\right).$

18. $\dfrac{9x^2 + 6xy - 8y^2}{2x + y} \div (3x - 2y)^2 \div \left(2 - \dfrac{x - 2y}{2x + y}\right).$

19. $\left(\dfrac{a}{c} + \dfrac{c}{a}\right) \div \left(\dfrac{a^6 + c^6}{a^3c^3}\right)\left(a^2 - c^2 + \dfrac{c^4}{a^2}\right) \cdot \dfrac{1}{ac^2}.$

20. $\dfrac{2a - 5}{2a^2 + 2} \div \dfrac{4a^4 - 25a^2}{4 - 4a^4} \cdot \left(3a^2 - \dfrac{a^3 - 8a^2}{a - 1}\right).$

21. $\dfrac{8m^3 - 125n^3}{m^2 + mn} \div \left(\dfrac{2m}{5n} - \dfrac{5n}{2m}\right) \div \left[3mn\left(2m + 5n + \dfrac{25n^2}{2m}\right)\right].$

22. $\left(\dfrac{4y}{x} - \dfrac{15y^2}{x^2} + 4\right) \div \left(4 - \dfrac{16y}{x} + \dfrac{15y^2}{x^2}\right)\left(3 - \dfrac{4x + 20y}{2x + 5y}\right).$

23. $\left(\dfrac{9c^2 - 4d^2}{6c^2}\right) \div \left(d + 4c + \dfrac{15c^2}{4d}\right) \cdot \dfrac{15c^2d + 6cd^2}{9c^2d + 24cd^2 - 20d^3}.$

24. $\left(6x - 11 - \dfrac{7}{x}\right) \div \left(2 + \dfrac{11}{x} + \dfrac{5}{x^2}\right) \div \left(\dfrac{1}{3x^3 - 75x}\right).$

25. $\left(x^2 - y^2 + \dfrac{4xy(y + x)}{x - y}\right) \div \left(\dfrac{x^2 + y(y + 2x)}{2x^2 - 3xy + y^2}\right),$

68. Complex fractions. A **complex fraction** is a fraction containing a fractional expression either in its numerator or in its denominator or in both.

EXAMPLE

Simplify $\dfrac{x - 3 - \dfrac{10}{x}}{1 - \dfrac{2}{x} - \dfrac{15}{x^2}}$.

Solution: Reducing the numerator and the denominator to simple fractions,

$$\frac{x - 3 - \dfrac{10}{x}}{1 - \dfrac{2}{x} - \dfrac{15}{x^2}} = \frac{\dfrac{x^2 - 3x - 10}{x}}{\dfrac{x^2 - 2x - 15}{x^2}}.$$

Performing the indicated division,

$$\frac{\dfrac{x^2 - 3x - 10}{x}}{\dfrac{x^2 - 2x - 15}{x^2}} = \frac{(x - 5)(x + 2)}{x} \cdot \frac{x^2}{(x - 5)(x + 3)}$$

$$= \frac{x^2 + 2x}{x + 3}.$$

Check: Let $x = 1$.

Then $\dfrac{1 - 3 - \frac{10}{1}}{1 - \frac{2}{1} - \frac{15}{1}} = \dfrac{1 + 2}{1 + 3}$, or $\dfrac{-12}{-16} = \dfrac{3}{4}$, or $\dfrac{3}{4} = \dfrac{3}{4}$.

To simplify a complex fraction we have the

RULE. *Reduce both the numerator and the denominator to simple fractions, then perform the indicated division.*

EXERCISES

Simplify:

1. $\dfrac{4 - \frac{1}{4}}{2 + \frac{1}{2}}$.

2. $\dfrac{\frac{4}{9} + 1}{\frac{7}{2} - 2}$.

3. $\dfrac{9 - (\frac{1}{5})^2}{4 - \frac{4}{5}}$.

4. $\dfrac{\frac{3}{5} + \frac{4}{7}}{2 - \frac{3}{5} \cdot \frac{4}{7}}$.

5. $\dfrac{(\frac{8}{5})^2 - 2}{3 \cdot \frac{8}{5}}$.

6. $\dfrac{4 - \frac{3}{2} + \frac{2}{3}}{3 - \frac{2}{3} + \frac{3}{2}}$.

7. $\dfrac{\frac{2^3}{27} + 1}{\frac{9}{2} - 1}$.

8. $\dfrac{2\frac{1}{2} - 3\frac{1}{3} + 4\frac{3}{4}}{2\frac{1}{2} \cdot 3\frac{1}{3} - 4\frac{3}{4}}$.

9. $\dfrac{2 - \frac{9}{2}}{(\frac{1}{2})^2 - (\frac{1}{2})^3 - 12(\frac{1}{2})^4}$.

10. $\dfrac{a/b}{c/d}$.

11. $\dfrac{\dfrac{1+x}{x}}{1-\dfrac{1}{x^2}}$.

15. $\dfrac{a-\dfrac{9}{a}}{\dfrac{1}{a^2}-\dfrac{1}{a^3}-\dfrac{12}{a^4}}$.

19. $\dfrac{1+\dfrac{b}{a}-\dfrac{20\,a}{b}}{\dfrac{b}{a}-\dfrac{8\,a}{b}-2}$.

12. $\dfrac{c+\dfrac{c}{d}}{1+\dfrac{1}{d}}$.

16. $\dfrac{\dfrac{m^3}{n^3}+1}{m+\dfrac{n^2}{m}-n}$.

20. $\dfrac{\dfrac{16}{x}-x}{\dfrac{24}{x^4}+\dfrac{10}{x^3}+\dfrac{1}{x^2}}$.

13. $\dfrac{9-\dfrac{b^2}{4\,a^2}}{1-\dfrac{b}{6\,a}}$.

17. $\dfrac{2+\dfrac{1}{a-2}+a}{a+\dfrac{1}{a+2}-2}$.

21. $\dfrac{x+\dfrac{x^2+y^2}{y}}{\dfrac{x}{y}-1}$.

14. $\dfrac{\dfrac{a^2}{b^2}-\dfrac{b^2}{a^2}}{a+\dfrac{b^2}{a}}$.

18. $\dfrac{\dfrac{a}{b}}{\dfrac{c}{b}-\dfrac{a}{\dfrac{b}{c}}}$.

22. $\dfrac{2+\dfrac{a}{b}}{\dfrac{(a-2\,b)^2}{4\,ab}+2}$.

23. $\dfrac{\left(\dfrac{2\,x^2}{x-y}\right)^2}{\dfrac{8\,x^3}{(x-y)^3}}$.

27. $\dfrac{\dfrac{9}{8}x-\dfrac{9\,y}{8}-\dfrac{7\,y^2}{2\,x}}{\dfrac{3\,x}{4}+\dfrac{9}{4}y+\dfrac{5\,y^2}{3\,x}}$.

24. $\dfrac{\dfrac{a-b}{a}-\dfrac{a+b}{b}}{\dfrac{a-b}{b}+\dfrac{a+b}{a}}$.

28. $\dfrac{\dfrac{x}{2\,ax+3\,bx+6\,ab+x^2}}{\dfrac{1}{x+2\,a}-\dfrac{1}{x+3\,b}}$.

25. $1-\dfrac{\left(1-\dfrac{c^4}{9}\right)-\left(1-\dfrac{c^4}{16}\right)}{1-\dfrac{7\,c^4}{144}}$.

29. $\dfrac{\left(\dfrac{3\,a+4\,b}{3\,a}\right)^2-\dfrac{6\,b}{a}}{8\,a-\dfrac{(3\,a+2\,b)^2}{3\,b}}$.

26. $\dfrac{\dfrac{a}{1+a}+\dfrac{1-a}{a}}{\dfrac{a}{1+a}-\dfrac{1-a}{a}}$.

30. $\dfrac{1-\dfrac{x^2-1}{5\,x^2-6\,x+1}}{1+\dfrac{3\,x+2}{5\,x-1}}$.

CHAPTER XVII

EQUATIONS CONTAINING FRACTIONS

69. Monomial denominators. Equations containing fractions with monomial denominators are easily solved. Yet unless each fraction preceded by a minus sign is handled with care, errors will be frequent.

EXAMPLE

Solve the equation $\dfrac{2}{7}\left(9 + \dfrac{5x}{3}\right) - \dfrac{3(2x-1)}{5} + \dfrac{5x}{3} = 2x.$

Solution: Performing the indicated multiplication,

$$\frac{18}{7} + \frac{10x}{21} - \frac{6x-3}{5} + \frac{5x}{3} = 2x.$$

Multiplying each member by the L.C.M. of the denominators, 105, and canceling,

$$\overset{15}{\frac{18}{7}}\cdot 105 + \overset{5}{\frac{10x}{21}}\cdot 105 - \frac{6x-3}{5}\cdot\overset{21}{105} + \frac{5x}{3}\cdot\overset{35}{105} = 2x\cdot 105.$$

$$270 + 50x - (6x-3)21 + 175x = 210x.$$
$$270 + 50x - 126x + 63 + 175x = 210x.$$

Combining like terms, $\qquad\qquad 99x + 333 = 210x.$

Then $\qquad\qquad\qquad\qquad\qquad -111x = -333.$

Whence $\qquad\qquad\qquad\qquad\qquad x = 3.$

Check: $\dfrac{2}{7}\left(9 + \dfrac{15}{3}\right) - \dfrac{3(6-1)}{5} + \dfrac{15}{3} = 6.$

$$4 \quad - \quad 3 \quad + \; 5 = 6, \text{ or } 6 = 6.$$

For solving equations containing fractions with monomial denominators, we have the

RULE. *Free the equation of any parentheses it may contain. Find the L.C.M. of the denominators of the fractions and multiply each fraction and each integral term of the equation by it, using cancellation wherever possible.*

Transpose and solve as usual.

EXERCISES

Find the roots of the following and verify results:

1. $\dfrac{x}{2} + \dfrac{x}{3} = 10.$ *(x = 12)*

4. $\dfrac{2x+3}{5} - \dfrac{1}{3}(x-3) = 2.$

2. $\dfrac{4}{3}x + \dfrac{2}{5}x = 5\frac{1}{5}.$

5. $\dfrac{4x+2}{11} - \dfrac{1}{5}(x+5) = 0.$

3. $\dfrac{x+5}{4} - \dfrac{2x+4}{9} = 1.$

6. $\dfrac{3}{4}(x+1) - \dfrac{5x-7}{6} = \dfrac{7}{3}.$

7. $\dfrac{x+6}{10} + \dfrac{3}{2}(x+4) = -3.$

8. $\dfrac{5x-12}{6} - \dfrac{4}{11}(2x-7) = \dfrac{1}{3}.$

9. $2x - 1 - \dfrac{12x-7}{6} - \dfrac{1}{6} = 0.$

10. $\dfrac{10x-7}{6} + \dfrac{5}{2}\left(\dfrac{2}{5} - x\right) = \dfrac{15x-11}{3}.$

11. $\dfrac{5x}{6} - \dfrac{1}{2} - \dfrac{3}{8}\left(x - \dfrac{5}{3}\right) + \dfrac{7}{32} = 0.$

12. $\dfrac{5}{x} + \dfrac{4}{3} = \dfrac{9}{x}.$

13. $\dfrac{9x}{4} - \dfrac{3}{4} - \dfrac{3x-7}{3} + 4 = -\dfrac{17}{24}.$

14. $\dfrac{c}{3x} - \dfrac{c}{5x} = \dfrac{1}{15}.$

15. $\dfrac{1}{2x} - \dfrac{13}{24} = \dfrac{8}{3x}.$

16. $\dfrac{2a-3x}{6a} + \dfrac{5a-2x}{5a} + \dfrac{41}{30} = 0.$

17. $\dfrac{x}{a} - \dfrac{1}{3}(a - 3x) + \dfrac{19a}{3} = -6.$

18. $\dfrac{cx}{3} - \dfrac{n}{5}(3x - 5cn) = cn\left(\dfrac{2c}{3} - \dfrac{n}{5}\right).$

19. $2x - b - \dfrac{b}{a}(3x - 4b) + 2a = \dfrac{2(2a^2 - b^2)}{a}.$

20. $(x + 5)(x - 6) = x(x - \tfrac{5}{2}).$

21. $\left(x + \dfrac{3}{4}\right)\left(3 + \dfrac{x}{2}\right) = \dfrac{x}{2}(x - 5) + 8\tfrac{1}{8}.$

22. $(x - \tfrac{1}{2})(x + \tfrac{3}{7}) = (x - 1)(x + 2) + 1\tfrac{11}{14}.$

23. $(x - \tfrac{3}{2})(x + \tfrac{2}{3}) - (x - \tfrac{1}{3})^2 - 1\tfrac{1}{9} = 0.$

24. $(x + \tfrac{2}{5})^2 - (x - \tfrac{1}{2})(x + \tfrac{1}{5}) + \tfrac{31}{50} = 0.$

PROBLEMS

1. One fourth of a certain number plus $\tfrac{1}{12}$ of that number equals 16. Find the number.

2. The difference between $\tfrac{1}{3}$ of a certain number and $\tfrac{1}{17}$ of it is 70. Find the number.

3. The sum of two numbers is 38. One tenth of the greater number equals $\tfrac{1}{9}$ of the less. Find the numbers.

4. The width of a rectangle is $\tfrac{4}{5}$ of its length. The perimeter is 216 centimeters. Find the area of the rectangle.

5. What number must be added to the numerator of the fraction $\tfrac{4}{7}$ so that the resulting fraction will be $\tfrac{1}{5}$ of the number?

6. Three fourths of a certain number is $\tfrac{1}{3}$ the sum of the next two consecutive numbers. Find the numbers.

7. A certain odd number divided by 11 is equal to $\tfrac{1}{24}$ of the sum of the next two consecutive odd numbers. Find the numbers.

8. What number added to both terms of the fraction $\tfrac{10}{17}$ gives a fraction whose value is $\tfrac{5}{7}$?

9. Separate 42 into two parts such that $\tfrac{1}{6}$ of their difference is $\tfrac{1}{3}$.

10. One fourth the difference of three times a certain number and 4 equals $\tfrac{1}{7}$ the difference of five times the number and 4. Find the number.

11. Separate 112 into two parts such that their quotient is $\frac{2}{5}$.

12. There are two numbers whose sum is 24. If their difference be divided by their sum, the quotient will be $3\frac{5}{6}$ less than the difference of the two numbers. Find the numbers.

13. The quotient of 27 plus seven times a certain number, divided by twice the number equals the quotient of 90 plus five times the number, divided by three times the number. Find the number.

14. A's age is $\frac{5}{2}$ B's age. In 10 years A's age will be twice B's age. Find their ages now.

15. The age of A is $\frac{2}{3}$ that of B. Fourteen years ago A's age was $\frac{1}{2}$ B's age. Find their ages now.

16. A is 16 years older than B. Eight years ago B was $\frac{3}{5}$ as old as A. Find their ages now.

17. Jupiter has 4 more moons than Uranus, and Saturn 2 more than twice as many as Uranus; Mars has 6 fewer than Jupiter, and Neptune half as many as Mars. These planets have together 25 moons. How many has each?

18. A triangle has the same area as a trapezoid. The altitude of the triangle is 30 meters and its base is 8 meters. The altitude of the trapezoid is $\frac{1}{3}$ that of the triangle, and one base equals the base of the triangle. Find the other base of the trapezoid.

19. A marksman hears the bullet strike the target 3 seconds after the report of his rifle. If the average velocity of the bullet is 1925 feet per second and the velocity of sound is 1100 feet per second, find the distance to the target and the length of time the bullet was in the air.

20. A gunner using one of the best modern rifles would hear the projectile strike the target 2640 yards distant in $9\frac{2}{3}$ seconds after the report of the gun, provided the projectile maintained throughout its flight the same velocity it had on leaving the gun. Find this velocity if sound travels 1100 feet per second.

70. Equations containing fractions with polynomial denominators.
The method of solving equations of this type is illustrated in
the examples which follow.

1. Solve the equation $\dfrac{x^2}{2\,x^3 - 2} = \dfrac{2\,x}{3\,x^2 + 3\,x + 3} - \dfrac{1}{6\,x - 6}$.

Solution : Factoring the denominators and rewriting,

$$\frac{x^2}{2\,(x-1)\,(x^2 + x + 1)} = \frac{2\,x}{3\,(x^2 + x + 1)} - \frac{1}{6\,(x-1)}.$$

Multiplying both members of the equation by the L.C.M. of the
denominators, $6\,(x-1)\,(x^2 + x + 1)$, and canceling,

$$\frac{x^2}{2\cancel{(x-1)(x^2+x+1)}} \cdot \overset{3}{\cancel{6(x-1)(x^2+x+1)}}$$

$$= \frac{2\,x}{3\cancel{(x^2+x+1)}} \cdot \overset{2}{\cancel{6}}(x-1)\cancel{(x^2+x+1)} - \frac{1}{\cancel{6(x-1)}} \cdot \cancel{6(x-1)}(x^2+x+1).$$

Then $\qquad\qquad 3\,x^2 = 4\,x^2 - 4\,x - x^2 - x - 1.$

Transposing, $\quad 3\,x^2 - 4\,x^2 + 4\,x + x^2 + x = -1.$

Combining like terms, $\qquad\qquad 5\,x = -1,$ or $x = -\tfrac{1}{5}.$

Check : $\qquad \dfrac{\frac{1}{2\,5}}{-\frac{2}{12\,5} - 2} = \dfrac{-\frac{2}{5}}{\frac{3}{2\,5} - \frac{3}{5} + 3} - \dfrac{1}{-\frac{6}{5} - 6}.$

$$\frac{-5}{252} = \frac{-10}{63} - \frac{-5}{36}.$$

Multiplying by 252, $\quad -5 = -40 + 35$ or $-5 = -5.$

In solving equations containing fractions with polynomial
denominators, the student should write the denominators and
their L.C.M. in factored form, as in the preceding solution.
With this exception, the rule on page 156 applies to all equations containing fractions.

Whenever both members of an equation are multiplied by *an
expression containing the unknown*, roots *may* be introduced by
the process. In fact, an apparent root may thus be obtained
for a statement which no number whatever can satisfy.
Such statements are frequently called "impossible equations,"
although, strictly speaking, they are not equations at all.

2. Solve $\dfrac{3x-2}{x-2} = \dfrac{4x-4}{x-2} + 1.$ (A)

Solution: $\dfrac{3x-2}{x-2}(x-2) = \dfrac{4x-4}{x-2}(x-2) + 1 \cdot (x-2).$

Then $3x - 2 = 4x - 4 + x - 2.$

Transposing, $3x - 4x - x = -4 - 2 + 2.$

Combining like terms, $-2x = -4.$

Whence $x = 2.$

On attempting to check, the fraction $\dfrac{3x-2}{x-2}$ becomes $\dfrac{4}{0}.$ Since division by zero has no meaning, 2 is not a root of (A), nor can any number be found which is.

The preceding example illustrates the need of checking; for *an equation has a root*, and a false statement in the form of an equation has none. Moreover the example emphasizes the point that any result we obtain from the solution of an equation is a root, not because we obtain it by correctly performing certain operations, as clearing of fractions, transposing, etc., but because it satisfies the original equation.

The reason that no root can be obtained for the statement $\dfrac{3x-2}{x-2} = \dfrac{4x-4}{x-2} + 1$ is because an impossible number relation is implied therein. This can be shown by solving the equation as follows:

Transposing, $\dfrac{3x-2}{x-2} - \dfrac{4x-4}{x-2} - 1 = 0.$

Reducing the left-hand member to a fraction,

$$\dfrac{3x - 2 - 4x + 4 - x + 2}{x-2} = 0,$$

or $\dfrac{-2x+4}{x-2} = 0.$

Factoring the numerator and reducing to lowest terms,

$$\dfrac{-2(x-2)}{x-2} = 0,$$

or $-2 = 0.$

That is, the impossible condition that $-2 = 0$ was implied in stating (A).

The reason that the impossible condition appears by this method of solution before we check, is to be found in the fact that we did not multiply both members of the equation by any expression containing x, as we did in the first solution.

EXERCISES

Solve and check:

1. $\dfrac{32}{x} = 5.$

5. $\dfrac{4}{x} - \dfrac{12 + x}{3x} = \dfrac{4}{3}.$

2. $\dfrac{25}{3x} = 5.$

6. $\dfrac{5}{6} - \dfrac{3x - 5}{4x} + \dfrac{x - 2}{3x} = 0.$

3. $5x + \dfrac{x - 2}{4} = 4x + 7.$

7. $\dfrac{x + 5}{5x} - \dfrac{3(x + 1)}{x} = 3\tfrac{1}{5}.$

4. $3x - \dfrac{x - 1}{4} - \dfrac{8x}{5} = 6.$

8. $5x - 4x\left(3 - \dfrac{2}{x}\right) + \dfrac{1}{4} = 3.$

9. $x - \dfrac{3x}{5}\left(\dfrac{10}{x} - 4\right) + 3\tfrac{3}{5} = 18.$

10. $\dfrac{8x - 7}{4x} + 3\tfrac{1}{2} = \dfrac{\tfrac{3}{2} - x}{x}.$

17. $\dfrac{x - 3}{x + 4} = \dfrac{x - 9}{x + 5}.$

11. $\dfrac{2x - 3}{3 + 2x} = 4.$

18. $\dfrac{x - 2}{x + 2} + \dfrac{4}{x + 2} + 2 = 0.$

12. $\dfrac{x - 2}{x - 3} = \dfrac{15}{16}.$

19. $\dfrac{3x}{4} - \dfrac{2}{x - 2} = \dfrac{3x - 2}{4}.$

13. $\dfrac{5}{7x + 5} - \dfrac{1}{8} = 0.$

20. $\dfrac{4}{x - 3} + \dfrac{3x + 4}{6} = \dfrac{x}{2}.$

14. $\dfrac{3x^2 - 7x - 4}{4x^2 - 10x - 8} = \dfrac{3}{4}.$

21. $\dfrac{2x + 3}{x - 5} + 4 = \dfrac{x + 8}{x - 5}.$

15. $\dfrac{1}{x - 2} = \dfrac{3}{x - 3}.$

22. $\dfrac{x}{4} - \dfrac{5}{4x - 12} = \dfrac{2x + \tfrac{5}{4}}{3}.$

16. $\dfrac{1}{x - 3} = \dfrac{x - 6}{x + 3} + \dfrac{x}{x + 3}.$

23. $\dfrac{x - 4}{x + 5} + \dfrac{7}{5} = \dfrac{3}{x + 5}.$

24. $\dfrac{x + 4}{15x - 5} - \dfrac{x}{5} = \dfrac{2x + \tfrac{20}{3}}{10}.$

25. $\dfrac{4}{3x + 6} + \dfrac{5}{7x + 14} + 43 = 0.$

26. $\dfrac{7}{4x - 12} + \dfrac{47}{220} = \dfrac{-3}{5x - 15}.$

27. $\dfrac{4x}{x+3} - \dfrac{6}{2x+6} = \dfrac{10x+11}{3x+9}.$

28. $\dfrac{3}{x-2} = \dfrac{5}{x^2-25} + \dfrac{3x}{x^2-25}.$

29. $\dfrac{1}{x-3} + \dfrac{2}{x+3} = \dfrac{-3}{x^2-9}.$

30. $\dfrac{x+2}{x-2} = \dfrac{10-x^2}{4-x^2} - \dfrac{10}{x^2-4}.$

31. $\dfrac{x-4}{x-5} + \dfrac{x-15}{x+4} = \dfrac{2x^2-10x-1}{x^2-x-20}.$

32. $\dfrac{x+2}{x+3} + \dfrac{x+3}{x+2} = \dfrac{4x+9}{x^2+5x+6}.$

71. Equations containing decimals. The method of solving an equation containing decimals is illustrated in the following examples.

EXAMPLES

1. Solve the equation $.4x + .7 = 9.7 - .05x.$

Solution: Multiplying by 100, $\qquad\qquad 40x + 70 = 970 - 5x.$
Transposing and collecting, $\qquad\qquad\quad 45x = 900.$
Dividing by 45, $\qquad\qquad\qquad\qquad\quad x = 20.$
Check: $.4 \times 20 + .7 = 9.7 - .05 \times 20,\ 8.7 = 8.7.$

In equations containing fractions, if decimals occur in any denominator, multiply both terms of such fractions by such a power of ten as will reduce the decimals in the denominators to integers. Then clear the equation of fractions and proceed as in the foregoing example.

2. Solve the equation $\dfrac{4x-3.8}{.5} + \dfrac{1.5x}{.38} + 10x = 9.08.$

Multiplying both terms of the first fraction by 10, and both terms of the second fraction by 100,

$$\frac{40x-38}{5} - \frac{150x}{38} + 10x = 9.08.$$

The equation can now be cleared of fractions and then solved as usual.

EXERCISES

Solve and check:

1. $.3x + 4 = .25$.

2. $.15x - .4x = 235x - 2352.5$.

3. $1.3x + 8.24 = -5.26 - 3.2x$.

4. $3x - 1.245x + .6x = 1.5 + .355x$.

5. $3.5x + .0564 - .1x = 4.9128 - .02x$.

6. $.12(2x + .05) - .15(1.5x - 2) = 0.246$.

7. $\dfrac{.01x + .003}{6} + \dfrac{.02x + .0008}{7} = .0017$

8. $\dfrac{.3(x + 5)}{8} - \dfrac{4(.25x - .35)}{7} = \dfrac{14.325}{56}$.

9. $\dfrac{0.5(6 - .2x)}{.80} - \dfrac{.3(.4x - 3)}{.16} = 5$.

10. $\dfrac{.32x}{.05} + \dfrac{.045x}{.125} = 13.52$.   11. $\dfrac{33}{x + 5} + \dfrac{3.75}{.5(x - 8.5)} = 0$.

Note. The introduction into Europe of the Arabic notation for numbers was one of the important events of the Middle Ages. This notation originated among the Hindus at least as early as 700 A.D. It was adopted by the Arabs, and was introduced by the Moors into Spain during the twelfth and thirteenth centuries. Any one who has tried to multiply two numbers in the Roman notation, like MDCCVII by MCXVIII, will realize the difficulties that surrounded arithmetical operations before the Arabic system was taught. Before the introduction of this system, one of the principal uses for arithmetic was the determination of the day of the month on which Easter came. Roger Bacon in the thirteenth century urged the theologians "to abound in the power of numbering," so that they might carry out these computations. Business accounts were kept on the abacus, a contrivance of wires and sliding balls on which arithmetical operations can be performed with great rapidity.

Though computation in the decimal system was common in Europe from the thirteenth century, the final step in perfecting the notation was not taken until about 1600, when Sir John Napier made use of the decimal point in the modern sense. It was not until the beginning of the eighteenth century that it came into general use.

72. Literal equations. At this point the student should review the solution on page 82.

the solution on page 82.

EXERCISES

Solve and check:

1. $5cx - 8c^2 = 4c^2 - cx.$ 4. $ax + bx = a^2 + ab.$

2. $2(x+1) - 4k = 2.$ 5. $cx + b^2 = bx + bc.$

3. $3(2x - a) = 2(x - 2a).$ 6. $mx + n^2 = m^2 - nx.$

7. $6ac + cx + 4a^2 = 2ax + 3c^2 + 2ca.$

8. $5ax - 5a^2 + 6b^2 = 7ab + 3bx.$

9. $\dfrac{x}{2a} = b.$ 13. $\dfrac{x}{a} + \dfrac{x}{b} = a + b.$

10. $\dfrac{3ab}{x} = a.$ 14. $\dfrac{c^2}{x} - c = \dfrac{d^2}{x} + d.$

11. $\dfrac{a}{x} + \dfrac{3a}{2x} = \dfrac{5}{4}.$ 15. $\dfrac{ax}{2b} - 4b^2 = \dfrac{2bx}{a} - a^2.$

12. $\dfrac{4a}{3x} + \dfrac{4a}{x} = \dfrac{3}{2} + \dfrac{5a}{6x}.$ 16. $\dfrac{x}{c} + \dfrac{c - 2x}{3} - 3c = -4.$

17. $\dfrac{x}{a} + \dfrac{x}{c} + ac = bc + ab + \dfrac{x}{b}.$

18. $\dfrac{3b + 4x}{5b} + \dfrac{3b + 2x}{4b} = \dfrac{1}{20}.$

19. $\dfrac{ax}{2} - \dfrac{3b}{5}\left(x - \dfrac{2ab}{3}\right) = ab\left(\dfrac{a}{2} - \dfrac{b}{5}\right).$

20. $\dfrac{2x - 3b}{a} + \dfrac{2}{b}\left(\dfrac{3x}{2} - a\right) + 5 + \dfrac{9b}{a} = \dfrac{4a}{b}.$

21. $\dfrac{x - m^2}{x - n^2} = \dfrac{n}{m}.$ 22. $\dfrac{x}{c} - \dfrac{d}{c} = \dfrac{x + 2c}{d} - 3.$

23. $\dfrac{b}{b(b - x)} + \dfrac{3}{a(b - x)} + \dfrac{3a + 9}{2ab} = 0.$

24. $\dfrac{c}{a(x + c)} + \dfrac{a}{c(x - a)} = \dfrac{c^2 - ac + 2a^2}{2ac(x - a)}.$

25. $\dfrac{1}{ab} + 1 - \dfrac{ab}{x} + \dfrac{1}{abx} = 0.$ **26.** $\dfrac{a^2}{bx} + \dfrac{b^2}{ax} = \dfrac{1}{a} + \dfrac{1}{b}.$

27. $\dfrac{c^2}{dx} - \dfrac{d^2}{cx} - \dfrac{3c - 3d}{x} = \dfrac{c - d}{cd}.$

28. $\dfrac{a + x}{b + x} - \dfrac{a - x}{b - x} = \dfrac{2}{x^2 - b^2}.$

29. $\dfrac{\dfrac{x}{a - b} - a}{\dfrac{x}{a - b} + a} + 1 = \dfrac{2}{a^2 + ab + 1}.$

30. $\dfrac{\dfrac{a}{2} + \dfrac{x}{3}}{\dfrac{a}{3} - \dfrac{x}{2}} + \dfrac{7a}{4a - 6x} = -7.$

31. $\dfrac{a^2 + ac}{x + 3c} + \dfrac{2cx(a + c)}{x^2 + 5cx + 6c^2} = \dfrac{a^2 + 2ac + c^2}{x + 2c}.$

73. Meaning of primes and subscripts. Different but related values are often represented by the same letter, with smaller figures or letters written at the right and above or below the letter used; as, y', y'', x_0, $4x_3$, $t_m^2 \, t_w$. These are read *y prime, y second, x sub zero, 4 x sub three, the square of t sub m, and t sub w* respectively. Primes and subscripts must not be treated as exponents, and the student should carefully note that x_0 and x_3 are as different numerically as a and b.

The notation just explained is very convenient in physics, where L_1 and L_2 may denote different but related lengths; W_1 and W_2 may represent two different weights; and t_0, t_1, and t_2 may mean three unequal but related intervals of time.

Primes are cumbersome and easily confused with exponents; hence subscripts are preferable.

The following equations are taken from algebra, geometry, and physics, where it is often necessary to express one of the quantities (weight, time, distance, etc.) in terms of the others.

EXERCISES

1. Solve for R, $K = 2\pi RH$.

2. Solve for a, $A = \dfrac{ab}{2}$.

3. Solve for R, $C = 2\pi R$.

4. Solve for r and t, $d = rt$.

5. Solve for a and A, $\dfrac{a}{A} = \dfrac{D}{360}$.

6. Solve for C, $\dfrac{D}{360} = \dfrac{l}{C}$.

7. Solve for r, $C = \dfrac{E}{R + r}$.

8. Solve for r and n, $C = \dfrac{E}{R + nr}$.

9. Solve for r and n, $C = \dfrac{n \cdot e}{R + nr}$.

10. Solve for F, $C = \tfrac{5}{9}(F - 32)$.

11. Solve for W_2, $\dfrac{W_1}{W_2} = \dfrac{L_1}{L_2}$.

12. Solve for r and t, $A = P(1 + rt)$.

13. Solve for P_2, $\dfrac{V_1}{V_2} = \dfrac{P_2}{P_1}$.

14. Solve for n and l, $s = \dfrac{n(a + l)}{2}$.

15. Solve for a, l, and r, $s = \dfrac{rl - a}{r - 1}$.

16. Solve for θ, $\dfrac{D}{180} = \dfrac{\theta}{\pi}$.

17. Solve for t_1, $V_1 = V_0(1 + .00365\, t_1)$.

18. Solve for b_2, $A = \dfrac{(b_1 + b_2)a}{2}$.

19. Solve for x, $\dfrac{a}{b} = \dfrac{x}{c - x}$.

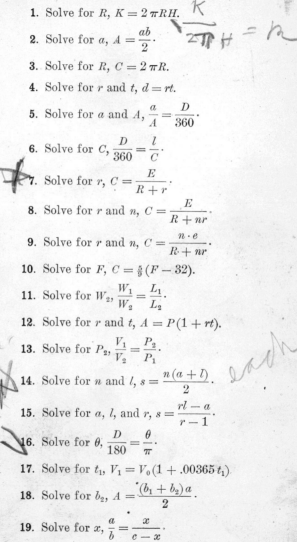

20. Solve for F, D_1, and D_0, $\dfrac{1}{F} = \dfrac{1}{D_1} + \dfrac{1}{D_0}$.

21. $C(t_m - t_1)H_c + W_c(t_m - t_1) = W_h(t_2 - t_m)$.

Find the value of t_m in the preceding equation, when $C = 80$, $t_1 = 20$, $t_2 = 99$, $H_c = .09$, $W_c = 1000$, and $W_h = 800$.

22. $C(t_m - t_w)H_c + W(t_m - t_w) = I(t - t_m)H_I$.

Solve the preceding equation for t, when $C = 80$, $t_m = 54$, $t_w = 18$, $H_c = .09$, $W = 100$, $I = 440$, and $H_I = .11$.

74. The lever. The adjacent figure is a diagram of a machine called a *lever*. AC is a stiff bar resting on a single support at B.

This support is called the *fulcrum* and AB and BC are spoken of as *arms* of the lever.

Those who have played with a teeter board have had some experience with a lever, and they have found that, in order to balance, the heavier of two persons must sit nearer the fulcrum than the lighter one does.

Thus, if $AB = 3$ feet and $BC = 4$ feet, a boy at A who weighs 100 pounds will balance a boy at C who weighs 75 pounds; for $3 \cdot 100 = 4 \cdot 75$.

In general, if the length of the arms of a lever are l_1 and l_2 and the corresponding weights are W_1 and W_2, a balance results when

$$l_1 W_1 = l_2 W_2.$$

PROBLEMS

1. A, 4 feet from the fulcrum, balances B, who is 6 feet from it. A weighs 96 pounds. Find the weight of B.

2. A, who weighs 100 pounds, balances B, who weighs 120 pounds. B is 80 inches from the fulcrum. How far from it is A?

3. A, who weighs 125 pounds, balances B, who weighs 100 pounds. The distance between them is 9 feet. How far is each from the fulcrum?

4. A and B together weigh 210 pounds. They balance when A is 3 feet 9 inches from the fulcrum, and B is 5 feet from it. Find the weight of each.

5. A weighs 90 pounds and is 4 feet from the fulcrum. B weighs 60 pounds and is 3 feet from the fulcrum and on the same side of it as A. C, who weighs 108 pounds, is on the opposite side of the fulcrum. How far from it must C be in order to balance both A and B?

PROBLEMS

1. Separate 300 into two parts such that their quotient is 5.

2. Separate 60 into two parts such that $\frac{2}{3}$ of the greater will equal $\frac{3}{4}$ of the smaller.

3. Separate 45 into two parts such that the sum of $\frac{4}{9}$ of the greater and $\frac{2}{3}$ of the smaller will be 24.

4. Separate $\frac{2}{5}$ into two parts such that $\frac{1}{3}$ of one part will equal $\frac{3}{4}$ of the other.

5. Find two numbers whose sum is 95, such that the greater divided by the less gives a partial quotient of 4 and a remainder of 5.

Solution:	Let $x =$ the smaller number.
Then	$95 - x =$ the greater number.

Now $\dfrac{\text{Dividend}}{\text{Divisor}} = \text{Partial Quotient} + \dfrac{\text{Remainder}}{\text{Divisor}}.$

Therefore $\dfrac{95 - x}{x} = 4 + \dfrac{5}{x}.$

Multiplying by x, $95 - x = 4x + 5.$
Solving, $x = 18,$
and $95 - x = 77.$

Check: $\underline{18\,|\,77\,\lfloor 4}$
$\underline{72}$
5

6. Separate 126 into two parts such that one divided by the other gives a partial quotient of 6 and a remainder of 7.

7. The sum of two numbers is 1906. The greater divided by the less gives a partial quotient of 41 and a remainder of 16. Find the numbers.

8. Separate $\frac{8}{5}$ into two parts such that their product is less by $\frac{2}{3}$ than the square of the greater part.

9. Separate 71 into two parts such that 40 exceeds $\frac{2}{3}$ of one part as much as the other exceeds 16.

10. A boy's age is now $\frac{2}{3}$ of what it will be 12 years hence. How old is he?

11. Two thirds of a man's age now, equals $\frac{6}{5}$ of what it was 30 years ago. Find his present age.

12. One sixth of a man's age 8 years ago equals $\frac{1}{8}$ of his age 12 years hence. What is his age now?

13. A man invests part of $3100 at 6% and the remainder at 5%. The 6% investment yields annually $18.60 less than the 5% investment. Find the sum invested at 5%.

14. A man invests part of $5360 at 5% and the remainder at 6%. The yearly income from the 5% investment is $63.40 more than that from the 6% investment. Find the sum invested at 6%.

15. A part of $3880 is invested at 4% and the remainder at 6%. The total yearly income is $171.20. Find the amount invested at 6%.

16. A collection of five-cent pieces and quarters contains 80 coins. Their total value is $16. How many are there of each?

17. Twenty-eight coins, dimes and quarters, have the value of $5.05. How many are there of each?

18. The square of half a certain even number is 11 less than $\frac{1}{4}$ the product of the next two consecutive even numbers. Find the numbers.

19. The square of $\frac{4}{3}$ of a certain even number is 2864 less than $1\frac{7}{9}$ times the product of the next two consecutive odd numbers. Find the number.

20. A rectangle is four times as long as it is wide. If it were 4 meters shorter and $1\frac{1}{2}$ meters wider, its area would be 11 square meters more. Find its length and its breadth.

21. The length of a certain rectangle is $2\frac{1}{2}$ times its width. If it were 5 meters longer and 4 meters narrower, its area would be 50 square meters less. Find its dimensions.

22. It costs as much to sod a square piece of ground at 20 cents per square meter as to fence it at 80 cents per meter. Find the side of the square.

23. A rectangular court is twice as long as it is wide. It costs as much to fence it at 50 cents per yard as to sod it at 15 cents per square yard. Find its dimensions.

24. A rectangular picture $2\frac{1}{2}$ times as long as wide is surrounded by a frame 2 inches wide. The area of the frame is 128 square inches. Find the dimensions of the picture.

25. A square court has the same area as a rectangular court whose length is $2\frac{7}{9}$ yards greater and whose width is $2\frac{1}{2}$ yards less. Find the dimensions and area of each.

26. A man bought apples at 18 cents per dozen. He sold $\frac{1}{5}$ of them at the rate of 3 for 4 cents, and the remainder at the rate of 4 for 3 cents, losing 76 cents. How many did he buy?

27. A can do a piece of work in 2 days, B in 3 days, and C in 4 days. How long will it take them, working together?

Solution: Let x represent the number of days required by A, B, and C together to do the work.

Then $\dfrac{1}{x} =$ the fractional part of the work the three together do in one day.

By the conditions of the problem A does $\frac{1}{2}$ of the work in one day, B does $\frac{1}{3}$ of the work in one day, and C does $\frac{1}{4}$ of the work in one day.

Therefore
$$\frac{1}{2} + \frac{1}{3} + \frac{1}{4} = \frac{1}{x}.$$

Solving,
$$x = 1\tfrac{2}{13}.$$

Check:
$$\frac{1}{2} + \frac{1}{3} + \frac{1}{4} = \frac{1}{1\frac{2}{13}}, \quad \text{or} \quad \frac{13}{12} = \frac{13}{12}.$$

28. A can do a piece of work in $2\frac{1}{2}$ days and B in $3\frac{3}{4}$ days. How many days will they require, working together?

29. A can do a piece of work in 2 days, B in $2\frac{1}{3}$ days, and C in $3\frac{1}{2}$ days. How many days will they require, working together?

30. A can do a piece of work in 8 days, and A and B together can do it in $4\frac{4}{5}$ days. How long would it take B alone?

31. A can do a piece of work in $3\frac{1}{2}$ days, B in $2\frac{4}{5}$ days, and A, B, and C together can do it in $1\frac{1}{6}$ days. In how many days can C do the work alone?

32. A can do a piece of work in 12 days and B in 15 days. After A works 3 days alone, A and B finish the work. How long do they work together?

33. Two bicyclists start at the same time to ride from A to B, 80 miles distant. One travels 4 miles an hour more than the other. The faster bicyclist reaches B and at once returns, meeting the slower one 64 miles from A. Find the rate of each.

Solution: A careful reading shows that the two travel at different rates, that they travel different distances, but that the time is the same for each. Hence the equation must be formed by expressing the time t, or d/r, for each, and equating the two expressions for t.

The two together cover twice the distance from A to B, or 160 miles. As the slower one traveled 64 miles, the faster travels $160-64$, or 96, miles. If x equals the rate of the slower bicyclist in miles per hour, we have:

	d miles	r miles per hour	$\dfrac{d}{r}$, or t hours
Slower bicyclist	64	x	$\dfrac{64}{x}$
Faster bicyclist	96	$x + 4$	$\dfrac{96}{x+4}$

Hence
$$\frac{64}{x} = \frac{96}{x+4}.$$

Solving, we obtain $x = 8$, the rate of the slower bicyclist in miles per hour, and $x + 4 = 12$, the rate of the faster bicyclist.

Check: $\frac{64}{8} = 8$, and $\frac{96}{12} = 8$.

34. A man travels at a uniform rate from A to B, 120 miles distant. He travels the first 70 miles without stopping. The remainder of the journey, including a delay of 2 hours, requires the same time as the first part. Find his rate.

Solution: By reading the problem we discover that the distances covered in the first and second portions of the journey are different, that the time of travel is not the same for each, but that the rate throughout is the same. Hence the equation will be formed by finding two expressions for the rate r, or d/t, and setting them equal to each other. If x equals the number of hours required to travel 70 miles, we have:

	d miles	t hours	$\dfrac{d}{t}$, or r
First part of journey	70	x	$\dfrac{70}{x}$
Second part of journey	50	$x-2$	$\dfrac{50}{x-2}$

Hence
$$\frac{70}{x} = \frac{50}{x-2}.$$

Solving, we obtain $x = 7$, the time in hours occupied in traveling the first 70 miles. And $70 \div 7 = 10$, the rate per hour.

Check: $70 \div 10 = 7$, and $7 - 5 = 2$.

35. A bicyclist traveling 10 miles an hour was overtaken $5\frac{2}{3}$ hours after he started by an automobile which left the same starting point 1 hour and 40 minutes later. What was the rate of the automobile?

36. Two bicyclists, A and B, start at the same time to ride from X to Y, 63 miles distant. A travels 3 miles per hour less than B. The latter reaches Y and at once returns, meeting A 9 miles from Y. Find the rate of each.

37. A leaves a certain point and travels at the rate of $4\frac{1}{2}$ miles an hour. Two and one half hours later B leaves the same point and travels in the opposite direction at the rate of $10\frac{1}{2}$ miles an hour. How much time must elapse after A starts before they will be 40 miles apart?

38. A bicyclist traveled to a certain point and returned, making the trip in 18 hours. The total distance was 160 miles, and the rate going was 8 miles an hour. At what rate did he return?

39. A and B start at the same time from two towns 150 miles apart and travel toward each other. Their respective rates are 9 and 12 miles an hour. A rests 3 hours and B rests $4\frac{1}{2}$ hours before they meet. How far has each of them traveled when they meet?

40. A and B leave the same place at the same time for a point 63 miles distant. A travels $3\frac{1}{2}$ times as fast as B. The former reaches the point and returns immediately, meeting B 8 hours from the time of starting. Find the rates of A and B.

41. A man rows $4\frac{1}{4}$ miles per hour in still water. He finds that it requires 5 hours to row upstream a distance which it requires 3 hours to row down. Find the rate of the current.

HINT. Let x equal the rate of the current. Then $4\frac{1}{4} - x$ equals the rate upstream and $4\frac{1}{4} + x$ equals the rate downstream.

42. A man who can row 4 miles per hour in still water rows up a stream the rate of whose current is 2 miles per hour. After rowing back he finds that the entire trip took 12 hours. How far does he row upstream?

43. A man who can row $4\frac{1}{3}$ miles an hour in still water rows downstream and returns. The rate of the current is $2\frac{1}{4}$ miles per hour and the time required for the trip is 13 hours. How many hours does he require to return?

44. A and B together can do a piece of work in $1\frac{1}{5}$ days. A alone can do the work in one day less than B. Find the time each requires alone.

HINT. Let $x =$ the number of days required by A alone.
Then $x + 1 =$ the number of days required by B alone.

Therefore $\dfrac{1}{x} + \dfrac{1}{x+1} = \dfrac{1}{\frac{6}{5}} = \dfrac{5}{6}$.

Whence $5x^2 - 7x - 6 = 0$, which may be solved by factoring.

45. A and B together can do a piece of work in $2\frac{2}{5}$ days. B alone can do the work in two days less time than A. Find the number of days required by each alone.

46. A man rows upstream and back, a total distance of 20 miles, in 6 hours. His rate upstream is $2\frac{1}{2}$ miles per hour. Find the rate of the current and his rate in still water.

47. A farmer pays $96 for a number of sheep. He sells all but 2 of them for $100, and gains $2 on each sheep sold. Find the number of sheep bought.

48. A piece of cloth is bought for $64. Four yards are cut off and the remainder is sold, at an advance of $2 per yard, for $72. Find the cost per yard.

49. A train runs 100 miles. On the return trip it increases its rate 5 miles per hour and makes the run in one hour less time. Find the rate going and returning.

50. An automobile makes a run of 120 miles. The chauffeur then increases the speed 4 miles per hour and returns over the same route in 5 hours less time. Find the rate going and returning.

51. Two automobiles travel 72 miles over the same route. One travels 2 miles per hour more than the other and makes the run in 30 minutes less time. Find the rate of each.

52. A and B start at the same time from two points 144 miles apart and travel toward each other. A's rate is 4 miles less than B's. The latter, having been delayed 3 hours on the way, has traveled the same distance as A when they meet. Find the rate of each.

53. A and B start from the same place at the same time and travel in opposite directions. B is delayed 2 hours on the way, and at the end of a certain time the two are 172 miles apart. If A has traveled 28 miles farther than B and one mile more per hour, find the rate of each.

CHAPTER XVIII

RATIO AND PROPORTION

75. Ratio. The **ratio** of one number, a, to a second number, b, is the quotient obtained by dividing the first by the second, or $\dfrac{a}{b}$.

The ratio of a to b is also written $a : b$.

It follows from the above that all ratios of numbers are fractions and all fractions may be regarded as ratios.

Thus $\dfrac{3}{2}$, $\dfrac{c}{2x}$, $\dfrac{a+b}{a-b}$, and $\dfrac{\sqrt{2}}{\sqrt[3]{5}}$ are ratios.

The dividend, or numerator, in a ratio is called the **antecedent**, and the divisor, or denominator, is called the **consequent**.

We may speak of the ratio of two concrete numbers if they have a common unit of measure. The ratio of 5 feet to 3 feet is $\frac{5}{3}$, the common unit of measure being 1 foot. Obviously no ratio exists between 5 years and 3 feet.

Measurement is the process of finding the numerical relation (ratio) of whatever is measured to a standard unit of measure. Thus, when we say a distance is 100 yards, we mean that it is 100 times the length of the *standard* yard. For the United States the standard yard is the distance between two scratches on a certain gun-metal bar. This bar, along with the standard pound, the standard gallon, etc., is kept at the Bureau of Weights and Measures in Washington, D.C.

If we say a piece of paper contains 54 square inches, we are expressing by the number 54 the ratio of the surface of the paper to the surface of a square whose side is one inch.

Every measurement, then, is the determination of a ratio, either exact or approximate.

176

Note. Until comparatively recent times there was no unity among the various nations in regard to the standards of measurement. Just as we now have English, French, and American money, and are obliged to change when we go from one country to another, so until recently the different countries had their own standards of measurement. The yard and the foot are now in common use in English-speaking countries, but in France and Germany the meter is the standard.

In earlier times there was even greater confusion. Among the Hebrews the unit of length was the cubit, which, tradition tells us, was the distance from the end of the king's longest finger to the point of his elbow. Our word *foot* is a reminder of the time when the length of the king's foot was the standard. But with the advance of civilization and the increase of trade between different nations more or less uniformity in standards of measurement has been secured.

EXERCISES

Simplify the following ratios by writing them as fractions and reducing the fractions to their lowest terms:

1. $5 : 10$.
2. $10 : 5$.
3. $16\,a^2 : 8\,a$.

4. $3\frac{1}{16} : 3\frac{1}{2}$.
5. $8\frac{2}{3} : 5\frac{7}{9}$.
6. 3 days : 9 hours.

7. 150 lb. : 1 ton.
8. $(x^2 - y^2) : (x + y)$.
9. $(a^3 + b^3) : (a + b)$.

10. $\left(1 - \dfrac{1}{a^2}\right) : \left(1 + \dfrac{1}{a}\right)$.

11. $\left(2 + \dfrac{1}{x^2}\right) : \left(4 - \dfrac{1}{x^4}\right)$.

12. $\dfrac{1}{x - 3} : \dfrac{1}{x^2 - 5\,x + 6}$

13. $(x^2 - xy + y^2) : (x^3 + y^3)$.

14. $\left(x^2 - \dfrac{y^3}{x}\right) : \left(1 - \dfrac{y}{x}\right)$.

15. $\left(\dfrac{16}{x} - x\right) : \left(\dfrac{24}{x^4} + \dfrac{10}{x^3} + \dfrac{1}{x^2}\right)$.

16. Separate 40 into two parts which are in the ratio of $2 : 3$.

Hint. Let $2\,x =$ one part, and $3\,x =$ the other. Then $2\,x + 3\,x = 40$, etc.

17. Separate 16 into two parts which are in the ratio of $5 : 3$.

18. Separate 84 into two parts which are in the ratio of $3:11$.

19. Separate 36 into three parts which are to each other as $2:3:4$.

20. Separate 135 into three parts which are to each other as $4:5:6$.

21. What number added to both terms of the ratio $\frac{5}{8}$ gives as the result the ratio $\frac{21}{28}$?

22. What number subtracted from both terms of the ratio $\frac{13}{27}$ gives as the result the ratio $\frac{2}{9}$?

23. If a is a positive number, which is the greater ratio, $\frac{4+2a}{4+3a}$ or $\frac{4+3a}{4+4a}$?

Hint. Reduce the fractions to equivalent fractions having a common denominator, and then compare the numerators of the resulting fractions.

24. If a and b are positive numbers, which is the greater ratio, $\frac{a+4b}{a+5b}$ or $\frac{a+6b}{a+7b}$?

25. If a positive number is added to both terms of a proper fraction, what change is produced in the numerical value of the fraction?

76. Proportion. Four numbers, a, b, c, and d, are in **proportion** if the ratio of the first pair equals the ratio of the second pair.

This proportion is written $a:b=c:d$, or $\frac{a}{b}=\frac{c}{d}$.

The first and fourth terms (a, d) are called the **extremes**, and the second and third terms (b, c) are called the **means**.

Since a proportion is an equation, any operation which may properly be performed on an equation may be performed on a proportion.

Then in the proportion $\frac{a}{b}=\frac{c}{d}$ both members may be multiplied by bd, giving $ad = bc$.

Therefore, *In any proportion the product of the means equals the product of the extremes.*

EXERCISES

Find the value of x in the proportions:

1. $\dfrac{3}{4} = \dfrac{6}{x}$.

2. $\dfrac{4}{7} = \dfrac{16}{x}$.

3. $\dfrac{3}{2} = \dfrac{x}{5}$.

4. $3 : x = 7 : 9$.

5. $x : 4 = 3 : 6$.

6. $\dfrac{4}{3} = 2 : \dfrac{1}{x}$.

7. $\dfrac{2}{3} = \dfrac{\frac{1}{x}}{4}$.

8. $\dfrac{2}{\frac{1}{x}} = \dfrac{3\frac{1}{3}}{4}$.

9. $\dfrac{1}{x} : 2 = 3 : 4\frac{1}{2}$.

10. $\dfrac{a}{b} = \dfrac{c}{x}$.

11. $a : b = c : \dfrac{1}{x}$.

12. $\dfrac{a}{x^2} = \dfrac{1}{x} : a^3$.

13. $4 : 3\frac{1}{3} = 3 : x - 3$.

14. $5 : x - 3 = 7 : 2x + 6$.

A **mean proportional** between two numbers, a and b, is the number m, if $\dfrac{a}{m} = \dfrac{m}{b}$. This means that $m^2 = ab$, or $m = \pm\sqrt{ab}$.

Since $\dfrac{2}{\pm 4} = \dfrac{\pm 4}{8}$, $+4$ is a mean proportional between 2 and 8, as is also -4.

A **third proportional** to two numbers, a and b, is the number t, if $\dfrac{a}{b} = \dfrac{b}{t}$.

In $\dfrac{3}{6} = \dfrac{6}{12}$, 12 is a third proportional to 3 and 6.

A **fourth proportional** to three numbers, a, b, and c, is the number f, if $\dfrac{a}{b} = \dfrac{c}{f}$.

Since $\dfrac{5}{12} = \dfrac{10}{24}$, 24 is a fourth proportional to 5, 12, and 10.

EXERCISES

Find the mean proportionals between:

1. 1 and 4.

2. 4 and 9.

3. 16 and 4.

4. 3 and 12.

5. $(a - b)^2$ and 4.

6. $\frac{1}{2}$ and $\frac{1}{8}$.

7. $\frac{1}{3}$ and $\frac{1}{27}$.

8. $\dfrac{4}{a^3}$ and $\dfrac{9}{ax^2}$.

9. Find a third proportional to the numbers in Exercises 1–7 which precede.

Find a fourth proportional to:

10. 1, 2, and 3.

11. 4, 5, and 6.

12. 7, 14, and 5.

13. 5, 12, and a.

14. 7, 21 x, and 6 x.

15. a, a^2, and a^3.

16. a^3, a^5, and a^4.

17. $a + b$, $a - b$, and $a^2 - b^2$.

18. $\dfrac{a - b}{2}$, $\dfrac{1}{a + b}$, and $a^2 - b^2$.

If $ps = qr$ is divided by qs, we obtain

$$\frac{p\cancel{s}}{q\cancel{s}} = \frac{\cancel{q}r}{\cancel{q}s}, \text{ or } \frac{p}{q} = \frac{r}{s}. \tag{1}$$

Also $ps = qr$ divided by rs gives

$$\frac{p}{r} = \frac{q}{s}. \tag{2}$$

And $qr = ps$ divided by pr gives

$$\frac{q}{p} = \frac{s}{r}. \tag{3}$$

Therefore, *If the product of any two numbers* (**ps**) *equals the product of two other numbers* (**qr**), *one pair may be made the means and the other pair the extremes of a proportion.*

If $\dfrac{a}{b} = \dfrac{c}{d}$, then from (1) and (2), $\dfrac{a}{c} = \dfrac{b}{d}$: Here $\dfrac{a}{c} = \dfrac{b}{d}$ is said to be obtained from $\dfrac{a}{b} = \dfrac{c}{d}$ by **alternation**.

If $\dfrac{a}{b} = \dfrac{c}{d}$, then from (1) and (3), $\dfrac{b}{a} = \dfrac{d}{c}$. Here $\dfrac{b}{a} = \dfrac{d}{c}$ is said to be obtained from $\dfrac{a}{b} = \dfrac{c}{d}$ by **inversion**.

EXERCISES

Write as a proportion in three ways:

1. $3 \cdot 4 = 2 \cdot 6$.

2. $5 \cdot 6 = 3 \cdot 10$.

3. $3 \cdot 6 = 2 \cdot x$.

4. $a \cdot d = b \cdot c$.

5. $(a + b)(a - b) = 2 \cdot 3$.

6. $(a + b)(a - b) = (a + 2)(a + 3)$.

Write as a proportion:

7. $a^2 - b^2 = 2 \cdot 3$.   **9.** $a^2 - 5a + 6 = 4 \cdot 2$.

8. $a^2 - 2ab + b^2 = 3 \cdot 6$.   **10.** $a^2 - 7a + 12 = (a + b)^2$.

11. $a^2 - 6a + 9 = a^2 - 10a + 16$.

12. $x^2 - 4xy + 4y^2 = a^2 + 10ab + 25b^2$.

13. $xy = 4$.   **15.** $ab = 1$.   **17.** $mnp = xyz$.

14. $xy = 3$.   **16.** $abc = de$.   **18.** $ab = a + b$.

Write as a proportion so that x is the fourth term:

19. $3 \cdot 4 = 5 \cdot x$.   **22.** $px = qr$.

20. $4x = 9 \cdot 7$.   **23.** $acx = bd$.   **25.** $x = \dfrac{ab}{c}$.

21. $ab = cx$.   **24.** $1 = ax$.   **26.** $xy = y + 1$.

Write by alternation:

27. $\frac{2}{3} = \frac{4}{6}$.   **29.** $4 : 5 = 6 : x$.

28. $\dfrac{4}{3} = \dfrac{x}{y}$.   **30.** $3 = \dfrac{a}{b}$.

Write by inversion:

31. $4 : 8 = 3 : 6$.   **35.** $3 : \dfrac{1}{x} = \dfrac{2}{a}$.

32. $\dfrac{3}{2} = \dfrac{a}{b}$.

33. $P : P_1 = W_1 : W$.   **36.** $\dfrac{1}{x} : \dfrac{1}{y} = \dfrac{1}{z}$.

34. $\dfrac{V_1}{V_2} = \dfrac{P_2}{P_1}$.   **37.** $\dfrac{N_1}{N_2} = \dfrac{\sqrt{T_2}}{\sqrt{T_1}}$.

If four numbers, a, b, c, and d, are in proportion, they are in proportion by **addition**, **subtraction**, and **addition and subtraction**.

Addition. Let
$$\frac{a}{b} = \frac{c}{d}. \tag{1}$$

Adding 1 to both members,
$$\frac{a}{b} + 1 = \frac{c}{d} + 1, \tag{2}$$

or
$$\frac{a + b}{b} = \frac{c + d}{d}. \tag{3}$$

Here (3) is said to be obtained from (1) by *addition*.

Subtraction. Let $\dfrac{a}{b} = \dfrac{c}{d}.$ (1)

Subtracting 1 from both members,

$$\frac{a}{b} - 1 = \frac{c}{d} - 1,$$ (2)

or $\qquad\qquad\qquad \dfrac{a-b}{b} = \dfrac{c-d}{d}.$ (3)

Here (3) is said to be obtained from (1) by *subtraction*.

Addition and Subtraction. Let $\dfrac{a}{b} = \dfrac{c}{d}.$ (1)

Then $\qquad\qquad \dfrac{a+b}{b} = \dfrac{c+d}{d}$ (addition), (2)

and $\qquad\qquad \dfrac{a-b}{b} = \dfrac{c-d}{d}$ (subtraction). (3)

Dividing (2) by (3), $\qquad \dfrac{a+b}{a-b} = \dfrac{c+d}{c-d}.$ (4)

Equation (4) is said to be obtained from (1) by *addition and subtraction*.

Addition, subtraction, and addition and subtraction are often called composition, division, and composition and division respectively.

EXERCISES

Write by addition:

1. $\frac{2}{3} = \frac{4}{6}.$

2. $4 : 12 = 8 : 24.$

3. $a : x = 1 : 2.$

4. $4 : 3 = f : x.$

5. $\dfrac{A_1}{A_2} = \dfrac{S_1^2}{S_2^2}.$

6. Write Exercises 1–4, preceding, by subtraction.

7. Write Exercises 1–4, preceding, by addition and subtraction.

8. If $\dfrac{a}{b} = \dfrac{c}{d},$ prove $\dfrac{a+b}{a} = \dfrac{c+d}{c}.$

9. If $\dfrac{a}{b} = \dfrac{c}{d},$ prove $\dfrac{a-b}{a} = \dfrac{c-d}{c}.$

10. If $\dfrac{a}{b} = \dfrac{c}{d},$ prove $\dfrac{2a+b}{b} = \dfrac{2c+d}{d}.$

11. If $\dfrac{a}{b} = \dfrac{c}{d},$ prove $\dfrac{a+3b}{b} = \dfrac{c+3d}{d}.$

Write Exercises 12 and 13 by addition and subtraction and solve the resulting equations for x.

12. $\dfrac{3x+4}{3x-4} = \dfrac{3+2}{3-2}$.   **13.** $\dfrac{6x+3}{6x-3} = \dfrac{2a+b}{2a-b}$.

A series of equal ratios. If $\dfrac{a}{b} = \dfrac{c}{d} = \dfrac{e}{f}$,   (1)

then $\dfrac{a+c+e}{b+d+f} = \dfrac{a}{b} = \dfrac{c}{d} = \dfrac{e}{f}$.   (2)

Proof: Let $\dfrac{a}{b} = \dfrac{c}{d} = \dfrac{e}{f} = r$.   (3)

Then $a = br$,   (4)

$c = dr$,   (5)

$e = fr$.   (6)

Adding (4), (5), and (6), $a + c + e = br + dr + fr$.   (7)

Factoring in (7) $a + c + e = (b + d + f)r$.   (8)

Therefore $\dfrac{a+c+e}{b+d+f} = r$.   (9)

Hence, by (3), $\dfrac{a+c+e}{b+d+f} = \dfrac{a}{b} = \dfrac{c}{d} = \dfrac{e}{f}$.   (10)

This result may be expressed verbally: *In a series of equal ratios the sum of the antecedents is to the sum of the consequents as any antecedent is to its consequent.*

EXERCISES

Test the truth of the preceding result in Exercises 1–4:

1. $\frac{1}{2} = \frac{3}{6} = \frac{5}{10}$.   **3.** $3 : 4 = 6 : 8 = 12 : 16$.

2. $\dfrac{1}{a} = \dfrac{2}{2a} = \dfrac{3b}{3ab}$.   **4.** $\dfrac{1}{x-y} = \dfrac{a}{ax-ay} = \dfrac{b}{bx-by}$.

5. Taken in the same order, the sides of two triangles are 3, 4, 5, and 9, 12, 15 respectively. What is the ratio of the sides of the first triangle to the corresponding sides of the second? Compare this ratio with the ratio of the perimeter of the first triangle to the perimeter of the second.

6. If $\dfrac{a}{b} = \dfrac{c}{d} = \dfrac{e}{f}$, prove $\dfrac{2a+3c+4e}{2b+3d+4f} = \dfrac{a}{b}$.

MISCELLANEOUS EXERCISES IN PROPORTION

1. If $a : b = 4 : x$, and $a : b = 4 : \dfrac{1}{x}$, find x.

2. If $\dfrac{a}{b} = \dfrac{9}{y}$, and $\dfrac{a}{b} = \dfrac{1}{\dfrac{1}{y}}$, find y.

3. If $p : r = 7 : 6$, and $q : r = 3 : 5$, find the ratio $p : q$.

4. If $p : q = 4 : a$, and $q : r = a : 7$, find the ratio $p : r$.

5. The sides of a triangle are 8, 10, and 12. The side 12 is divided into the ratio of the other two sides. Find the two parts.

6. The perimeter of a triangle is 63. Two sides are 18 and 24 and the other side is divided in the ratio of these two. Find the two parts of the third side.

7. A flagstaff casts a shadow 12 yards long; at the same time a man 5 feet 10 inches tall casts a shadow 35 inches long. How high is the pole?

Fact from Geometry. If one triangle is similar to another, the sides of the first taken in any order are proportional to the sides of the second taken in the same order.

8. The sides of a triangle are 10, 15, and 20 respectively. In a similar triangle the side corresponding to 10 is 12. Find the other sides. Compare the ratio of the two corresponding sides with the ratio of the perimeters.

9. The sides of a triangle are 9, 10, and 17. The perimeter of a similar triangle is 108. Find the sides of the second triangle.

Fact from Geometry. A line *parallel* to one side of a triangle divides the other two sides into four proportional parts.

Thus in triangle ABC which follows, line DE is parallel to side BC, and $\dfrac{AD}{DB} = \dfrac{AE}{EC}$.

Also a line parallel to one side of a triangle forms with the other two sides a second triangle *similar* to the first.

In the following figure triangle ADE is similar to triangle ABC. Therefore $\dfrac{AD}{AB} = \dfrac{AE}{AC} = \dfrac{DE}{BC}$.

10. In triangle ABC:

(*a*) If $AD = 6$, $DB = 4$, and $AE = 10$, find EC.

(*b*) If $DB = 4$, $AD = 8$, and $DE = 6$, find BC.

(*c*) If $DB = 4$, $AD = 8$, and $AC = 10$, find AE.

(*d*) If $AB = AC = 16$, and $AD = 10$, find AE.

11. Draw a triangle and letter the vertices F, G, and H respectively. Draw RK parallel to FG, R being on side HF and K on side HG. Then if:

(*a*) $FG = 15$, $RK = 10$, $HR = 8$, find HF.

(*b*) $FG = 20$, $RK = 16$, $HF = 10$, find RF.

(*c*) $FG = 20$, $RK = 15$, $RF = 6$, find HR.

(*d*) $FG = 18$, $RK = 15$, $KG = 4$, find HK.

Fact from Geometry. The line joining the middle points of two sides of a triangle is parallel to the third side.

12. Two sides of a triangle are 30 centimeters and 24 centimeters respectively. The line joining their middle points is 12 centimeters long. Find the third side of the triangle.

13. The sides of a triangle are 10, 12, and 16 centimeters respectively. Find the lengths of the lines connecting the middle points of its sides.

14. In the *right-angled* triangle ABC, line BD is *perpendicular* to AC. Then BD is a mean proportional between AD and DC.

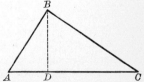

(*a*) If $AD = 9$ and $BD = 6$, find DC.

(*b*) If $AD = 4$ and $AC = 20$, find BD.

15. In the *semicircle ABC*, line *CD* is perpendicular to *AB*. Then *CD* is a mean proportional between *AD* and *DB*.

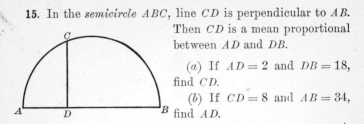

(*a*) If $AD = 2$ and $DB = 18$, find *CD*.

(*b*) If $CD = 8$ and $AB = 34$, find *AD*.

16. The distance *AB* between two points on opposite banks of a river was wanted. Stakes were set at *E*, *B*, *D*, and *C*, so that *BE* was parallel to *CD*, and so that *ABC* and *AED* were straight lines. The measured values of *DC*, *CB*, and *BE* were 480 feet, 160 feet, and 420 feet respectively. What was the computed value of *BA* ?

17. The perimeters of two similar triangles are 45 and 135 respectively. One side of the first is 11 and a second side is 19. Find the sides of the second triangle.

18. Two men start at the same time and travel in opposite directions. The ratio of their rates is $2:3$. In 5 hours they are 100 miles apart. Find the rate of each.

19. *A*, *B*, and *C* ate equally of a stock of provisions which *A* and *B* furnished. The values of what *A* and *B* contributed were in the ratio of 7 to 8 respectively. *C* paid $30 for what he ate. How should *A* and *B* have divided the money ?

20. A clock provided with hands to indicate the minute, the hour, and the day of the month showed correct time at 4 P.M. on February 21, 1900. The clock gained 10 minutes daily. What was the correct time when the clock indicated 4 P.M. on the 28th of the next month ?

CHAPTER XIX

GRAPHICAL REPRESENTATION

77. Temperature curve. The curve $ABCDEF$ is called a **graph**. It was made by a recording thermometer. Such instruments are provided with an arm carrying a pen, which moves up as the temperature rises, and down as it falls. A clock movement runs a strip of cross-ruled paper under the pen and thus a continuous line is traced on the paper. The following record extends from 2 P.M. of Wednesday, February 19, 1908, to 10.30 A.M.

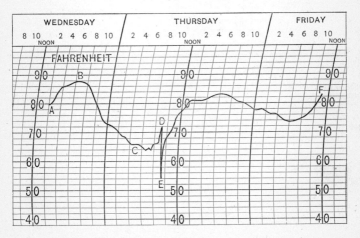

of the Friday following. The numbers 50, 60, 70, 80, and 90 denote degrees Fahrenheit. There are 5 spaces from 50° to 60°. Hence one space corresponds to 2 degrees. The numbers 2, 4, 6, 8, and 10 indicate the time of day. Whether this is A.M. or P.M. can be determined by the position of these numbers with respect to the heavy curved lines marked NOON. The point A

on the graph informs us that at 2 P.M. Wednesday the temperature was 80 degrees. The point B between 6 P.M. and 7 P.M. Wednesday marks the highest temperature recorded.

The point C tells us that the temperature was about $65\frac{1}{2}$ degrees at 6 A.M. Thursday.

The preceding record was made indoors, and the sudden fall from D to E was caused by the opening of a door leading into a cold hallway. The portion of the graph from D to E shows that the temperature of the room fell approximately 18 degrees in about 30 minutes

EXERCISES

By reference to the graph (p. 187) answer the following:

1. With what temperature does the record begin? end?

2. What is the highest temperature recorded? the lowest?

3. About what time was the highest temperature recorded? the lowest?

4. How often did the instrument record a temperature of 80 degrees? 72 degrees? 78 degrees? 62 degrees?

5. At what times did it record a temperature of 80 degrees? 72 degrees? 78 degrees? 62 degrees?

6. To what practical use can a graph such as the one here explained be put?

78. Falling body curve. The curved line $OABDC$ in the adjacent figure is another graph. It represents closely the relation between the distance a sphere of lead, if allowed to drop through the air, will fall in any number of seconds from one to eight. Time measured in seconds from the instant the sphere begins to fall is *represented* on the line OX. One inch on OX corresponds to 4 seconds of time, $\frac{1}{2}$ inch to 2 seconds, $\frac{1}{10}$ inch to $\frac{2}{5}$ of a second, etc. The distance measured in feet through which the sphere falls is *represented* on the line OY. One inch on OY corresponds to 320 feet, $\frac{1}{10}$ of an inch to 32 feet, etc. The point A on the curve, just above 2, corresponds to a time of 2 seconds. *A* is opposite the number 64 on *OY*. This means that in 2 seconds the lead sphere falls 64 feet. Similarly *B* corresponds to a time of 4 seconds and a distance of 256 feet. That is, the lead sphere falls 256 feet in 4 seconds.

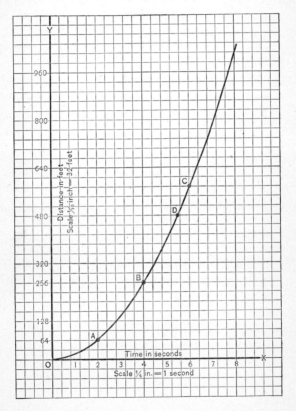

The question, "How far does a body fall in 6 seconds?" can be answered by reference to the graph, thus: The point on the curve corresponding to 6 seconds is *C*, just above 6 on *OX*. The point on *OY* opposite *C* corresponds to 576 feet. Therefore in 6 seconds a body falls 576 feet.

EXERCISES

By reference to the graph (p. 189), answer the following:

1. How far does a body fall in 8 seconds? 3 seconds? 7 seconds? $2\frac{1}{2}$ seconds? 6.2 seconds?

The question, "How long will it take a body to fall 480 feet?" can be answered by reference to the curve, thus: Opposite 480 on OY is the point D on the curve. D is directly over a point midway between 5 and 6 on OX. Therefore, to fall 480 feet a body requires $5\frac{1}{2}$ seconds.

By reference to the graph, answer the following:

2. How many seconds does a body require to fall 400 feet? 196 feet? 100 feet? 25 feet? 120 feet? 750 feet?

The two preceding graphs are pictorial representations of the relation between two variables. In the first graph the variables were time and temperature, both of which, in the period under consideration, were constantly changing. In the second graph the variables were time and distance. It must be borne in mind that the correctness of any graph is limited by the fact that we cannot measure any physical quantity with perfect accuracy, and that we cannot draw the graph itself with absolute precision. This makes results obtained graphically only approximately correct, but close enough, nevertheless, to be extremely useful for many purposes.

79. Graph of an equation. A relation between two variable numbers not connected with physical quantities, such as temperature and time, can also be represented by a graph. The question, "What two numbers added give five?" may be expressed by the equation $x + y = 5$. Here x and y are *any* two numbers whose sum is 5.

It can be seen by inspection that if x is 1, y is 4, and if x is 2, y is 3. Or we may proceed as follows: Give x any value, say 3; then the equation becomes $3 + y = 5$. Transposing and solving, $y = 2$. Similarly give x the value $3\frac{1}{2}$; then $3\frac{1}{2} + y = 5$, whence $y = 1\frac{1}{2}$. Proceeding in this way, we may obtain a few of the many related pairs of values of x and y, which may be tabulated as follows ·

	A	B	C	D	E	F	G	J	H	I	K	R
x	1	$1\frac{1}{2}$	2	3	$3\frac{1}{5}$	4	5	0	6	7	-1	-2
y	4	$3\frac{1}{2}$	3	2	$1\frac{4}{5}$	1	0	5	-1	-2	6	7

Now in the figure we lay off equal spaces on OX from O, and on OY from O each $\frac{2}{10}$ of an inch, and agree to have the values of x correspond to distances measured from OY parallel to OX, and

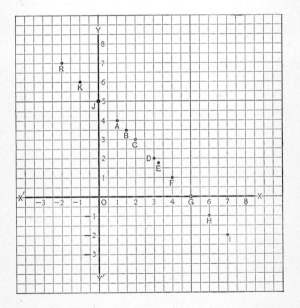

the values of y to distances measured from OX parallel to OY. Then the point A corresponds to the first pair of numbers, $x = 1$, $y = 4$. In like manner, B corresponds to the second pair of numbers, $x = 1\frac{1}{2}$, $y = 3\frac{1}{2}$. Similarly C, D, E, and F correspond respectively to the third, fourth, fifth, and sixth pairs of numbers.

Apparently A, B, C, etc., are points on a straight line. Even points B and E, corresponding to fractional values of x and y, are in line with the others. The inference seems warranted, then, that a **straight line** drawn from A to F would be a *portion* of the graph of the equation $x + y = 5$.

If the line AF is continued, it meets OX at G. The distance of G to the right of OY is 5 and its distance above OX is zero. Evidently point G corresponds to the seventh pair of numbers, $x = 5$, $y = 0$. Similarly FA extended cuts OY at point J whose distance from OX is 5 and whose distance to the right of OY is zero. Therefore this point corresponds to the eighth pair of numbers, $x = 0$, $y = 5$.

If AF is extended below OX, it passes through points H and I. The point H is just under the sixth space mark on OX and 1 space below OX, and the point I is just under the seventh space mark on OX and 2 spaces below OX. The point H must correspond to the ninth pair of numbers, $x = 6$, $y = -1$, and I to the tenth pair, $x = 7$, $y = -2$. This leads us to extend the line YO **downward** and divide it into spaces equal to those above O, and to number the *consecutive* points of division with the **negative numbers**, -1, -2, -3, etc.

Since the point K is opposite the sixth space mark on OY and 1 space to the left of OY, it corresponds to the eleventh pair of numbers, $x = -1$, $y = 6$. Similarly R corresponds to the twelfth pair, $x = -2$, $y = 7$. This leads us to extend XO to the **left** and, dividing it into equal spaces, to number the *consecutive* points of division with **negative numbers**, -1, -2, -3, etc.

Then the line RI extended indefinitely in both directions would be the *complete* graph of the equation $x + y = 5$. Moreover, every point on this line would correspond to a pair of numerical values of x and y which satisfy this equation. These numerical values would include all the possible integers and fractions both positive and negative. The truth of this will become clearer as we proceed.

80. Definitions and assumptions. The preceding explanations and questions should tend to make clear that in constructing the graph of an equation in two variables a number of assumptions must be made. These assumptions and some necessary definitions are now stated. It is agreed:

I. To have two lines at right angles to each other, as $X'OX$, called the **x-axis,** and $Y'OY$, called the **y-axis,** as in the following figure.

II. To have a line of definite length as a unit of distance. Then the number 2 will correspond to a distance of twice the unit, the number $4\frac{1}{2}$ to a distance of $4\frac{1}{2}$ times the unit, etc.

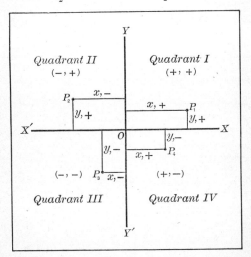

III. That the distance (measured parallel to the x-axis) from the y-axis to any point in the surface of the paper be the **x-distance** (or abscissa) of the point, and the distance (measured parallel to the y-axis) from the x-axis to the point be the **y-distance** (or ordinate) of the point.

IV. That the x-distance of a point to the *right* of the y-axis be represented by a *positive* number, and the x-distance of a point to the *left* by a *negative* number; also the y-distance of a point *above* the x-axis be represented by a *positive* number, and the y-distance of a point *below* the x-axis by a *negative* number. Briefly, *distances measured from the axes to the **right** and **upward** are **positive**, to the **left** and **downward, negative**.*

V. That every point in the surface of the paper corresponds to a *pair of numbers*, one or both of which may be positive, negative, integral, or fractional.

VI. That of a given pair of numbers the first be the measure of the x-distance and the second the measure of the y-distance. Thus the point (2, 3) is the point whose x-distance is 2 and whose y-distance is 3.

VII. That the point of intersection of the axes be called the **origin**.

The values of the x- and the y-distances of a point are often called the **coördinates** of the point.

Though not an absolute necessity, cross-ruled paper is a great convenience in all graphical work. Excellent results, however, can be obtained with ordinary paper and a rule marked in inches and fractions of an inch for measuring distances. Hence the graphical work which follows should not be omitted because it is found inconvenient to obtain cross-ruled paper for class use.

EXERCISES

Draw two axes and locate the following points, using $\frac{1}{2}$ inch or 1 centimeter as the unit distance.

1. (3, 5); (− 3, 5); (− 3, − 5); (+ 3, − 5).

2. (4, − 2); (− 6, 4); (− 1, − 2); (+ 2, − 4).

3. (0, 4); (0, − 4); (4, 0); (− 4, 0).

4. (2, 2); (0, 2); (− 2, 6); (2, 0).

5. (0, − 5); (− 5, 0); (0, 0).

6. If one coördinate of a point is zero, where is it located? Where, if both are zero?

Locating points as in the preceding exercise is called *plotting* the points.

1. Find and tabulate six pairs of values of x and y which satisfy the equation $x + 2y = 8$. Draw two axes and, using $\frac{1}{2}$ inch as the unit distance, plot each of the points. Are the six points in a straight line? Where do all the points lie whose x- and y-distances satisfy the equation $x + 2y = 8$? What, then, is the graph of the equation $x + 2y = 8$? Does $x = 4$, $y = 4$, satisfy this equation? Plot the point (4, 4). Is it on the graph of the equation? If the x- and y-distances of a point satisfy the equation $x + 2y = 8$, where is the point located? If the x- and y-distances do not satisfy the equation $x + 2y = 8$, where is the point located?

Find and tabulate six pairs of values for x and y which satisfy each of the following equations. Use numbers not greater than 10. Have at least one negative value for x and one negative value for y. Then plot the six corresponding points.

2. $3x + 2y = 6$.	**4.** $x + y = 0$.	**6.** $x = 3y$.
3. $3x - 4y = 12$.	**5.** $x - y = 0$.	**7.** $y = 2x$.

The preceding work should be enough to *convince* the student that the graph of an equation of the first degree in x and y is a *straight line*. It can be proved that the graph of any equation of the first degree (linear) in two variables is a straight line, but the student would not understand the proof were it given now. Therefore it will be *assumed* that the graph of every linear equation in two variables is a straight line. And as a straight line is determined by *any two* of its points, it will be sufficient in graphing a linear equation in two variables to plot any *two points* whose x- and y-distances satisfy the equation, and then to draw through these two points a straight line. The two points most convenient to plot are usually the two in which the line cuts the axes. Occasionally these points come very close together, and consequently they will not determine accurately the position of the line. In such cases one should decide on two values of x rather far apart (such as 0 and 5, or

0 and — 5) and compute the corresponding values of y. Two such points will fix the position of the line more accurately.

If a line goes through the origin (as in Exercise 6 preceding), $x = 0$, $y = 0$, will do for one point, but a point outside the axes must be taken for the second one.

Example: Graph the equation $2x + 5y = 10$. In this equation if $x = 0$, $y = 2$; and if $y = 0$, $x = 5$. Here the point $(0, 2)$ is on the y-axis in the adjacent figure, 2 units above the origin, and the point $(5, 0)$ is on the x-axis, 5 units to the right of the origin. The straight line through these two points is the graph of $2x + 5y = 10$.

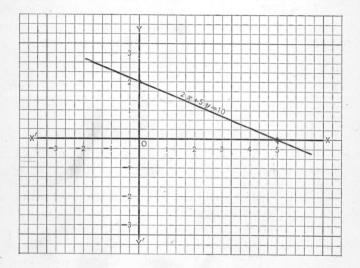

Check: If an error has been made in obtaining the value of x or y from the equation, or in plotting the values found, it can be quickly detected by plotting a third point, the values of whose x- and y-distances satisfy the equation. If this third point lies on the line determined by the first two points, the line has been correctly located; if it does not, a mistake has been made.

EXERCISES

Graph the following linear equations:

1. $x + y = 6.$ 4. $3x + 4y = 12.$ 7. $x - 2y = 0.$

2. $x - y = 5.$ 5. $4x - 3y = 12.$ 8. $3x - y = 0.$

3. $x + 2y = 8.$ 6. $2x + 4y = 9.$ 9. $x = 4.$

HINT. The equation $x = 4$ is equivalent to the equation $x + 0y = 4.$ This last is satisfied by $x = 4$ and *any* value of y. Thus the pairs of values $(4, 3)$; $(4, 6)$; $(4, 0)$; $(4, -2)$, etc., satisfy the equation $x + 0y = 4$. Plotting these points, it is evident that the required graph is a line parallel to the y-axis and 4 units to the right of it.

10. $x = -6.$ 12. $y = -2.$ 14. $y = 0.$

11. $y = 5.$ 13. $x = 0.$ 15. $x = \pm 3.$

16. If a point is on a line, do the values of its x- and its y-distances satisfy the equation of the line?

17. If the values of the x- and the y-distances of a point satisfy the equation of a line, is the point located on the graph of the equation?

18. Is the point $(3, 4)$ on the line whose equation is $3x - 4y = 12$? Is $(0, 4)$? Is $(4, 0)$?

19. Can you determine without reference to the graph itself if the point $(2, 6)$ is on any of the graphs of the equations in Exercises 1–9 above? If so, on which ones?

20. Which of the graphs of the equations in Exercises 1–15 pass through the origin?

In a linear equation containing one or more variables the *constant* term is the term which does not contain a variable.

Thus in the equation $3x + 4y = 12$, 12 is called the constant term. Also in $ax + by = c$, the constant term is c.

21. What is the value of the constant term in the equations whose graphs pass through the origin? What can be said of its value in those equations whose graphs do not pass through the origin?

22. Can you tell, then, by looking at a linear equation whether its graph goes through the origin or not? Explain.

23. Can you tell from the equation when a line is parallel to the *x*-axis? the *y*-axis? Explain.

It should now be clear that:

The equation of a line is satisfied by the values of the x-distance and the y-distance of any point on that line.

Any point the values of whose x-distance and whose y-distance satisfy the equation is on the graph of the equation.

81. Graphical solution of linear equations in two variables. If we construct the graphs of the two equations $x + 2y = 8$ and

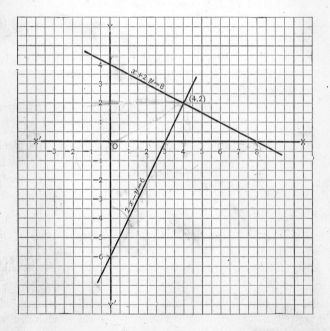

$2x - y = 6$ as indicated in the adjacent figure, it is seen that for the point of intersection of the graphs *x* is 4 and *y* is 2.

Since the point (4, 2) is on both graphs, it should satisfy both equations. Substituting these values (4 for x and 2 for y) in each equation, we get the identities $4 + 4 = 8$, and $8 - 2 = 6$. Thus the **graphical solution** of two linear equations consists in plotting the two equations and finding from the graph the value of x and the value of y at the point of intersection. Since two straight lines *can intersect in but one point*, there can be but *one pair of values of x and y* which satisfies a pair of linear equations in two variables.

EXERCISES

Solve graphically the following pairs of linear equations, and verify by substituting in each pair of equations the x and y values of the point of intersection as obtained from their graphs:

1. $x + y = 6,$
    $x + 2y = 8.$

2. $x - y = 4,$
    $2x + y = 5.$

3. $x + y = 6,$
    $x - y = 4.$

4. $x + y + 8 = 0,$
    $x - y - 2 = 0.$

5. $2x + y + 2 = 0,$
    $2x + 2y + 7 = 0.$

6. $4x - y = -1,$
    $x - 2y = 5.$

7. $2x + 5y = 10,$
    $x + 4y = 8.$

8. $x + 6y = 12,$
    $2x + 3y = 12.$

9. $x + 2y = 10,$
    $x = 3y.$

10. $x + y + 6 = 0,$
    $x = y.$

11. $x + y = 4,$
    $x + y = 6.$

12. $x + 2y = 4,$
    $x + 2y = 10.$

13. $2x - y = 6,$
    $4x - 2y = 8.$

14. $x + y = 6,$
    $x - 4 = 0.$

15. $x - y = 7,$
    $y + 2 = 0.$

16. $x = 2y,$
    $x - 4 = 0.$

17. $3x - y = 0,$
    $y + 3x = 0.$

18. $x - 3 = 0,$
    $y + 2 = 0.$

Biographical note. RENÉ DESCARTES. One of the two or three most important advances ever made in mathematics was the discovery that algebraic equations could be represented geometrically. This great discovery was made by René Descartes (1596–1650), the French philosopher. Though never rugged in health, he took part in several campaigns when a young man, and it is said that during a weary winter spent in camp in Austria he first conceived the ideas that resulted in this important work. Though his writings read very differently from a modern book on the same subject, yet he developed all of the essentials of graphical representation. He saw that a letter, that is, a coördinate, might represent either a positive or a negative number, and so enforced upon mathematicians the conviction that negative integers are indeed numbers, and that they are useful in algebraic operations. After his time they were not usually ruled out as absurd or impossible, as was commonly the case before. He also introduced the modern exponential notation, though he did not use negative or fractional exponents. To Descartes is due the use of the last letters of the alphabet for the unknown and the first letters for the known numbers. Thus he would have written the equation $x^3 - 8x + 16 = 40$ in the form $x^3* - 8x + 16 \infty 40$. Though the sign $=$ was used long before his time, he did not accept it. The asterisk he used to indicate that a certain power of the variable was lacking.

82. Graphical representation of statistics.

Scientific data and numerical statistics from the business world are frequently exhibited with striking clearness and brevity by means of graphs. The character of the graph obtained in any case depends on the relation between the plotted numbers. Sometimes the resulting graph is a smooth curve, and then again it may be an irregular continuous line made up of straight lines of various lengths.

EXERCISES

1. A healthy man 21 years old can insure his life with a certain company for $1000 by making an annual payment of $18.40. The annual payment at a few other ages is given in the following table:

Age	Payment	Age	Payment
25	$20.14	50	$45.45
30	22.14	55	56.93
35	26.35	60	72.83
40	30.94	65	95.14
45	37.08	70	126.66

Construct a curve showing the relation between a man's age and the annual payment necessary to insure his life for $1000, as follows: Let one inch on the vertical axis correspond to

Rene des Cartes Philosophe
et Gentilhomme François né en Tourai
ne et decedé en Suede l'an 1650 agé de 54 ans.

Definir la Nature et de l'ame et du Corps,
De la Terre et du Ciel decouvrir les ressorts,
D'un être souverain demontrer l'existence,
Voila quel fut l'employ de René du Perron,
Et luy seul eut plus de Science
Que n'en eurent ensemble, Aristote et Platon.

RENÉ DESCARTES

4. The public debt of the United States at five-year intervals between 1860 and 1905 is given in millions of dollars in the following table:

YEAR	MILLIONS OF DOLLARS	YEAR	MILLIONS OF DOLLARS
1860	64	1885	1872
1865	2680	1890	1549
1870	2480	1895	1717
1875	2232	1900	2132
1880	2128	1905	2293

Draw a graph of the preceding data, representing 5 years by one inch on the horizontal axis and 500 million dollars by one inch on the vertical axis.

5. The number of bushels of wheat produced in the United States each year from 1892 to 1908 is given in the following table:

YEAR	MILLIONS OF BUSHELS	YEAR	MILLIONS OF BUSHELS
1892	399	1901	522
1893	515	1902	748
1894	396	1903	670
1895	460	1904	637
1896	467	1905	552
1897	427	1906	692
1898	530	1907	735
1899	675	1908	634
1900	547		

Construct a graph from the data given.

(Let one inch on the vertical axis represent 100 million bushels, and one inch on the horizontal axis represent 4 years.)

5 years, and one inch on the horizontal axis to $20. The
locate the points corresponding to the preceding data. Lastly
connect these points by a smooth curve.

2. In a straight line across a river the depths in feet at
points 50 feet apart were as follows:

0.0	16.3	5.3
2.2	14.9	5.0
4.1	13.0	3.4
6.4	9.8	2.0
8.8	8.0	1.5
12.0	6.9	1.0
15.1	5.7	0.0

From the preceding table construct a curve showing the
outline (profile) of the bed of the river at the point where
the survey was made.

(Let one inch on the vertical axis equal a depth of 20 feet
and one inch on the horizontal axis equal 125 feet.)

3. Starting with 100,000 persons at the age of 10, the number still living at certain ages is given in the following table:

AGE	NUMBER SURVIVING	AGE	NUMBER SURVIVING
10	100,000	55	64,563
15	96,285	60	57,917
20	92,637	65	49,341
25	89,032	70	38,569
30	85,441	75	26,237
35	81,822	80	14,474
40	78,106	85	5,485
45	74,173	90	847
50	69,804	95	3

Construct a curve showing the relation between the num
of survivors and their age.

(Let one inch on the vertical axis represent 20,000 per
and one inch on the horizontal axis represent 10 years.)

Include

CHAPTER XX

LINEAR SYSTEMS

83. Definitions. A **linear** equation in **one** unknown has but one root; that is, the value of the unknown in such equations is a *constant*.

A **linear** equation in **two** unknowns is satisfied by an unlimited number of pairs of values for the two unknowns. Any change in the value of one is always accompanied by a change in the value of the other. Hence the unknowns are really **variables,** as they were called in the chapter on graphs.

Two or more equations involving two or more variables are referred to as a **system** of equations.

A system of equations satisfied by the same values of the variables is called a **simultaneous** system.

A **set** of values (one for each variable) which satisfies an equation in two or more variables is sometimes called a *solution* of the equation; and a set which satisfies a system is often called a solution of the system. In this book, however, the word *solution* will be used to denote the *process of solving* either a single equation or a system. The values of the unknown which satisfy an equation in one unknown will be called *roots*, and a set of values for the variables satisfying an equation in two or more variables, or a system of such equations, will be called a **set of roots.**

An equation having one root or a limited number of roots is called a **determinate equation.**

Thus $2x = 10$ and $n^2 - 5n = -6$ are determinate equations; for the first is satisfied by $x = 5$ only, and the second is satisfied by $n = 2$, or 3 only.

A system of equations which is satisfied by one set of roots or a limited number of sets of roots is a **determinate system**.

Thus the system $\begin{cases} x + 2y = 12, \\ 4x - y = 3, \end{cases}$ is a determinate system ; for it is satisfied by only one set of roots : $\begin{cases} x = 2, \\ y = 5. \end{cases}$ The system $\begin{cases} x^2 + y^2 = 25, \\ x + y = 7, \end{cases}$ is determinate also, for it is satisfied by only two sets of roots : $\begin{cases} x = 4, \\ y = 3, \end{cases}$ and $\begin{cases} x = 3, \\ y = 4. \end{cases}$

An equation which is satisfied by an unlimited number of sets of roots is called an **indeterminate equation**.

As we have seen, $x + y = 6$ is an indeterminate equation.

Also $x + y + z = 10$ is an indeterminate equation, for $x = 2$, $y = 3$, and $z = 5$ satisfy it as well as $x = 4$, $y = 5$, and $z = 1$, etc.

A system of equations which is satisfied by an unlimited number of sets of roots is called an **indeterminate system**.

Such a system as $\begin{cases} x + y + z = 8, \\ 2x - 3y - z = 9, \end{cases}$ is indeterminate, for many sets of roots which satisfy both equations can easily be found. For example, the set of roots $x = 7$, $y = 2$, and $z = -1$ satisfies the system. Another set of roots for the system is $x = 5$, $y = -1$, and $z = 4$.

84. Solution by addition or subtraction. The method of solving a system of two linear equations by addition or subtraction is illustrated in the

EXAMPLES

1. Solve the system $\begin{cases} x + 4y = 4, & \quad (1) \\ x - 2y = 16. & \quad (2) \end{cases}$

Solution : Eliminate x first, thus :

$(1) - (2)$, $\qquad\qquad 6y = -12.$ $\qquad\qquad (3)$

$(3) \div 6$, $\qquad\qquad y = -2.$ $\qquad\qquad (4)$

Substituting -2 for y in *either* (1) or (2), say (1),

$$x - 8 = 4. \qquad\qquad (5)$$

Solving (5), $\qquad\qquad x = 12.$

Check : Substituting 12 for x and -2 for y in (1) and (2) gives the obvious identities $\begin{cases} 12 - 8 = 4, \\ 12 + 4 = 16. \end{cases}$

2. Solve the system $\begin{cases} 13\,x + 3\,y = 14, & (1) \\ 7\,x - 2\,y = 22. & (2) \end{cases}$

Solution : Eliminate y first, as follows :

$(1) \cdot 2$,	$26\,x + 6\,y = 28.$	(3)
$(2) \cdot 3$,	$\underline{21\,x - 6\,y = 66.}$	(4)
$(3) + (4)$,	$47\,x \qquad = 94.$	(5)
$(5) \div 47$,	$x = 2.$	(6)

Substituting 2 for x in (2), $14 - 2\,y = 22.$ (7)

Solving (7), $\qquad\qquad\qquad y = - 4.$

Check : Substituting 2 for x and -4 for y in (1) and (2) gives

$$\begin{cases} 26 - 12 = 14, \text{ or } 14 = 14. \\ 14 + 8 = 22, \text{ or } 22 = 22. \end{cases}$$

Either x or y could have been eliminated first. The multipliers necessary to eliminate x are 7 and 13, while the multipliers necessary to eliminate y are the *more convenient numbers* 2 and 3.

When the notation $(3) - (4)$ is used in a solution, it indicates the subtraction of the first member of equation (4) from the first member of equation (3), the subtraction of the second member of equation (4) from the second member of equation (3), and the writing of the two results as equation (5). And the process of adding in a similar way the members of the two equations is indicated by writing $(3) + (4)$.

The notation $(3) \cdot 6$ indicates that both members of equation (3) are multiplied by 6, and $(3) \div 6$ indicates that both members of equation (3) are divided by 6.

With the meanings just explained it is customary to speak of the addition or the subtraction of two equations, and of the multiplication or division of an equation by a number.

The method of the preceding solutions is stated in the

RULE. *If necessary, multiply the first equation by a number and the second equation by another number, such that the coefficients of the same variable in both the resulting equations will be numerically equal.*

If these coefficients have like signs, subtract one equation from the other ; if they have unlike signs, add and solve the equation thus obtained.

Substitute the value just found, in the simplest of the preceding equations which contains both variables, and solve for the other variable.

CHECK. Substitute for each variable in the *original* equations its value as found by the rule. If the resulting equations are not obvious identities, simplify them until they become such.

An attempt to solve by the rule the pair

gives

$$3x - 6y = 40, \tag{1}$$
$$x - 2y = 8, \tag{2}$$
$$3x - 6y = 40, \tag{3}$$
$$3x - 6y = 24. \tag{4}$$

Subtracting, $0 = 16$, an impossibility. This result indicates that (1) and (2) do not form a simultaneous system.

A system of equations like (1) and (2) is called an **incompatible** or **inconsistent system.**

The graphs of a pair of incompatible linear equations are parallel lines (see Exercises 11–13, p. 199).

An attempt to solve by the rule the system $\begin{cases} x + 2y = 8, \\ 3x + 6y = 24, \end{cases}$ gives $0 = 0$. Here the second equation divided by 3 gives the first. Therefore any set of roots of the first is a set of the second. If we choose to regard the two equations as really different, which is not at all necessary, we say that they have an *infinite* (unlimited) number of sets of roots.

EXERCISES

Solve the following systems of equations and check results:

1. $x + 2y = 7,$
   $5x - 2y = 11.$

2. $2x + y = 4,$
   $3x - y = 21.$

3. $7m - n = 2,$
   $n - 2m = -3.$

4. $10h - k = -3,$
   $12h + 12k = 102.$

5. $7r - 8s = -30,$
   $r + 11s = 20.$

6. $8x + y = 7,$
   $11x + 2y = 28.$

7. $5l + 2p = 0,$
   $3l + p = 3.$

8. $10v + 2u = 22,$
   $u + 5v = 11.$

9. $12x + 5y = 14,$
   $3x - 10y = 8.$

10. $2x - y = -1,$
    $15x - 9y = 20.$

11. $\begin{cases} 3s - t = 12, \\ 2t - 6s = 10. \end{cases}$

14. $\begin{cases} 27h + 32k = 6, \\ 16k - 9h = 8. \end{cases}$

12. $\begin{cases} 5x - 3w = 2, \\ 15x + 12w = -5. \end{cases}$

15. $\begin{cases} 2r + 25r_1 = 15, \\ 3r = 10r_1 - 44. \end{cases}$

13. $\begin{cases} x_1 - 6x_2 = 7, \\ 12x_2 - x_1 = 0. \end{cases}$

16. $\begin{cases} 12n - 2m = 18, \\ 3m = 18n + 10. \end{cases}$

85. Solution by substitution. The method of solving a system of two linear equations by substitution is illustrated in the

EXAMPLE

Solve the system $\quad \begin{cases} 3x - 13y = 41, & (1) \\ 8x + 11y = 18. & (2) \end{cases}$

Solution: From (1), $\qquad\qquad 3x = 13y + 41.$ $\qquad$ (3)

Solving (3) for x in terms of y, $\qquad x = \dfrac{13y + 41}{3}.$ $\qquad$ (4)

Substituting $\dfrac{13y + 41}{3}$ for x in (2),

$$8\frac{(13y + 41)}{3} + 11y = 18. \qquad (5)$$

$(5) \cdot 3, \qquad\qquad 8(13y + 41) + 33y = 54.$ $\qquad$ (6)

Simplifying, $\qquad\quad 104y + 328 + 33y = 54.$ $\qquad$ (7)

Collecting, $\qquad\qquad\qquad\qquad 137y = -274.$ $\qquad$ (8)

$(8) \div 137, \qquad\qquad\qquad\qquad y = -2.$ $\qquad$ (9)

Substituting -2 for y in (4), $\qquad x = \dfrac{-26 + 41}{3} = 5.$

Check: Substituting 5 for x and -2 for y in (1) and (2) gives the obvious identities $15 + 26 = 41$ and $40 - 22 = 18$.

The method of the preceding solution is stated in the

RULE. *Solve either equation for one variable in terms of the other.*

Substitute this value in the equation from which it was not obtained and solve the resulting equation.

Substitute the definite value just found, in the simplest of the preceding equations which contains both variables, and solve, thus obtaining a definite value for the other variable.

CHECK. As on page 206.

EXERCISES

Solve by the method of substitution:

1. $x - 2y = 8,$
   $3x + 2y = 7.$

2. $x - 2y = -12,$
   $4x - y = 1.$

3. $14m - 2n = 1,$
   $n - 6m = 0.$

4. $6h + 10k = 19,$
   $2k = 3h.$

5. $3s + 12 = 3 + t,$
   $t = s + 1.$

6. $18 + 2p = q,$
   $p + q = -9.$

7. $3r + 15s = 7,$
   $12 + 5s = -r.$

8. $20y - 3z = 1,$
   $z - 6y = 0.$

9. $.75p + 1.5q = 3,$
   $q = p - 16.$

10. $\dfrac{3x - 20}{2} = \dfrac{2x + 5y}{3},$
    $10 = x - y.$

11. $\dfrac{1}{7 + 2m_1} = \dfrac{-7}{m_2 - 1},$
    $m_1 = m_2 + 3.$

12. $\dfrac{5R_1 + 2R_2}{2} = 2(R_2 + 2),$
    $R_1 - \tfrac{2}{3}R_2 = 0.$

86. Simultaneous equations containing fractions. The method of solving a system of two linear equations containing fractions is illustrated in the

EXAMPLE

Solve the system
$$\begin{cases} \dfrac{8x}{3} - \dfrac{59}{6} = \dfrac{3y}{2}, & (1) \\[2mm] \dfrac{3x}{4} = -2y - \dfrac{9}{2}. & (2) \end{cases}$$

Solution: $(1) \cdot 6,$ $16x - 59 = 9y.$ (3)
Transposing in (3), $16x - 9y = 59.$ (4)
$(2) \cdot 4,$ $3x = -8y - 18.$ (5)
Transposing in (5), $3x + 8y = -18.$ (6)
$(4) \cdot 3,$ $48x - 27y = 177.$ (7)
$(6) \cdot 16,$ $\underline{48x + 128y = -288.}$ (8)
$(7) - (8),$ $-155y = 465.$ (9)
$(9) \div -155,$ $y = -3.$
Substituting -3 for y in (4), $16x + 27 = 59.$
Whence $x = 2.$

Check: Substituting 2 for x and -3 for y in (1),

$$\frac{16}{3} - \frac{59}{6} = \frac{-9}{2},$$

or

$$\frac{-9}{2} = \frac{-9}{2}.$$

Substituting 2 for x and -3 for y in (2),

$$\tfrac{6}{4} = 6 - \tfrac{9}{2},$$

or

$$\tfrac{3}{2} = \tfrac{3}{2}.$$

As in the foregoing solution, it is usually best to clear the equations of fractions and write them in the form of (4) and (6) before attempting to eliminate one of the variables. Equations (4) and (6) are in what is called the **general form** of a linear equation in two variables. This form is represented for all such equations by $ax + by = c$. Here a, b, and c denote numbers, or known literal expressions.

EXERCISES

Solve the following systems of equations and check results:

1.
$$\frac{2x}{3} + 4y = \frac{26}{3},$$
$$3x - \frac{7y}{2} = -4.$$

2.
$$m - \frac{3n}{5} = \frac{18}{5},$$
$$\frac{8n}{3} + 7m = -16.$$

3.
$$\frac{5R_1}{6} + \frac{R_2}{4} = 7,$$
$$\frac{2R_1}{3} - \frac{R_2}{8} = 3.$$

4.
$$3k - \frac{12h}{5} = 18,$$
$$\frac{11k}{10} + \frac{17h}{2} = 53\tfrac{1}{2}.$$

5.
$$\frac{2x}{9} - \frac{y}{2} = -1,$$
$$x = \frac{9y}{4} - 4\tfrac{1}{2}.$$

6.
$$.4x + .9y = 5.7,$$
$$2x - y = 1.$$

7.
$$12m = \frac{11y}{9} + 17,$$
$$\frac{2m}{3} - \frac{49}{12} = \frac{5y}{12}.$$

8.
$$9s = \frac{t}{3} + \frac{23}{4},$$
$$\frac{7t}{3} - \frac{9}{4} = \frac{-3s}{4}.$$

9.
$$.04m + .75n = 10,$$
$$.8m - 1.25n = 5.$$

$$28\,x - 16\,y = 56,$$

10. $\dfrac{2\,x + 7}{2} - y = 4.$

11. $\dfrac{r + 3}{7} - \dfrac{l}{5} = 0,$

$$5\,r + 2 = 7\,l.$$

12. $\dfrac{x + 3}{5} + \dfrac{y + 4}{10} = \dfrac{3}{2},$

$$\dfrac{7\,x + 1}{3} - \dfrac{11\,y - 4}{7} = 4.$$

13. $\dfrac{20\,m + 9}{7} = \dfrac{n}{7} + 1,$

$$m + \dfrac{29}{5} = n.$$

14. $\dfrac{1}{x} + \dfrac{1}{y} = \dfrac{5}{6},$

$$\dfrac{1}{x} - \dfrac{1}{y} = \dfrac{1}{6}.$$

HINT. Solve Exercise 14 without clearing of fractions.

15. $\dfrac{1}{m_1} + \dfrac{1}{m_2} = \dfrac{2}{15},$

$$\dfrac{1}{m_1} - \dfrac{1}{m_2} = -\dfrac{1}{3}.$$

16. $\dfrac{6}{x} + \dfrac{7}{y} = \dfrac{3}{2},$

$$\dfrac{7}{x} - \dfrac{6}{y} + 5\tfrac{1}{3} = 0.$$

17. $\dfrac{1}{x} + \dfrac{1}{y} = 10,$

$$\dfrac{3}{x} + \dfrac{3}{y} = 14.$$

18. $\dfrac{5}{x} + 12 = 17,$

$$\dfrac{2}{x} - 15\,y = 0.$$

19. $\dfrac{4\,r + q}{6\,r + q} = \dfrac{2}{5},$

$$\dfrac{2\,r}{3} - q = 5.$$

20. $\dfrac{1}{t_2} + \dfrac{2}{t_1} = \dfrac{40}{t_1 t_2},$

$$2\,t_2 - 3\,t_1 = 0.$$

21. $\dfrac{5\,m + 3\,n - 1}{3} = n + \dfrac{1}{3},$

$$\dfrac{25\,m}{10\,m + 2\,n} = 1.$$

22. $\dfrac{k + 5}{k + 1} = \dfrac{l + 2}{l - 2},$

$$\dfrac{11\,k + 4}{l + k + 1} = 4.$$

23. $\dfrac{2\,x_1 - 3\,x_2}{x_2 - 4\,x_1} = 3,$

$$\dfrac{8}{x_2 + x_1} + \dfrac{8}{x_1 - x_2} = 0.$$

24. $3\,x - 2\,y = 7,$

$$\dfrac{2}{x - 5} = -\dfrac{5}{y - 4}.$$

25. $\dfrac{2}{6 + s} - \dfrac{4}{4 - t} = 0,$

$$\dfrac{t}{4} + \dfrac{s}{2} + 2 = 0.$$

26. $\dfrac{2}{n_1 + 2 + n_2} = \dfrac{1}{5\,n_2 + 3\,n_1 - 5},\quad n_1 + 2\,n_2 = 4.$

In the following problems the student should state *two* equations in *two* unknowns. Instead of using x and y, the *first letter* of the word denoting an unknown should be used to represent that unknown. Thus in Problem 6 below, n would represent the number of nickels and q the number of quarters.

The course here suggested is desirable for many reasons, and it should be followed in all problems containing two or more unknowns, unless the words denoting two of the unknowns begin with the same letter.

PROBLEMS

1. The difference of two numbers is 25 and their sum is 46. Find the numbers.

2. The quotient of two numbers is 6 and their sum is 49. Find the numbers.

3. Find two numbers whose difference is 36 and whose quotient is 3.

4. The value of a certain fraction is $\frac{2}{3}$. If 3 be added to the numerator and 1 to the denominator, the value of the resulting fraction is $\frac{3}{4}$. Find the fraction.

5. The greater of two numbers divided by the less gives a partial quotient of 3 and a remainder of 6. The less divided by the greater gives a fraction which is .7 less than 1. Find the numbers.

6. A collection of nickels and quarters, containing 77 coins, amounted to $9.85. How many coins of each kind were there?

7. If $\frac{4}{5}$ be subtracted from the numerator and $\frac{1}{9}$ added to the denominator of a certain fraction, the value of the resulting fraction is $\frac{2}{3}$. The sum of the numerator and the denominator of the original fraction is 19. Find the fraction.

8. The difference between the numerator and the denominator of a certain proper fraction is 24. If $\frac{2}{3}$ be added to the numerator and $\frac{1}{4}$ be taken from the denominator, the value of the resulting fraction is $\frac{3}{14}$. Find the fraction.

9. Two weights balance when one is 12 inches and the other 8 inches from the fulcrum. If the first weight increased by 2 pounds is placed 10 inches from the fulcrum, the balance is maintained. Find the two weights.

10. Two weights balance when one is 12 inches and the other 18 inches from the fulcrum. If the first weight is decreased 12 pounds, the other weight must be moved 3 inches nearer the fulcrum to balance. Find the weights.

11. Two weights balance when one is 15 inches and the other 10 inches from the fulcrum. The smaller weight is moved one inch nearer the fulcrum and decreased 6 pounds. Then the larger weight is decreased 12 pounds and a balance results. Find the two weights.

12. A's age is now twice B's. Seven years ago B was $\frac{1}{3}$ as old as A. Find the age of each now.

13. In 5 years A will be twice as old as B. Five years ago A was three times as old as B. Find the age of each now.

14. The perimeter of a rectangle is 232 feet and the length is 8 feet more than twice the width. Find the dimensions of the rectangle.

15. A part of $1000 is invested at 6% and the remainder at 5%. The yearly income from both is $54. Find the number of dollars in each investment.

16. A part of $2000 is invested at $4\frac{1}{2}\%$ and the remainder at $3\frac{1}{2}\%$. The yearly income from the $3\frac{1}{2}\%$ investment exceeds the other yearly income by $10. Find the number of dollars in each investment.

17. A part of $5000 is invested at 4% and the remainder at 6%. The 4% investment yields $126 more in 5 years than the one at 6% does in 3 years. Find the number of dollars in each investment.

18. Ten rubles are worth 10 cents less than 20 marks, and 12 marks are worth 4 rubles and a dollar. Find the value of a ruble and a mark in cents.

19. Five francs are worth 19 cents more than 2 florins, and the sum of 3 francs and one florin is worth 5 cents less than one dollar. Find the value of a florin and a franc in cents.

20. The sum of the two digits of a 2-digit number is 9. If 45 be subtracted from the number, the result will be expressed by the digits in reverse order. Find the number.

Solution: Let $t =$ the digit in tens' place,
and $u =$ the digit in units' place.
Then $t + u = 9.$ (1)

But t standing in tens' place has *its numerical value multiplied by* 10. Therefore the number is represented by the binomial $10\,t + u$, and the number formed by the digits in reverse order is represented by the binomial $10\,u + t$.

Hence $10\,t + u - 45 = 10\,u + t.$ (2)
Simplifying (2), $t - u = 5.$ (3)
Solving (1) and (3), $t = 7,$
and $u = 2.$

Hence the number is 72.

Check: $7 + 2 = 9.$
$72 - 45 = 27.$

21. The sum of the digits of a 2-digit number is 7. If 27 be added to the number, the result is expressed by the digits in reverse order. Find the number.

22. The tens' digit of a 2-digit number is twice the units' digit. If 36 be subtracted from the number, the result is expressed by the digits in reverse order. Find the number.

23. If a 2-digit number be divided by the sum of its digits, the quotient is 4. If 36 be added to the number, the result is expressed by the digits in reverse order. Find the number.

24. If a 2-digit number be increased by 3 and then the result be divided by the sum of its digits, the quotient is 9. If the number be divided by three times the units' digit, the quotient is 17. Find the number.

25. If a 2-digit number be divided by the sum of its digits, the quotient is 7. If the number formed by the digits in reverse order be divided by the sum of the digits and 3, the quotient is 3. Find the number.

26. The sum of the reciprocals of two numbers is $\frac{5}{24}$, and the difference of their reciprocals is $\frac{1}{24}$. Find the numbers.

27. The difference of the reciprocals of two numbers is $1\frac{1}{6}$. The quotient of the greater number divided by the less is $1\frac{7}{8}$. Find the numbers.

28. If 15 grams be taken from one pan of a balance and placed in the other, the sum of the weights in the first will be $\frac{1}{2}$ the sum of those in the second. But if 85 grams be taken from the second and placed in the first, the sums of the weights in each pan will then be the same. Find the weight in each pan at first.

29. A gives B \$20; then B has twice as much money as A. B then gives A \$75 and has left $\frac{1}{3}$ as much as A. How many dollars had each at first?

30. The circumference of the fore wheel of a carriage is 2 feet less than that of the rear wheel. The fore wheel makes as many revolutions in going 155 feet as the rear wheel in going 186 feet. Find the circumference of each wheel.

31. If the length and the width of a rectangle be each increased one foot, the area will be increased 18 square feet. But if the length and the width be each decreased one foot, the area will be decreased by 16 square feet. Find the length and the breadth.

32. A and B working together can do a piece of work in $2\frac{2}{5}$ days. A works 50% more rapidly than B. How many days would each require alone?

33. A and B together can do a piece of work in $7\frac{1}{5}$ days. They work together for 5 days, and A finishes the job by himself in $3\frac{2}{3}$ days. How many days would each require alone?

34. If the length of a rectangle be increased by 4 feet and the width decreased by 2 feet, the area is increased 8 square feet. But if the length be decreased by 1 foot and the width increased by 3 feet, the area is increased 33 square feet. Find the dimensions of the rectangle in feet and its area in square yards.

35. A rectangle has the same area as one 10 feet longer and 6 feet narrower. It also has the same area as one 4 feet longer and 3 feet narrower. Find the dimensions of the rectangle.

36. The products of three pairs of numbers are equal. One number in the second pair is 2 greater, and one in the third pair 3 greater, than the first number in the first pair. The other numbers in the second and third pairs are respectively 15 less and 18 less than the second number of the first pair. Find each pair of numbers.

37. If the number of men who together purchased a piece of land had been 3 more, each would have had to pay $200 less than he did ; but if the number of men had been 4 less, each would have had to pay $500 more than he did. Find the number of men and the price of the land.

38. A man rows 10 miles downstream in 2 hours and returns in 2 hours and 30 minutes. Find the rate of the river and his rate in still water.

Hint. Let x = the man's rate in still water in miles an hour, and y = the rate of the river in miles an hour. Then his rate downstream is $x + y$ miles an hour, and upstream $x - y$ miles an hour.

39. A boat goes downstream 36 miles in 3 hours and upstream 24 miles in 3 hours. Find its rate in still water and the rate of the current.

40. The rate of a boat in still water is $8\frac{1}{2}$ miles an hour. It goes down the river from A to B in 14 hours. It returns one half the distance from B to A in 10 hours. Find the rate of the river and the distance from B to A.

41. A boat which runs 12 miles an hour in still water goes downstream from A to C in 7 hours. It returns upstream to B, 36 miles below A, in 5 hours. Find the distance from A to C and the rate of the stream.

42. A train leaves A one hour late and runs from A to B at 25% more than its usual rate, arriving on time. If it had run from A to B at 24 miles an hour, it would have been 10 minutes late. Find the distance from A to B and the usual rate of the train.

43. A train leaves A 40 minutes late. It then runs to B at a rate 20% greater than usual, and arrives 16 minutes late. Had it run 15 miles of the distance from A to B at the usual rate and the rest of the trip at the increased rate, it would have been 22 minutes late. Find the usual rate and the distance from A to B.

44. The rate of a passenger train is 66 feet a second and the rate of a freight train 44 feet a second. When they run on parallel tracks in opposite directions they pass each other in 15 seconds. The length of the freight train is twice the length of the passenger train. Find the length of each.

45. The rate of a passenger train is 45 miles an hour and that of a freight train is 30 miles an hour. The freight train is 350 feet longer than the passenger train. When the trains run on parallel tracks in the same direction they pass each other in 1 minute and 15 seconds. Find the length of each.

46. The length of a freight train is 1540 feet and the length of a passenger train 660 feet. When they run on parallel tracks in opposite directions they pass each other in 20 seconds, and when they run in the same direction they pass each other in 1 minute and 40 seconds. Find the rates of the trains.

47. Two bicyclists travel in opposite directions around a quarter-mile track and meet every 22 seconds. When they travel in the same direction, the faster passes the slower once every 3 minutes and 40 seconds. Find the rate of each rider.

87. Literal equations in two variables. Linear systems in which the variables have literal coefficients are solved by the method of § 84.

EXERCISES

In Exercises 1–16 consider a, b, c, d, and these letters with subscripts, as known numbers; solve for the other letters involved and check. Solve Exercises 17–20 for x and y.

1. $3x + 7y = 17a,$
$10x - 4y = 2a.$

2. $3x - y = 10b,$
$4x + 9y = 3b.$

3. $5m - 4n = 10a - 4,$
$m - 2na = 0.$

4. $11h + 5k = 33c,$
$\dfrac{h}{c} - \dfrac{k}{2c} = 3.$

5. $12R_1 - 11R_2 = a + 12b,$
$R_1 + R_2 = 2a + b.$

6. $8p + 9q = 4a + 9a_1,$
$\dfrac{p}{2} - 3q = \dfrac{a - 12a_1}{4}.$

7. $\dfrac{7cx}{3} - \dfrac{5y}{2} = -3c,$
$x + \dfrac{11y}{4} = 11c + 3.$

8. $7.5x + 3y = 6a,$
$.25x + .5y = 0.$

9. $\dfrac{h}{2a} - \dfrac{2k}{a} = -5,$
$\dfrac{3h}{a} - \dfrac{7k}{4a} = \dfrac{3}{4}.$

10. $dr + 3s = 1 - d,$
$7dr + 36s = 7 - 12d.$

11. $h - k = 0,$
$4 - \dfrac{h + k}{5c} = \dfrac{h - k}{2c}.$

12. $(a + b)n = 1 - cm,$
$(a + b)m - 1 = -cn.$

13. $\dfrac{m}{b_1 - b_2} + \dfrac{n}{b_1 + b_2} = 2,$
$m + n = 2b_1.$

14. $\dfrac{1}{x} + \dfrac{1}{y} = 2b,$
$\dfrac{2}{x} - \dfrac{3}{y} = 5c - b.$

15. $\dfrac{1}{x + a_1} + \dfrac{1}{y} = \dfrac{a_1 + a_2}{2a_1a_2},$
$\dfrac{a_1}{x + a_1} - \dfrac{a_2}{y} = 0.$

16. $\dfrac{m + 2a}{n - a} = 1,$
$\dfrac{\frac{6}{5}n - a}{3m - 2a} - \dfrac{2n}{5m} = 0.$

17. $kx - ry = 0,$
$x + y - h = 0.$

18. $x + dy = 3,$
$d(x - 3) - y = 0.$

19. $ax - by = c,$
$x + y = b.$

20. $ax + by = c,$
$dx + ey = f.$

GENERAL PROBLEMS

1. If one book costs a dollars, what will c books cost?

2. If a books cost b dollars, what will one book cost? c books?

3. (a) Find the perimeter and the area of a rectangle whose length is a and whose width is b. (b) Then find the perimeter and the area of a second rectangle whose dimensions are three times the first. (c) The perimeter of the second is how many times the perimeter of the first? (d) The area of the second is how many times the area of the first?

4. The base of a triangle is 8. The altitude is 10. Find the area.

5. The base of a triangle is b. The altitude is 8. Find the area.

6. The base of a triangle is b. The altitude is a. Find the area.

7. The base of a triangle is $a + b$. The altitude is $a - b$. Find the area.

8. The base of a triangle is $x - 2y$. The altitude is $x + 2y$. Find the area.

9. The area of a triangle is k. The base is b. Find the altitude.

10. The altitude of a triangle is a inches and the base is 10 inches. If 2 inches be taken from the altitude, how much must the base be increased so that the area will be the same as before?

11. The altitude of a triangle is a feet, the base is b feet. The altitude is increased h feet and the base decreased so that the area is the same as before. How many feet are taken from the base?

12. The sum of two numbers is s and their difference is d. Find the numbers.

13. The first of two numbers is a times the second, and the first minus the second is b. Find the numbers.

14. The sum of two numbers is b, and the quotient of the first divided by the second is a. Find the numbers.

15. If a be added to the numerator of a certain fraction, the value of the resulting fraction is 2. If b be added to the denominator, the value of the resulting fraction is 1. Find the fraction.

16. If the numerator of a certain fraction be increased by 1, the value of the resulting fraction is x. If the denominator of the fraction be decreased by 2, the value of the resulting fraction is y. Find the numerator and the denominator.

17. The value of a certain fraction is b. If 2 be added to the numerator, the value of the resulting fraction is c. Find the numerator and the denominator.

18. A boy who weighs a pounds and one who weighs b pounds balance at the opposite ends of a teeter board whose length is l feet. How far is the fulcrum from each end of the board?

19. A certain number of books at 80 cents each and another number at $1.10 each cost together h dollars. If the price of the books had been interchanged, the total cost would have been k dollars. Find the number of each kind.

20. Two books cost c dollars. The first cost d cents more than the second. Find the cost of each.

21. A and B have together k dollars. A gives h dollars to B and then they have equal sums. How many dollars had each at first?

22. If A gives h dollars to B, they will have equal sums. If B gives k dollars to A, A will have twice as much as B. How many dollars has each?

23. If A gives $10 to B, B will have h dollars more than A. But if B gives k dollars to A, A will have three times as much as B. How many dollars has each?

24. A and B have together $40. A gives h dollars to B, after which B gives k dollars to A. Then they have equal sums. How many dollars had each at first?

25. A gives r dollars to B and then has $\frac{1}{2}$ as much money as B. Then B gives $8 to A and has left $\frac{3}{4}$ as much money as A. How many dollars had each at first?

26. A part of $1000 is invested at $a\%$ and the remainder at $b\%$. The yearly income from both investments is c dollars. How many dollars are there in each investment?

27. A portion of x dollars is invested at 5% and the remainder at 4%. The yearly income is y dollars. How many dollars are there in each investment?

28. A works three times as fast as B. Together they can do a piece of work in c days. How many days would each require alone?

29. A works h times as fast as B. Together they can do a piece of work in 4 days. How many days would each require alone?

30. A and B together can do a piece of work in h days. A can do $\frac{2}{3}$ of the work in 6 days. How many days does each require alone?

31. A and B together can do a piece of work in 5 days. A can do $\frac{2}{5}$ of it in k days. How many days does each require alone?

32. B requires twice as much time as A to do a piece of work which they can do together in n days. How many days does each require alone?

33. A and B together can do a piece of work in p days. A works q times as fast as B. How many days does each require alone?

34. A man travels n miles and then returns to his starting point. Going, his rate is 3 miles an hour; returning, it is 4 miles an hour. How many hours did the entire journey take?

35. A and B start at the same time from two towns k miles apart and travel toward each other until they meet. A travels 3 miles an hour and B travels 5 miles an hour. In how many hours do they meet? How far does each travel?

36. In Problem 34, what would the required time have been, if the rate going had been p miles an hour and the rate returning q miles an hour?

37. In Problem 35, what would have been the respective distances if A had rested h hours on the way before he met B?

38. A and B start at the same time from two points c miles apart and travel toward each other until they meet. A travels p miles an hour and B travels q miles an hour. In how many hours do they meet?

39. In Problem 38, how many miles does each travel?

40. A man rides in a carriage d miles and returns on foot at the rate of 3 miles an hour. The time of riding is h hours less than the time of walking. Find the rate of the carriage.

41. In the preceding problem, if the rate of walking had been c miles an hour, what would have been the rate of the carriage?

42. A man rides a distance of p miles and walks back at the rate of q miles an hour. The entire trip took t hours. Find his rate of riding.

43. A and B start from the same point at the same time and travel in opposite directions for n hours. They are then 50 miles apart. A travels 2 miles an hour more than B. Find the rate of each.

44. In Problem 43, what would have been the respective rates if A had traveled k miles an hour more than B, and at the end of n hours they were h miles apart?

45. A man has just t hours at his disposal. How far can he ride in a carriage which travels p miles an hour, and yet have time to walk back at the rate of q miles an hour?

88. Determinate systems in three and four variables. Consider the equations:

$$m + n + p = 6. \tag{1}$$
$$2\,m + 3\,n + 4\,p = 16. \tag{2}$$
$$3\,m + 4\,n + 5\,p = 22. \tag{3}$$
$$m + 2\,n + 3\,p = 10. \tag{4}$$
$$6\,m + 9\,n + 12\,p = 48. \tag{5}$$

Equation (3) is (1) plus (2); (4) is (2) minus (1); (5) is (2) multiplied by 3. Hence we speak of (3), (4), and (5), with respect to (1) and (2), as **derived** equations. Equations (1) and (2) are spoken of as **independent** with respect to each other, because neither can be derived from the other as (3), (4), and (5) were derived from (1) and (2).

A system of three *independent equations* of the first degree in three variables, no two equations being *incompatible*, has *one* set of roots and *only* one.

The method of obtaining the set of roots of a determinate system is illustrated in the following

EXAMPLE

Solve the system
$$\begin{cases} m + 6\,n - 5\,p = 23, & (1) \\ 3\,m - 8\,n + 4\,p = -1, & (2) \\ 7\,m - 10\,n + 10\,p = 0. & (3) \end{cases}$$

Solution: Eliminate one variable, say p, between (1) and (2) thus:

$(1) \cdot 4,$	$4\,m + 24\,n - 20\,p = 92.$	(4)
$(2) \cdot 5,$	$15\,m - 40\,n + 20\,p = -5.$	(5)
$(4) + (5),$	$19\,m - 16\,n = 87.$	(6)

Now eliminate p between (2) and (3) as follows:

$(2) \cdot 5,$	$15\,m - 40\,n + 20\,p = -5.$	(7)
$(3) \cdot 2,$	$14\,m - 20\,n + 20\,p = 0.$	(8)
$(7) - (8),$	$m - 20\,n = -5.$	(9)

The equations (6) and (9) contain *the same two* variables, m and n.

$(6) \cdot 1,$	$19\,m - 16\,n = 87.$	(10)
$(9) \cdot 19,$	$19\,m - 380\,n = -95.$	(11)
$(10) - (11),$	$364\,n = 182.$	(12)
$(12) \div 364,$	$n = \tfrac{1}{2}.$	(13)

Substituting $\frac{1}{2}$ for n in (9), $m - 10 = -5$. $\hspace{2cm}$ (14)

Solving (14), $\hspace{4cm} m = 5$. $\hspace{2cm}$ (15)

Substituting $\frac{1}{2}$ for n and 5 for m in (1),

$$5 + 3 - 5p = 23. \hspace{2cm} (16)$$

Solving (16), $\hspace{4cm} p = -3$.

Check: Substituting 5 for m, $\frac{1}{2}$ for n, and -3 for p in (1), (2), and (3),

$$5 + 3 + 15 = 23, \text{ or } \ 23 = 23.$$
$$15 - 4 - 12 = -1, \text{ or } -1 = -1.$$
$$35 - 5 - 30 = 0, \text{ or } \ \ 0 = 0.$$

For the solution of a simultaneous system of linear equations in three variables we have the

RULE. *Decide from an inspection of the coefficients which variable is most easily eliminated.*

Using any two equations, eliminate that variable.

With one of the equations just used, and the third equation, again eliminate the same variable.

The last two operations give two equations in the same two variables. Solve these two equations by the rule, pp. 205–206.

Substitute the two values found in the simplest of the original equations and solve for the third variable.

CHECK. Substitute the values found in each of the *original* equations and simplify results.

Four or more independent equations in three variables have no common set of roots.

In general a system of $n + 1$ independent linear equations in n variables has no set of roots; a system of n independent linear equations in n variables, no two of which are incompatible, has one set of roots; and a system of $n - 1$ independent linear equations in n variables, no two of which are incompatible, has an infinite number of sets of roots.

A system of four independent equations in four variables may be solved as follows:

Use the first and second equation, then the first and third, and lastly the first and fourth, and eliminate the same variable each time. This gives a system of *three* equations in the *same three* variables, which can be solved by the rule given above.

EXERCISES

Solve the following systems:

1.
$$m + n - 2p = 13,$$
$$m - 3n - p = -3,$$
$$m - n + 4p = -17.$$

2.
$$x + y + 3z = \tfrac{7}{2},$$
$$x - 2y + 4z = 7,$$
$$2x - 11y - 24z = 5.$$

3.
$$x + y + z = -1,$$
$$3x - y - 5z = 13,$$
$$5x + 3y + 2z = 1.$$

4.
$$2h + 3k - 4l = -26,$$
$$3h - k + 27l = 87\tfrac{1}{2},$$
$$h + 5k + 33l = 74\tfrac{1}{2}.$$

5.
$$2m + 3n - 4p = -3,$$
$$m + n + 3p = -9,$$
$$m + 2n - 7p = 6.$$

6.
$$x + 8y + 5z = 1,$$
$$3x + 10z + 4y = -5,$$
$$x + 4z = 0.$$

7.
$$2h - 3l + 4k - 2 = 0,$$
$$3h - 3l - 15 = 0,$$
$$7h - 4k - 31 = 0.$$

8.
$$4r - 10s = 5,$$
$$6r - t = 3,$$
$$5s + 2t = -\tfrac{3}{2}.$$

9.
$$2a_1 - 3a_2 = 4,$$
$$3a_1 + a_3 = 5,$$
$$a_2 - 2a_3 = 2.$$

10.
$$3r_1 + 5r_2 = 74,$$
$$r_1 - 2r_3 = -16,$$
$$7r_3 - 4r_2 = 44.$$

11.
$$\frac{1}{m} + \frac{1}{n} - \frac{1}{p} = 1,$$
$$\frac{1}{m} + \frac{1}{n} + \frac{1}{p} = \frac{2}{3},$$
$$\frac{1}{m} - \frac{1}{n} + \frac{1}{p} = 0.$$

HINT. Solve Exercise 11 without clearing of fractions.

12.
$$\frac{2}{m} - \frac{3}{n} + \frac{10}{p} = -3,$$
$$\frac{4}{m} + \frac{5}{p} + \frac{6}{n} = 15,$$
$$\frac{1}{m} - \frac{1}{n} + \frac{5}{p} = -\frac{1}{2}.$$

13.
$$\frac{1}{A} + \frac{1}{B} = 2,$$
$$\frac{1}{A} + \frac{1}{C} = 3,$$
$$\frac{1}{B} + \frac{1}{C} = 4.$$

14.
$$r + s + t + u = 2.8,$$
$$r - s + t - u = 7.2,$$
$$r + 2s + 3t - 5u = 7,$$
$$r + s - 8t + u = -1.7.$$

15.
$$\frac{2}{x} + \frac{3}{y} = 26,$$
$$\frac{4}{y} - \frac{10}{z} = 3,$$
$$\frac{1}{x} + \frac{5}{z} = \frac{25}{2}.$$

Note. Perhaps the student wonders if a linear equation in three variables has a graphic representation. It may partially satisfy his curiosity to say that by means of three axes at right angles to each other such a representation, though beyond the scope of this book, is possible. Further, the points whose x, y, and z values satisfy the equation lie in a flat surface called a plane. Two such surfaces may intersect in a straight line, and the system of two equations which the surfaces represent is satisfied by the x, y, and z values of any point on this line. Three such surfaces may intersect in a single point, and the system which the surfaces represent is satisfied by the x, y, and z values of this point. In the systems of equations in three variables on page 224 the student is really finding the coördinates of the point of intersection of three planes. Those who desire more information on this subject are referred to books on analytic geometry.

Since space has but three dimensions, this method of representation of linear equations in two or three variables cannot be extended to equations containing four or more.

PROBLEMS

1. Find three numbers of which the sum of the first and second is 76, the second and third 54, and the first and third 58.

2. The sum of three numbers is 58. The sum and the quotient of two of them are 24 and 2 respectively. Find the numbers.

3. The perimeter of a triangle is 64 feet. Two of its sides are equal, and the third side is 10 feet longer than either of the first two. Find the length of each side.

4. The sum of two sides of a triangle is 52 feet and the difference is 12 feet. The perimeter of the triangle is 93 feet. Find the length of each side.

5. The sum of the two sides of a triangle which meet at one vertex is 41 feet, at another vertex 48 feet, and at the third vertex 43 feet. Find the length of each side.

6. The sum of three numbers is 26. The quotient of two of them is 9, and the sum of these two divided by the third is $3\frac{1}{3}$. Find the numbers.

Fact from Geometry. The sum of the three angles of any triangle (each angle being measured in degrees) is 180 degrees.

7. Two of the angles of a triangle are equal, and their sum is equal to the third. Find the number of degrees in each angle.

8. Two angles of a triangle are equal, and their sum is $\frac{1}{2}$ the third. How many degrees are there in each?

9. Angle A of a triangle is 17 degrees larger than angle B, and angle B is 20 degrees larger than angle C. How many degrees are there in each?

10. The sum of two angles of a triangle is 36 degrees more than the third, and the third is six times the difference of the first two. How many degrees are there in each?

11. A and B together can do a piece of work in 2 days, A and C in 3 days, and B and C in 4 days. Find the time required by each alone and by all together.

12. Two pumps together can fill a tank in 4 hours. The first of these and a third together can fill the tank in 6 hours. All three together can fill the tank in $3\frac{9}{13}$ hours. Find the number of hours required by each alone.

13. The sum of two fractions having the same denominator is 6. If 1 be added to the numerator of the first, and 1 be subtracted from the numerator of the second, the resulting fractions will be equal. If 22 be added to the denominator of each fraction, the sum of the resulting fractions is $\frac{1}{2}$. Find the fractions.

14. The sum of the digits of a 3-digit number is 15. The units' digit exceeds the tens' digit by 5. If 396 be added to the number, the result is expressed by the digits in reverse order. Find the number.

15. If the tens' and units' digits of a 3-digit number be interchanged, the resulting number is 54 greater than the number. If the tens' and hundreds' digits be interchanged, the resulting number is 360 less than the number. The sum of the digits is 10. Find the number.

16. The sum of the 4 digits of a 4-digit number is 9. The units' digit is twice the thousands' digit, and the tens' digit equals the hundreds' digit. If 2997 is added to the number, the result is expressed by the digits in reverse order. Find the number.

Fact from Geometry. The sum of the angles of any *quadrilateral* (a closed figure bounded by four straight lines) is 360 degrees.

17. Find the number of degrees in each angle of a quadrilateral in which the sum of the first and second angles is 200 degrees, the sum of the second and third 180 degrees, and the sum of the second, third, and fourth 255 degrees.

18. The sum of two opposite angles of a quadrilateral is 180 degrees and their difference is 30 degrees. The difference of the other two angles is 36 degrees. Find each angle.

19. The sum of two opposite sides of a quadrilateral is 30, the sum of the other two sides is 35, and two adjacent sides are equal. The sum of the equal sides is less by 17 than the sum of the other two. Find each side.

20. A, B, and C had together $300. A gave to B and C as many dollars as each of them had, after which B gave to A and C as many dollars as each of them then had. They then had equal amounts. How many dollars had each at first?

21. A, B, and C had together $192. A gave to B and C as many dollars as each of them had, after which B gave to A and C as many dollars as each of them then had; and, lastly, C gave to A and B as many dollars as each of them then had. They then had equal amounts. How many dollars had each at first?

CHAPTER XXI

SQUARE ROOT AND RADICALS

89. Square root of algebraic expressions. Since

$$[\pm (t + u)]^2 = t^2 + 2\,tu + u^2,$$

then the square root of

$$t^2 + 2\,tu + u^2 = \pm\,(t + u).$$

A study of this last form will enable us to extract the square root of any polynomial which is a perfect square. Obviously the square root of t^2 (the first term of the trinomial) is t, the first term of the root. If t^2 is subtracted from the trinomial, the remainder is $2\,tu + u^2$. The next term of the root (u) can be found by dividing the first term of the remainder ($2\,tu$) by $2\,t$, (twice the term of the root already found).

The work may be arranged thus:

$$t^2 + 2\,tu + u^2\,\underline{|\,t + u}$$
$$t^2$$

Trial divisor,	$2\,t$	$2\,tu + u^2$
Complete divisor,	$2\,t + u$	$2\,tu + u^2 = (2\,t + u)\,u.$

Therefore the required roots are $\pm\,(t + u)$.

The foregoing process is easily extended to extracting the square root of the polynomial $4\,x^4 - 20\,x^3 + 37\,x^2 - 30\,x + 9$, whose square root contains *three* terms, as follows:

$$4\,x^4 - 20\,x^3 + 37\,x^2 - 30\,x + 9\,\underline{|\,2\,x^2 - 5\,x + 3}$$

$(2\,x^2)^2 =$ $\quad 4\,x^4$	
First trial divisor, $2 \cdot 2\,x^2 = 4\,x^2$	$-20\,x^3 + 37\,x^2$
First complete divisor, $4\,x^2 - 5\,x$	$-20\,x^3 + 25\,x^2 = (4\,x^2 - 5\,x)\,(-5\,x)$
Second trial divisor,	
$2\,(2\,x^2 - 5\,x) = 4\,x^2 - 10\,x$	$12\,x^2 - 30\,x + 9$
Second complete divisor, $4\,x^2 - 10\,x + 3$	$12\,x^2 - 30\,x + 9 = (4\,x^2 - 10\,x + 3)\,3$

Therefore the required roots are $\pm (2x^2 - 5x + 3)$.

The term $2x^2$ was obtained by taking the square root of $4x^4$; the second term, $-5x$, by dividing $-20x^3$ by the first trial divisor, $4x^2$; and the third term, 3, by dividing $12x^2$ by $4x^2$, the first term of the second trial divisor.

The method just illustrated may be stated in the

RULE. *Arrange the terms of the polynomial according to descending powers of some letter in it.*

Extract the square root of the first term. Write the result (with plus sign only) as the first term of the root, and subtract its square from the given polynomial.

Double the root already found for the first trial divisor, divide the first term of the remainder by it, and write the quotient as the second term of the root.

Annex the quotient just found to the trial divisor, making the complete divisor; multiply the complete divisor by the second term of the root, and subtract the product from the last remainder.

If terms of the polynomial still remain, double the root already found for a trial divisor, divide the first term of the trial divisor into the first term of the remainder, write the quotient as the next term of the root, form the complete divisor, and proceed as before until the process ends, or until the required number of terms of the root have been found.

Inclose the root thus found in a parenthesis preceded by the sign $\pm$.

Note. The process of extracting the square root of numbers was familiar to mathematicians long before they knew how to find the square root of polynomials. This is consistent with the fact that the development of the methods of performing operations on literal number symbols generally followed and grew out of the similar operations on numerals. The application of the rules for extracting the square root of numbers to that of polynomials is generally ascribed to Recorde (1510–1558), who was the author of the earliest English work on algebra that we know. This book, which bears the title " The Whetstone of Wit," gives an accurate idea of the algebraical knowledge of the time, and had a very wide influence.

EXERCISES

Extract the square roots of:

1. $a^4 + 3 a^2 + 2 a^3 + 2 a + 1$.

2. $24 x^2 - 32 x + 16 + x^4 - 8 x^3$.

3. $21 c^2 + c^4 + 20 c - 10 c^3 + 4$.

4. $n^6 + 9 n^2 + 10 n^3 + 25 - 6 n^4 - 30 n$.

5. $19 a^2 - 11 a^4 + 4 a^6 - 30 a + 4 a^5 + 14 a^3 + 25$.

6. $c^4 - 4 c^3d + 6 c^2d^2 - 4 cd^3 + d^4$.

7. $30 xy^3 + 25 y^4 - 11 x^2y^2 - 12 x^3y + 4 x^4$.

8. $- 36 a^4x + 36 a^2x^2 + 9 a^6 - 24 a^3x^2 + 16 x^4 + 48 ax^3$.

9. $9 c^4 - 2 a^2b^2c^2 + 4 a^3b^3c + a^4b^4 - 12 abc^3$.

10. $2 a^2xc^3 - 4 xc^3 - 4 a^2x^2 + 4 x^2 + c^6 + a^4x^2$.

11. $4 - \dfrac{4 c^2}{5} + \dfrac{c^4}{25}$.   12. $\dfrac{9}{a^2} + \dfrac{a^2}{4} - 3$.

13. $x^4 - 4 x^3 + 5 x^2 - 2 x + \frac{1}{4}$.

14. $\dfrac{4 x^2}{y^2} + 7 + \dfrac{y^2}{4 x^2} + \dfrac{12 x}{y} - \dfrac{3 y}{x}$.

Solution: Arranging terms in descending powers of x and applying the rule just stated, we obtain the following:

$$\dfrac{4 x^2}{y^2} + \dfrac{12 x}{y} + 7 - \dfrac{3 y}{x} + \dfrac{y^2}{4 x^2} \left|\dfrac{2 x}{y} + 3 - \dfrac{y}{2 x}\right.$$

$$\left(\dfrac{2 x}{y}\right)^2 = \dfrac{4 x^2}{y^2}$$

$$2\left(\dfrac{2 x}{y}\right) = \dfrac{4 x}{y} \quad \left|\dfrac{12 x}{y} + 7\right.$$

$$\dfrac{4 x}{y} + 3 \quad \left|\dfrac{12 x}{y} + 9 = \left(\dfrac{4 x}{y} + 3\right)3\right.$$

$$2\left(\dfrac{2 x}{y} + 3\right) = \dfrac{4 x}{y} + 6 \quad \left|-2 - \dfrac{3 y}{x} + \dfrac{y^2}{4 x^2}\right.$$

$$\dfrac{4 x}{y} + 6 - \dfrac{y}{2 x} \quad \left|-2 - \dfrac{3 y}{x} + \dfrac{y^2}{4 x^2} = \left(\dfrac{4 x}{y} + 6 - \dfrac{y}{2 x}\right)\left(-\dfrac{y}{2 x}\right)\right.$$

Therefore the square roots are $\pm\left(\dfrac{2 x}{y} + 3 - \dfrac{y}{2 x}\right)$.

15. $x^4 + 6 x^3 + \dfrac{29 x^2}{3} + 2 x + \dfrac{1}{9}.$

16. $4 a^4 + \dfrac{4 a^3}{3} - \dfrac{35 a^2}{9} - \dfrac{2 a}{3} + 1.$

17. $\dfrac{9}{4} - \dfrac{127 m^2}{18} + \dfrac{25 m^4}{4} - 2 m + \dfrac{10 m^3}{3}.$

18. $9 c^4 - 12 c^3 + 4 c^2 - \dfrac{4}{c} + \dfrac{1}{c^4} + 6.$

19. $\dfrac{m^2}{n^2} + \dfrac{n^2}{m^2} + \dfrac{17}{4} - \dfrac{5 m}{n} + \dfrac{5 n}{m}.$

20. $\dfrac{a^4}{25 c^4} + \dfrac{2 a^2}{c^3} + \dfrac{117}{5 c^2} - \dfrac{40}{a^2 c} + \dfrac{16}{a^4}.$

21. $\dfrac{a^2}{4 c^4} + 9 + \dfrac{4 c^2}{25 a^4} - \dfrac{3 a}{c^2} + \dfrac{2}{5 ac} - \dfrac{12 c}{5 a^2}.$

22. Extract the fourth root of the expressions in Exercises 2 and 6 on the preceding page.

HINT. The fourth root of a number equals the square root of its square root.

90. Square root of arithmetical numbers. Since $1 = 1^2$, and $81 = 9^2$, a 1-digit or a 2-digit square has only *one* digit in its square root.

And as $100 = 10^2$, and $9801 = (99)^2$, a 3-digit or a 4-digit square has *two* digits in its square root.

Also $10,000 = 100^2$, and $998,001 = (999)^2$; hence a 5-digit or a 6-digit square has *three* digits in its square root.

The preceding examples illustrate the relation between the number of digits in a number and the number of digits in its square root. They also suggest a method of obtaining the first digit in the square root of any number.

For example, take the four numbers 78'43'56, 7'84'35, .98'01, and .03'27'40, and beginning at the decimal point in each number, point off periods of two digits each, as indicated. Any incomplete period on the right, as in .03'27'4, should be completed by annexing one zero; thus, .03′27′40. Now the first digit in the square root is the greatest integer whose square is less than or equal to the left-hand period. This is true whether the latter contains *two* digits or *one*. Therefore the first digit in the square root of 78′43′56 is 8, in the square root of 7′84′35 is 2, in the square root of .98′01 is 9, and in the square root of .03′27′40 is 1.

Moreover the number of digits in the square root of a perfect square is equal to the number of periods, provided any *single digit* remaining on the left is counted as a period.

Just how t and u are involved in the square of $(t + u)$, or $t^2 + 2tu + u^2$, is obvious on inspection, because the parts t^2, $2tu$, and u^2 cannot be united into one term. In the square of an arithmetical number, however, the parts are united. Thus $(53)^2 = (50 + 3)^2 = 2500 + 300 + 9 = 2809$. Now it is clear how 50 and 3 are involved in $2500 + 300 + 9$, but it is not plain from 2809 alone. Pointing off, however, enables us to discover at once the first digit, 5, which is equivalent to 5 tens, or 50. With the exception of pointing off, the method of extracting the square root of an arithmetical number does not differ greatly from the method of extracting the square root of an algebraic expression. In fact, the formula, the square root of $t^2 + 2tu + u^2 = \pm(t + u)$, can be used to explain the two processes.

If t denotes the tens and u the units, $t^2 + 2tu + u^2$ is closely related to $2500 + 300 + 9$, t^2 being 2500, or $(50)^2$; u^2 being 9, or 3^2; and $2tu$ being $2 \cdot 50 \cdot 3$. Therefore the process of extracting the square root of 2809 may be based on these relations and the work arranged as follows:

$$
\begin{array}{r l}
& 2809 \underline{|50 + 3} \\
t^2 = & 2500 \\
2t = 2 \cdot 50 = 100 & \overline{309} \\
2t + u = 100 + 3 & \underline{309 = (100 + 3)\,3 = (2t + u)\,u = 2tu + u^2}
\end{array}
$$

Therefore ± 53 are the two square roots of 2809.

If the number has three digits in its square root, the work and explanations may be arranged thus :

$$1'74'24 | 100 + 30 + 2$$

$t^2 = 10,000$ $10000 = 10$ tens squared

First trial divisor,

$2\,t = 2 \cdot 100 = 200$ 7424

First complete divisor,

$2\,t + u = 200 + 30 = 230$ $6900 = (2 \cdot 10 \text{ tens} + 30 \text{ units}) 30$

Second trial divisor,

$2\,t = 2 \cdot 130 = 260$ 524

Second complete divisor,

$2\,t + u = 260 + 2 = 262$ $524 = (2 \cdot 13 \text{ tens} + 2 \text{ units}) 2$

Therefore ± 132 are the square roots of 17,424.

When the method and reasons for the process have become familiar, the work may be shortened by omitting the explanations and unnecessary zeros as follows :

$$28'09 | 53 \qquad\qquad 1'74'24 | 132$$
$$25 \qquad\qquad\qquad 1$$
$$103 | 309 \qquad\qquad 23 | 74$$
$$\underline{309} \qquad\qquad \underline{69}$$
$$\qquad\qquad\qquad\qquad 262 | 524$$
$$\qquad\qquad\qquad\qquad \underline{524}$$

The method just illustrated for extracting the positive square root of a number is the one commonly used. For it we have the

RULE. *Begin at the decimal point and point off as many periods of two digits each as possible : to the left if the number is an integer, to the right if it is a decimal ; to both the left and the right if the number is part integral and part decimal.*

Find the greatest integer whose square is equal to or less than the left-hand period, and write this integer for the first digit of the root.

Square the first digit of the root, subtract its square from the first period, and annex the second period to the remainder.

Double the part of the root already found for a trial divisor, divide it into the remainder (omitting from the latter the right-hand digit), and write the integral part of the quotient as the next digit of the root.

Annex the root digit just found to the trial divisor to make the complete divisor, multiply the complete divisor by this root digit, subtract the result from the dividend, and annex to the remainder the next period for a new dividend.

Double the part of the root already found for a new trial divisor and proceed as before until the desired number of digits of the root have been found.

After extracting the square root of a number involving decimals, point off one decimal place in the root for every decimal period in the number.

CHECK. *If the root is exact, square it. The result should be the original number. If the root is inexact, square it and add to this result the remainder. The sum should be the original number.*

Sometimes in using a trial divisor we obtain too great a quotient for the next digit of the root. This happens in obtaining the second digit of the square root of 32,301, where 2 into 22 gives 11. Obviously 10 and 11 are both impossible. If 9 is tried, we get $9 \cdot 29$, or 261, which is greater than 223. Similarly 8 is too great. But $7 \cdot 27 = 189$, which is less than 223. Therefore 7 is the second digit of the root.

$$3'23'01 \underline{|1}$$
$$\underline{1}$$
$$2 \overline{|223}$$

With practice, in cases like the one just explained, the student will be able to look ahead and decide mentally on the proper digit of the root.

Occasionally the trial divisor gives a quotient less than 1. This indicates that the required root digit is 0, which should be written in the root. The next period should then be brought down. An instance of this kind occurs in finding the second digit in the square root of 9'42.49. The quotient of $4 \div 6$ is $\frac{2}{3}$, which is not an integer. Therefore the second digit of the root is less than 1. Then the next period, 49, should be brought down. The new trial divisor

$$9'42.49 \underline{|3}$$
$$9$$
$$6 \overline{|\ \ 42}$$

will be 60, which will give 7 as the third digit of the root. The work can easily be completed, giving 30.7 as the square root.

An attempt to extract the square root of 2 by annexing decimal periods of zeros and applying the rule becomes a never-ending process:

The number 2 has no exact square root, and no matter how far the work be carried, there is no final digit. As the work stands, we know that the square root of 2 lies between 1.414 and 1.415. It is correct to say that 1.414 is approximately the square root of 2, or that it is the square root of 2 to three decimal places. If a closer approximation is desired, it can be obtained by extracting the square root to four or more decimal places.

```
2.00'00'00 | 1.414
1
24 | 100
     96
281 | 400
      281
2824 | 11900
       11296
```

A common fraction, or the fractional part of a mixed number, should be reduced to a decimal before extracting the square root, unless the root is seen to be exact.

EXERCISES

Extract the square root, correct to three decimal places, of:

1. 6241.
2. 16129.
3. 223,729.
4. 2.

5. 5.
6. 7.135.
7. .6279.
8. .0451.

9. .0035.
10. $1\frac{1}{5}$.
11. $1\frac{6}{7}$.
12. $\frac{2}{21}$.

Fact from Geometry. In the adjacent right triangle $a^2 + b^2 = c^2$; a and b are called the **legs**; and c, the side opposite the right angle, is called the **hypotenuse**.

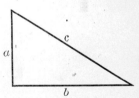

If leg a is 8 and leg b is 15, then substituting in $a^2 + b^2 = c^2$ gives $64 + 225 = c^2$. Whence $289 = c^2$, and $c = \pm 17$.

Since -17 is not a practical answer, it is rejected.

Find the hypotenuse and the area of a right triangle whose legs are:

13. 84 and 13.　　14. 133 and 156.　　15. 645 and 812.

Find the other leg and the area of a right triangle in which the hypotenuse and one leg are respectively:

16. 65 and 56.   **17.** 397 and 325.

In rectangle $ABCD$, line DB is called a **diagonal.**

18. Find the diagonal of a rectangle whose adjacent sides are 24 feet and 143 feet.

19. One diagonal of a rectangle is 401 and one side is 399. Find the other side and the area.

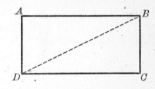

20. One diagonal of a rectangle is 677 and one side is 52. Find the perimeter of the rectangle.

21. A rectangle is 7 yards longer than it is wide. Its perimeter is 102 feet. Find one diagonal.

22. One diagonal of a square is 74 meters. Find the side.

23. The side of a square is 52 inches. Find one diagonal.

24. A rectangle is 2.4 times as long as it is wide. One diagonal is 52. Find the length and the width.

25. The width of a rectangle is 25% less than the length. The diagonal is 100. Find the area.

26. The length of a rectangle is 10. The diagonal is twice the shorter side. Find the width.

Fact from Geometry. A line drawn from one vertex of an equilateral triangle to the middle point of the opposite side is perpendicular to it.

Then in the equilateral triangle ABC, if D is the middle point of AC, BD is the altitude; and

$$\overline{BD}^2 = \overline{AB}^2 - \overline{AD}^2 = \overline{AB}^2 - \left(\frac{AC}{2}\right)^2.$$

27. If BC in the adjacent triangle is 6, find BD and the area of the triangle.

28. If AC is 10, find BD and the area of the triangle.

29. If BD is 10, find AB and the area of the triangle.

30. The perimeter of an equilateral triangle is 36. Find the altitude.

31. The altitude of an equilateral triangle is 25 centimeters. Find one side.

Note. A method of extracting the square root of numbers not unlike that in use to-day was employed by the Greek, Theon, about 350 A.D. In the Middle Ages square roots were extracted with a fair degree of accuracy by using the formulas of approximation:

$$(1) \quad \sqrt{a^2 + x} = a + \frac{x}{2\,a}. \qquad (2) \quad \sqrt{a^2 + x} = a + \frac{x}{2\,a + 1}.$$

The true value of the square root of the number was proved to be between the results obtained by these expressions. Thus if $\sqrt{65}$ was desired, it was noticed that $65 = 64 + 1$, and from (1)

$$\sqrt{65} = \sqrt{64 + 1} = \sqrt{8^2 + 1} = 8 + \frac{1}{2 \cdot 8} = 8\tfrac{1}{16},$$

while from (2)

$$\sqrt{65} = \sqrt{64 + 1} = \sqrt{8^2 + 1} = 8 + \frac{1}{2 \cdot 8 + 1} = 8\tfrac{1}{17}.$$

Thus the true value of $\sqrt{65}$ is between these two numbers. This method was known to the Arabs.

It should be kept in mind that the use of decimal fractions and of the decimal point was not common until the eighteenth century. Consequently the complete application of the method of extracting the square root given in the text is comparatively recent.

91. Radicals. All the numbers of algebra are in one or the other of two classes — **real** numbers and **imaginary** numbers.

Thus 3, -5, $\sqrt{2}$, $\tfrac{2}{3}$, and 1.763 are real numbers.

Real numbers are of two kinds — **rational** numbers and **irrational** numbers.

A **rational** number is a positive or a negative *integer* or a number which may be expressed as the *quotient of two such integers*.

Thus 7, $\tfrac{2}{5}$, 4.237 are rational numbers.

A rational number can be obtained from the number 1 by carrying out the operations of addition, subtraction, multiplication, and division, which are therefore called rational operations.

Any real number which is not a rational number is an **irrational** number.

Thus $\sqrt{2}$, $\sqrt[3]{4}$, $\sqrt[4]{7}$, are all irrational numbers, and cannot be expressed as the quotient of two integers.*

The $\sqrt{2}$ to six places is 1.414213. And it can be proved that the digits in the decimal portion never repeat themselves in groups of digits which have a definite order, however far the process of extracting the root be carried. Hence the decimal portion of the root is said to be non-repeating. For example, .121212 $\cdots$ is a repeating decimal. As a never-ending decimal which does not repeat cannot be expressed as the quotient of two integers, the $\sqrt{2}$ is an irrational number. The $\sqrt[3]{2}$, $\sqrt[5]{4}$, etc., are also irrational numbers. It is beyond the scope of this book, however, to show how their approximate values are obtained.

Symbols like $\sqrt{-1}$, $\sqrt{-4}$, $\sqrt[4]{-16}$, were mentioned on page 102. Such symbols arise when we express an even root of a negative number. These indicated roots are called **imaginary** numbers and will be treated later.

A **radical** is an indicated root of any algebraic expression.

Thus $\sqrt{4}$, $\sqrt{3}$, $\sqrt[3]{a}$, and $\sqrt{x^2 - 5x + 6}$ are *radicals*.

A **surd** is an irrational root of a rational number. Surds are always irrational numbers.

Thus $\sqrt{3}$, $\sqrt[3]{7}$, etc., are *surds*.

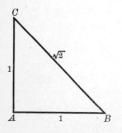

Though no irrational numbers can be expressed exactly in decimals, we can represent a few surds by the lengths of lines. Thus in the right triangle ABC, if $AB = AC = 1$ inch, $BC = \sqrt{2}$ inches. If AB were 2 inches and AC were 1 inch, BC would be $\sqrt{5}$ inches.

* See Hawkes's "Advanced Algebra," p. 52.

An irrational number is not necessarily a surd. The length of the circumference of a circle divided by the length of its diameter gives a number which is not rational. The symbol for this number is the Greek letter π (pronounced pī). The approximate value of π is $\frac{22}{7}$; more closely it is 3.1416. The number which π represents is a never-ending, non-repeating decimal whose value correct to ten decimals is 3.1415926535.

Strictly speaking, the $\sqrt{\pi}$ is not a surd, nor is an expression like $\sqrt{\sqrt{3}+2}$ a surd. The $\sqrt{\sqrt{3}}$ is a surd, for it can be written $\sqrt[4]{3}$, as we shall see later.

The **index** of a radical is the *numerical*, or *literal*, part of the radical sign.

The index determines the **order** of the radical and indicates the root to be extracted.

In $5\sqrt[3]{7}$, 3 is the index, the radical is of the third order, and the coefficient is 5.

The **radicand** is the number, or expression, under the radical sign.

In $\sqrt{9}$ and $\sqrt[3]{ax}$, 9 and ax are the radicands.

For a given index the **principal root** of a number is its *one real root*, if it has but one; or its *real positive root*, if it has two real roots.

The principal root of $\sqrt[3]{-27}$ is -3. That of $\sqrt[4]{16}$ is $+2$, not -2.

Radical expressions may be written in two ways, with **radical signs** or with **fractional exponents.** The relation between the two will now be explained. To do this it is necessary to extend the meaning of the term *exponent*, which, as defined on page 7, applied to integral exponents only. We shall assume that the laws which govern integral exponents hold for fractional exponents also.

The fact that $x^2 \cdot x^3 = x^5$, illustrates the more general law, $x^a \cdot x^b = x^{a+b}$, where a and b represent either integers or fractions.

Accordingly $x^{\frac{1}{2}} \cdot x^{\frac{1}{2}} = x^{\frac{1}{2}+\frac{1}{2}} = x^1$ or x. Since $x^{\frac{1}{2}}$ multiplied by itself gives x, $x^{\frac{1}{2}}$ *must be another way of writing the square root of x.*

Hence $\sqrt{x}$ may be written $x^{\frac{1}{2}}$.

Then $$4^{\frac{1}{2}} = \sqrt{4} = 2,$$

and $$(25\,a^2)^{\frac{1}{2}} = \sqrt{25\,a^2} = 5\,a.$$

Further, $$x^{\frac{1}{3}} \cdot x^{\frac{1}{3}} \cdot x^{\frac{1}{3}} = x^1 = x.$$

And since $x^{\frac{1}{3}}$ is one of the three equal numbers whose product is x, $x^{\frac{1}{3}}$ *is another way of writing the cube root of x.*

Therefore $\sqrt[3]{x}$ may be written $x^{\frac{1}{3}}$.

This means that $$8^{\frac{1}{3}} = \sqrt[3]{8} = 2,$$

and $$64^{\frac{1}{3}} = 4.$$

Similarly $$\sqrt[4]{x} = x^{\frac{1}{4}},$$

and $$\sqrt[5]{x} = x^{\frac{1}{5}}, \text{ etc.}$$

In general terms, $$\sqrt[n]{x} = x^{\frac{1}{n}}.$$

Now $$x^{\frac{3}{2}} = x^{\frac{1}{2}} \cdot x^{\frac{1}{2}} \cdot x^{\frac{1}{2}} = \left(x^{\frac{1}{2}}\right)^3 = \left(\sqrt{x}\right)^3,$$

and $$x^{\frac{3}{2}} = x^{3 \cdot \frac{1}{2}} = (x^3)^{\frac{1}{2}} = \sqrt{x^3}.$$

Hence $$\left(\sqrt{x}\right)^3 = \sqrt{x^3},$$

and $$4^{\frac{3}{2}} = \left(4^{\frac{1}{2}}\right)^3 = \left(\sqrt{4}\right)^3, \text{ or } \sqrt{4^3}$$

for both $\left(\sqrt{4}\right)^3$ and $\sqrt{4^3}$ equal 8.

In like manner, $$x^{\frac{2}{3}} = x^{\frac{1}{3}} \cdot x^{\frac{1}{3}} = \left(x^{\frac{1}{3}}\right)^2 = \left(\sqrt[3]{x}\right)^2.$$

But also $$\sqrt[3]{x^2} = (x^2)^{\frac{1}{3}} = (x \cdot x)^{\frac{1}{3}} = x^{\frac{1}{3}} \cdot x^{\frac{1}{3}} = x^{\frac{2}{3}}.$$

Therefore $$\left(\sqrt[3]{x}\right)^2 = \sqrt[3]{x^2}.$$

Again, $$8^{\frac{2}{3}} = \left(\sqrt[3]{8}\right)^2,$$

or $$\sqrt[3]{8^2} = 2^2 \text{ or } 4.$$

That is, $$\left(\sqrt[3]{8}\right)^2 = \sqrt[3]{8^2}.$$

In general terms, $$x^{\frac{a}{n}} = \sqrt[n]{x^a},$$

or, in words, x with an exponent $\dfrac{a}{n}$ means the nth root of x to the ath power.

The student should fix in mind that the *denominator* of the fractional exponent is the *index* of the root, and the *numerator* the *power* to which the radicand is raised.

EXERCISES

Write with radical signs:

1. $x^{\frac{4}{3}}$.

2. $x^{\frac{5}{2}}$.

3. $(cd)^{\frac{3}{2}}$.

4. $(2x)^{\frac{1}{3}}$.

5. $2x^{\frac{1}{3}}$.

6. $5a^{\frac{3}{4}}$.

7. $(5a)^{\frac{3}{4}}$.

8. $3rx^{\frac{2}{3}}$.

9. $h^{\frac{2}{3}}k^{\frac{2}{3}}$.

10. $7s^{\frac{2}{3}}(t+w)^{\frac{1}{2}}$.

11. $3a^{\frac{5}{2}}(bc)^{\frac{1}{3}}$.

12. $5^{\frac{1}{2}}x^{\frac{2}{3}}k^{\frac{1}{4}}$.

13. $4^{\frac{1}{3}}t^{\frac{1}{a}}$.

14. $2x^{\frac{1}{b}}y^{\frac{e}{d}}$.

Find the numerical values of:

15. $25^{\frac{1}{2}}$.

16. $27^{\frac{1}{3}}$.

17. $16^{\frac{1}{4}}$.

18. $4^{\frac{3}{2}}$.

19. $64^{\frac{2}{3}}$.

20. $125^{\frac{2}{3}}$.

21. $(-8)^{\frac{4}{3}}$.

22. $32^{\frac{1}{5}}$.

23. $81^{\frac{3}{4}}$.

24. $(-216)^{\frac{2}{3}}$.

25. $(\frac{1}{16})^{\frac{1}{2}}$.

26. $(\frac{1}{25})^{\frac{1}{2}}$.

27. $(\frac{1}{16})^{\frac{1}{4}}$.

28. $25^{\frac{1}{2}} \cdot 4^{\frac{5}{2}}$.

29. $4^{\frac{1}{2}} \cdot (\frac{1}{4})^{\frac{1}{2}}$.

30. $(-32)^{\frac{4}{5}}(-64)^{\frac{1}{3}}$.

31. $36^{\frac{1}{2}} \cdot (\frac{1}{9})^{\frac{1}{2}}$.

32. $9^{\frac{1}{2}} \cdot (\frac{1}{27})^{\frac{1}{3}}$.

33. $2(\frac{4}{9})^{\frac{1}{2}} \cdot (\frac{1}{8})^{\frac{1}{3}}$.

34. $\sqrt[5]{32} \cdot 4^{\frac{1}{2}}$.

35. $\sqrt[3]{8^2} \cdot 25^{\frac{3}{2}}$.

36. $121^{\frac{1}{2}} \cdot \sqrt{\frac{25}{121}}$.

37. $(-343)^{\frac{1}{3}} \cdot \sqrt{\frac{1}{49}}$.

38. $\frac{2}{3}(1\frac{69}{144})^{\frac{1}{2}} \div (2\frac{1}{16})^{\frac{1}{3}}$

Write with fractional exponents and simplify results:

39. $\sqrt[2]{a^3}$.

40. $\sqrt[2]{ax^4}$.

41. $3\sqrt{2x^5}$.

42. $\sqrt{9x}$.

43. $5\sqrt{16ax^2}$.

44. $\sqrt[3]{a^2}$.

45. $\sqrt[3]{ax^4}$.

46. $2\sqrt[3]{2x^2}$.

47. $3\sqrt[3]{8x^4}$.

48. $4\sqrt[3]{27ax^3}$.

49. $2\sqrt[4]{a^2x^3}$.

50. $4\sqrt[4]{16x}$.

51. $7\sqrt[5]{rs^7}$.

52. $5a\sqrt[5]{32m^2}$.

53. $12x^2\sqrt[3]{ax^3}$.

54. $c\sqrt[2]{(de)^3}$.

55. $uv\sqrt[2]{(u+v)^5}$.

56. $3\sqrt[2]{a^3} \cdot \sqrt[3]{x^2}$.

57. $2a\sqrt[5]{ax^2} \cdot \sqrt[3]{2m}$.

58. $\sqrt[n]{x^a} \cdot \sqrt[n]{y^b}$.

59. $\sqrt[n]{x^a} \cdot \sqrt[n]{x^{3a}}$.

92. Simplification of radicals. The form of a radical expression may be changed without altering its numerical value.

For example, $\dfrac{1}{\sqrt{2}}$ can be changed to $\dfrac{\sqrt{2}}{2}$, for each equals $.707+$.

Study the following changes of form:

1. $\sqrt{36} = \sqrt{4 \cdot 9} = \sqrt{4} \cdot \sqrt{9} = 2 \cdot 3 = 6.$
2. Similarly $\sqrt{8} = \sqrt{4 \cdot 2} = \sqrt{4} \cdot \sqrt{2} = 2\sqrt{2}.$
3. More generally, $\sqrt[2]{a^2 b} = \sqrt{a^2}\sqrt{b} = a\sqrt{b}.$
4. $\sqrt[3]{24} = \sqrt[3]{8 \cdot 3} = \sqrt[3]{8}\sqrt[3]{3} = 2\sqrt[3]{3}.$
5. More generally, $\sqrt[3]{a^3 b} = \sqrt[3]{a^3}\sqrt[3]{b} = a\sqrt[3]{b}.$
6. Finally, $\sqrt[n]{a^n b} = \sqrt[n]{a^n}\sqrt[n]{b} = a\sqrt[n]{b}.$

Note. Although the Arabs were by no means able to state all the rules explained in this chapter, it is interesting to note that they did recognize the truth of a few of them. For instance, a writer about 830 A.D. gives, in his own notation, of course, the facts contained in the formulas $a\sqrt{b} = \sqrt{a^2 b}$, and $\sqrt{a}\sqrt{b} = \sqrt{ab}$.

A radical is in its **simplest form** when the radicand:

(*a*) *Is integral.*

(*b*) *Contains no rational factor raised to a power which is equal to, or greater than, the order of the radical.*

(*c*) *Is not raised to a power, unless the exponent of the power and the index of the root are prime to each other.*

For the meaning of (*a*), (*b*), and (*c*) study carefully the

EXAMPLES

Of (*a*): 1. $\sqrt{\frac{3}{2}} = \sqrt{\frac{6}{4}} = \sqrt{\frac{1}{4} \cdot 6} = \sqrt{\frac{1}{4}}\sqrt{6} = \frac{1}{2}\sqrt{6}.$

2. $6\sqrt{\frac{1}{3}} = 6\sqrt{\frac{3}{9}} = 6\sqrt{\frac{1}{9} \cdot 3} = 6 \cdot \frac{1}{3}\sqrt{3} = 2\sqrt{3}.$

3. $\sqrt[3]{\frac{3}{16}} = \sqrt[3]{\frac{12}{64}} = \sqrt[3]{\frac{1}{64} \cdot 12} = \sqrt[3]{\frac{1}{64}}\sqrt[3]{12} = \frac{1}{4}\sqrt[3]{12}.$

4. $\sqrt{\dfrac{3}{5x}} = \sqrt{\dfrac{15x}{25x^2}} = \sqrt{\dfrac{1}{25x^2} \cdot 15x} = \dfrac{1}{5x}\sqrt{15x}.$

Of (*b*): 1. $\sqrt{4x^5} = \sqrt{4x^4 \cdot x} = \sqrt{(2x^2)^2 \cdot x} = 2x^2\sqrt{x}.$

2. $5\sqrt[3]{24x^5} = 5\sqrt[3]{8x^3 \cdot 3x^2} = 5\sqrt[3]{(2x)^3 \cdot 3x^2} = 10x\sqrt[3]{3x^2}.$

3. $\sqrt{16 - 8\sqrt{2}} = \sqrt{4(4 - 2\sqrt{2})} = 2\sqrt{4 - 2\sqrt{2}}.$

Of (*c*): 1. $\sqrt[4]{4} = \sqrt[4]{2^2} = 2^{\frac{2}{4}} = 2^{\frac{1}{2}} = \sqrt{2}.$

2. $\sqrt[6]{9} = \sqrt[6]{3^2} = 3^{\frac{2}{6}} = 3^{\frac{1}{3}} = \sqrt[3]{3}.$

3. $\sqrt[4]{a^2 b^4} = a^{\frac{2}{4}} b^{\frac{4}{4}} = a^{\frac{1}{2}} b = b\sqrt{a}.$

EXERCISES

Express in simplest form:

1. $\sqrt{12}$.

2. $\sqrt{32}$.

3. $\sqrt{75}$.

4. $2\sqrt{50}$.

5. $\sqrt[3]{40}$.

6. $\sqrt[3]{54}$.

7. $\sqrt{20}$.

8. $\sqrt[3]{3000}$.

9. $2\sqrt[3]{24}$.

10. $\sqrt{\frac{1}{2}}$.

11. $\sqrt{\frac{2}{5}}$.

12. $\sqrt{\frac{3}{8}}$.

13. $3\sqrt{\frac{9}{2}}$.

14. $5\sqrt{\frac{3}{5}}$.

15. $\sqrt[3]{\frac{1}{2}}$.

16. $4\sqrt[3]{\frac{1}{4}}$.

17. $8\sqrt[3]{\frac{7}{4}}$.

18. $\sqrt{1-(\frac{1}{2})^2}$.

19. $\sqrt{1+(\frac{1}{3})^2}$.

20. $\sqrt{2+(\frac{3}{5})^2}$.

21. $\sqrt[3]{1-(\frac{1}{2})^2}$.

22. $\sqrt[3]{4+(\frac{2}{3})^2}$.

23. $\sqrt[3]{1+(\frac{1}{3})^3}$.

24. $\sqrt[4]{25\,a^2}$.

25. $3\sqrt{4\,x^5}$.

26. $a\sqrt[6]{8\,x^3}$.

27. $x\sqrt[4]{49\,a^2x^2}$.

28. $\sqrt[6]{125\,x^{3a}y^{3m}}$.

29. $\sqrt{\dfrac{a^3}{27}}$.

30. $a\sqrt[3]{\dfrac{5}{2\,a^2}}$.

31. $\sqrt{R^2-\left(\dfrac{R}{2}\right)^2}$.

32. $\sqrt{R^2+\left(\dfrac{R}{2}\right)^2}$.

33. $\sqrt{\left(a+\dfrac{a}{3}\right)\left(a-\dfrac{a}{3}\right)}$.

34. $\sqrt[3]{R^3-\left(\dfrac{R}{2}\right)^3}$.

35. $(x-y)\sqrt{\dfrac{x+y}{x-y}}$.

36. $\sqrt{4+4\sqrt{2}}$.

37. $\sqrt{8-4\sqrt{2}}$.

38. $\sqrt{18+9\sqrt{3}}$.

39. $\sqrt{25\sqrt{5}-100}$.

40. $\sqrt[3]{16+8\sqrt{2}}$.

41. $\sqrt[3]{81+3\sqrt{243}}$.

42. $\sqrt{R^2-2\,R^2\sqrt{2}}$.

43. $\sqrt[4]{32-64\sqrt{3}}$.

44. $\sqrt{\dfrac{R^2+R^2\sqrt{3}}{2}}$.

45. $\sqrt{R^2-\left(\dfrac{R}{2}\right)^2\sqrt{2}}$.

46. $\sqrt{R^2\sqrt{2}-\dfrac{R^2}{2}}$.

47. $\sqrt{\dfrac{R^2}{3}-R^2\sqrt{3}}$.

Reversing the process of simplification,

$3\sqrt{2}=\sqrt{9}\sqrt{2}=\sqrt{18}$. And $2\sqrt[3]{3}=\sqrt[3]{8}\sqrt[3]{3}=\sqrt[3]{24}$.

· Express entirely under the radical sign:

48. $2\sqrt{2}$.　　　　**51.** $4\sqrt[3]{2}$.　　　　**54.** $2x^2\sqrt[3]{x^2}$.

49. $3\sqrt{5}$.　　　　**52.** $3\sqrt[3]{\frac{1}{3}}$.

50. $3\sqrt[3]{4}$.　　　　**53.** $x^2\sqrt{x^3}$.　　　**55.** $\frac{a}{2}\sqrt[3]{\frac{4}{a^2}}$.

56. $(a+2)\sqrt{\frac{1}{a^2-4}}$.　　　**57.** $\frac{x+3}{ax}\sqrt[3]{\frac{a^2x^2}{(x+3)^2}}$.

93. Addition and subtraction of radicals. Similar radicals are radicals of the same order with radicands which are identical or which can be made so by simplification.

Thus $3\sqrt[3]{ac^2}$ and $\sqrt[3]{ac^2}$ are similar radicals. Also $\sqrt{8}$ and $\sqrt{18}$ are similar, for $\sqrt{8}=2\sqrt{2}$ and $\sqrt{18}=3\sqrt{2}$.

Dissimilar radicals are radicals which are not similar.

The sum or difference of similar radicals can be expressed as one term, while the sum or the difference of dissimilar radicals can only be indicated.

Thus　　　　　$5\sqrt{2}$ plus $3\sqrt{2}=8\sqrt{2}$.

But　　　　　$5\sqrt{2}$ plus $3\sqrt[3]{2}=5\sqrt{2}+3\sqrt[3]{2}$.

EXAMPLES

Simplify and collect:

1. $2\sqrt{8}+\sqrt{18}-\sqrt{50}$.

Solution:　$2\sqrt{8}+\sqrt{18}-\sqrt{50}$.

Simplifying, $4\sqrt{2}+3\sqrt{2}-5\sqrt{2}$.

Collecting, $2\sqrt{2}$.

2. $\sqrt[3]{16a^3}+2\sqrt[3]{54a^3}-3\sqrt[3]{2a^3}$.

Solution:　$\sqrt[3]{16a^3}+2\sqrt[3]{54a^3}-3\sqrt[3]{2a^3}$.

Simplifying, $2a\sqrt[3]{2}+6a\sqrt[3]{2}-3a\sqrt[3]{2}$.

Collecting, $5a\sqrt[3]{2}$.

3. $15\sqrt{\frac{6}{5}}+\sqrt{\frac{3}{10}}-3\sqrt{\frac{5}{6}}+\sqrt{\frac{5}{3}}$.

Solution:　$15\sqrt{\frac{6}{5}}+\sqrt{\frac{3}{10}}-3\sqrt{\frac{5}{6}}+\sqrt{\frac{5}{3}}$.

Simplifying, $3\sqrt{30}+\frac{1}{10}\sqrt{30}-\frac{1}{2}\sqrt{30}+\frac{1}{3}\sqrt{15}$.

Collecting, $2\frac{3}{5}\sqrt{30}+\frac{1}{3}\sqrt{15}$.

EXERCISES

Simplify and collect:

1. $\sqrt{27} + \sqrt{12}$.

2. $\sqrt{45} - \sqrt{20}$.

3. $2\sqrt{200} - 3\sqrt{8}$.

4. $\sqrt[3]{56} + 2\sqrt[3]{189}$.

5. $2\sqrt[3]{320} - \sqrt[2]{50}$.

6. $\sqrt[4]{25} - \sqrt[2]{50}$.

7. $\sqrt[4]{32} + 5\sqrt[4]{162}$.

8. $5\sqrt{\frac{1}{2}} - \frac{3}{2}\sqrt{2}$.

9. $\sqrt{\frac{1}{3}} + 2\sqrt{\frac{4}{3}} - 3\sqrt{\frac{2}{3}}$.

10. $\sqrt{\frac{3}{10}} - \sqrt{120} - 2\sqrt{\frac{6}{5}}$.

11. $\sqrt{\frac{5}{18}} + 2\sqrt{\frac{32}{5}} - \sqrt{\frac{10}{9}}$.

12. $\sqrt[3]{\frac{6}{8}} - \sqrt[3]{12} + \sqrt[3]{6}$.

13. $a\sqrt[4]{4} + \sqrt{8\,a^2}$.

14. $R - \sqrt{\dfrac{3\,R^2}{4}}$.

15. $2x\sqrt[3]{54x} - 3\sqrt[3]{16\,x^4} + \sqrt[6]{4\,x^2}$.

16. $\sqrt[3]{81\,x^7} + x\sqrt[3]{375\,x^4} - \sqrt[12]{16\,x^4}$.

17. $\sqrt{a^3bc} - a\sqrt{abc} + ac\sqrt{\dfrac{b}{ac}}$.

18. $\sqrt{(m+n)^3} - n\sqrt[4]{(m+n)^2}$.

19. $\sqrt[3]{(a+b)^4} - \sqrt[3]{8\,a^3(a+b)} + \sqrt[6]{a^2 + 2\,ab + b^2}$.

20. $\sqrt[2]{a^3 + 4\,a^2 + 4\,a} - \sqrt[2]{a^3} - \dfrac{2}{a^3}\sqrt{a^7}$.

21. $\sqrt{x^3y^3} - x^2y^2\sqrt{\dfrac{1}{xy}} + xy\sqrt{2 + \dfrac{x^2 + y^2}{xy}}$.

22. $rs\sqrt[3]{rs} + \sqrt[3]{\dfrac{1}{r^2s^2}} - 2\sqrt[3]{r^4s^4}$.

23. $2\sqrt{\dfrac{y}{x}} - \sqrt{\dfrac{x}{y}} + \sqrt{2 + \dfrac{x^2 + y^2}{xy}}$.

24. $\sqrt{3\,x^2 - 18\,x + 27} - \sqrt{27\,(x^2 + 2\,x + 1)}$.

25. $\sqrt[3]{(a-3)^2(5\,a - 15)} + \sqrt[3]{40}$.

Note. Though methods of classifying irrational expressions are found in the works of Euclid, the Hindus and the Arabs were the first to develop this part of algebra in anything like the form used to-day. The word *surd* is derived from the mistranslation of a Greek word which means, not absurd or foolish, but inexpressible, that is, inexpressible in terms of rational numbers.

94. Multiplication of radicals. Radicals of the same order are multiplied as follows:

EXAMPLES

1. Multiply $3\sqrt{8}$ by $2\sqrt{5}$.

Solution: $3\sqrt{8} \cdot 2\sqrt{5} = 6\sqrt{40} = 6 \cdot 2\sqrt{10} = 12\sqrt{10}$.

2. Multiply $5\sqrt[3]{4\,ax^2}$ by $\sqrt[3]{2\,a^2x^2}$.

Solution: $5\sqrt[3]{4\,ax^2} \cdot \sqrt[3]{2\,a^2x^2} = 5\sqrt[3]{8\,a^3x^4} = 10\,ax\sqrt[3]{x}$.

3. Multiply $3\sqrt{5} - 4\sqrt{3}$ by $2\sqrt{5} + \sqrt{3}$.

Solution:
$$\begin{array}{l} 3\sqrt{5} - 4\sqrt{3} \\ 2\sqrt{5} + \sqrt{3} \\ \hline 30 -8\sqrt{15} \\ +3\sqrt{15} - 12 \\ \hline 30 -5\sqrt{15} - 12 = 18 - 5\sqrt{15}. \end{array}$$

4. Multiply $2\sqrt{a} + 5\sqrt{a-b}$ by $\sqrt{a} - \sqrt{a-b}$.

Solution:
$$\begin{array}{l} 2\sqrt{a} + 5\sqrt{a-b} \\ \sqrt{a} - \sqrt{a-b} \\ \hline 2\,a +5\sqrt{a^2-ab} \\ -2\sqrt{a^2-ab} - 5(a-b) \\ \hline 2\,a +3\sqrt{a^2-ab} - 5\,a + 5\,b = 5\,b - 3\,a + 3\sqrt{a^2-ab}. \end{array}$$

Radicals of different orders are multiplied as follows:

EXAMPLES

1. Multiply $\sqrt[2]{a}$ by $\sqrt[3]{c}$.

Solution: $\sqrt{a} = a^{\frac{1}{2}}$, and $\sqrt[3]{c} = c^{\frac{1}{3}}$.

Reducing the exponents of a and c to equivalent fractions having the least common denominator,

$$a^{\frac{1}{2}} = a^{\frac{3}{6}}, \text{ and } c^{\frac{1}{3}} = c^{\frac{2}{6}}.$$

But $\qquad a^{\frac{3}{6}} = \sqrt[6]{a^3}$ and $c^{\frac{2}{6}} = \sqrt[6]{c^2}$.

Then $\qquad \sqrt[2]{a} \cdot \sqrt[3]{c} = \sqrt[6]{a^3} \cdot \sqrt[6]{c^2} = \sqrt[6]{a^3c^2}$.

2. Multiply $\sqrt[3]{4}$ by $\sqrt[2]{3}$.

Solution: $\sqrt[3]{4} \cdot \sqrt[2]{3} = 4^{\frac{1}{3}} \cdot 3^{\frac{1}{2}} = 4^{\frac{2}{6}} \cdot 3^{\frac{3}{6}} = \sqrt[6]{4^2} \cdot \sqrt[6]{3^3} = \sqrt[6]{4^2 \cdot 3^3} = \sqrt[6]{432}$.

The method of multiplying radicals illustrated in the preceding examples may be stated in the

RULE. *If necessary, reduce the radicals to the same order.*

Find the products of the coefficients of the radicals for the coefficient of the radical part of the result.

Multiply together the radicands and write the product under the common radical sign.

Reduce the result to its simplest form.

The preceding rule does not hold for the multiplication of imaginary numbers, that is, for radicals of even order in which the radicands are negative. This case will be discussed later.

EXERCISES

Perform the indicated multiplications and simplify the products :

1. $\sqrt{2} \cdot \sqrt{8}$.

2. $\sqrt{3} \cdot \sqrt{27}$.

3. $5^{\frac{1}{2}} \cdot 20^{\frac{1}{2}}$.

4. $18^{\frac{1}{2}} \cdot 8^{\frac{1}{2}}$.

5. $\sqrt[3]{16} \cdot \sqrt[3]{4}$.

6. $\sqrt[3]{4} \cdot \sqrt[3]{12}$.

7. $(100)^{\frac{1}{3}} \cdot (30)^{\frac{1}{3}}$.

8. $\sqrt[4]{8} \cdot \sqrt[4]{32}$.

9. $\sqrt{\frac{12}{25}} \cdot \sqrt{75}$.

10. $\sqrt{\frac{2}{3}} \cdot \sqrt{\frac{27}{8}}$.

11. $\sqrt{11} \cdot \sqrt{\frac{1}{11}}$.

12. $a^{\frac{1}{2}} \cdot (bc)^{\frac{1}{2}}$.

13. $2\sqrt{x} \cdot \sqrt[2]{4\,x^3}$.

14. $5\sqrt[3]{2\,a} \cdot 3\sqrt[3]{16\,a}$.

15. $2\sqrt{Rs} \cdot 7\sqrt{r^3 s^3 t^2}$.

16. $\sqrt{\dfrac{a}{x}} \cdot \sqrt{\dfrac{4\,x}{a}}$.

17. $\sqrt{75\,a} \cdot (45\,a)^{\frac{1}{2}}$.

18. $\sqrt{2\,u} \cdot \sqrt{4\,v} \cdot \sqrt{6\,uv}$.

19. $5\sqrt{3\,m} \cdot 5\sqrt{3\,m}$.

20. $\left(3\sqrt[2]{3\,x}\right)^2$.

21. $\sqrt[3]{2} \cdot \sqrt{2}$.

22. $\sqrt{3} \cdot \sqrt[3]{3}$.

23. $\sqrt[3]{2} \cdot \sqrt{3}$.

24. $\sqrt{2} \cdot \sqrt[3]{3}$.

25. $\sqrt[3]{4} \cdot \sqrt{2}$.

26. $\sqrt{8} \cdot \sqrt[3]{8}$.

27. $\sqrt{3} \cdot \sqrt[3]{24}$.

28. $\sqrt{a} \cdot \sqrt[3]{a}$.

29. $\sqrt{a^3} \cdot \sqrt[3]{a^2}$.

30. $\sqrt{2\,a} \cdot \sqrt[3]{2\,a}$.

31. $\sqrt[3]{4\,x^2} \cdot \sqrt{2\,x}$.

32. $\sqrt[3]{\dfrac{5\,x}{a}} \cdot \sqrt[2]{\dfrac{a^3}{5\,x^2}}$.

33. $\left(x + a\sqrt{m}\right)\sqrt{m^3}$.

34. $\left(\sqrt{5\,a} - \sqrt{10\,a^2}\right)\sqrt{5\,a}$.

35. $\left(\sqrt{2} + \sqrt{3}\right)\left(\sqrt{2} - \sqrt{3}\right)$.

36. $\left(5\sqrt{3} - 4\right)\left(3\sqrt{3} + 8\right)$.

37. $\left(\sqrt{5} - \sqrt{3} - \sqrt{2}\right)\left(\sqrt{5} + \sqrt{3} + \sqrt{2}\right)$.

38. $\left(3\sqrt{2} + 2\sqrt{3} + \sqrt{30}\right)\left(\sqrt{2} + \sqrt{3} - \sqrt{5}\right).$

39. $\dfrac{6\,a + b\sqrt{2}}{2} \cdot \dfrac{6\,a + b\sqrt{2}}{2}.$

40. $\left(R - \dfrac{R}{2}\sqrt{3}\right)\left(2\,R + \dfrac{3\,R}{2}\sqrt{3}\right).$

41. $\sqrt{a+b} \cdot \sqrt{a-b} \cdot \sqrt{2\,a^2 - 2\,b^2}.$

42. $\left(2\sqrt{x-a} + \sqrt{a}\right)\left(-3\sqrt{x-a} - 5\sqrt{a}\right).$

43. $\left(3\sqrt[3]{x-a}\right)\left(-5\sqrt[3]{x-a}\right).$

44. $\sqrt{2 - \sqrt{2}} \cdot \sqrt{2 + \sqrt{2}}.$

45. $\sqrt{a - \sqrt{b}} \cdot \sqrt{2\,a - 2\sqrt{b}}.$

46. $\sqrt{\dfrac{R}{2}\sqrt{5} + R} \cdot \sqrt{\dfrac{R}{2}\sqrt{5} - R}.$

Square :

47. $\sqrt[3]{2}.$

48. $2\sqrt[3]{3}.$

49. $2\sqrt[3]{12}.$

50. $\sqrt{2 - \sqrt{2}}.$

51. $3\sqrt{x} + \sqrt{3}.$

52. $\left(2\sqrt[3]{3}\right)^2.$

53. $2\,a\sqrt[3]{8\,x}.$

54. $\sqrt[3]{2} + \sqrt[3]{3}.$

55. $\sqrt[3]{4 + 4\sqrt{3}}.$

56. $\dfrac{1}{3}\sqrt[3]{9 - 9\sqrt{2}}.$

57. $\sqrt{2} + \sqrt[3]{3}.$

58. $2\sqrt[4]{3} - \sqrt{2}.$

Cube :

59. $2\sqrt[2]{3}.$

60. $3\sqrt[2]{2}.$

61. $\left(\sqrt{2}\right)^2.$

62. $\left(\sqrt[2]{3}\right)^3.$

63. $\sqrt{3} - \sqrt{6}.$

64. $2\sqrt{2} + \sqrt{3}.$

65. $\sqrt[3]{3} - \sqrt[3]{2}.$

66. $\sqrt{2 + \sqrt{2}}.$

67. $\sqrt[3]{2} - \sqrt{3}.$

Simplify :

68. $R^2 + \left(\dfrac{R}{2}\sqrt{2 - \sqrt{2}}\right)^2.$

69. $\sqrt{R^2 - \left(\dfrac{R}{2}\sqrt{5} - \dfrac{R}{2}\right)^2}.$

70. $\left[R^2 - \left(\dfrac{R\sqrt{5} - R}{4}\right)^2\right]^{\frac{1}{2}}.$

71. $\left[\left(R - \dfrac{R}{2}\sqrt{3}\right)^2 + \left(\dfrac{R}{2}\right)^2\right]^{\frac{1}{2}}.$

72. $\left[R^2 - \left(\dfrac{R\sqrt{2 - \sqrt{3}}}{2}\right)^2\right]^{\frac{1}{2}}.$

73. $\sqrt{R^2 - \left(\dfrac{R\sqrt{2 - \sqrt{2}}}{2}\right)^2}.$

74. $\sqrt{\left(\dfrac{R\sqrt{2}}{2}\right)^2 + \left(R - \dfrac{R}{2}\sqrt{2}\right)^2}.$

75. $\left(\dfrac{R}{2}\sqrt{2+\sqrt{2}}\right)\left(\dfrac{R\sqrt{2-\sqrt{2}}}{2}\right)4.$

76. Find the value of $x^2 + 4x + 1$ if $x = -2 + \sqrt{3}$.

77. Find the value of $x^2 - 2x - 3$ if $x = 2 + \sqrt{5}$.

78. Find the values of $x^2 - 4x - 1$ if $x = 2 \pm \sqrt{5}$.

79. Find the values of $3x^2 + 3x - 5$ if $x = \frac{1}{2} \pm \frac{1}{2}\sqrt{13}$.

80. Do the values $x = 2 \pm \sqrt{3}$ satisfy the equation $x^2 - 4x + 1 = 0$?

81. Do the values $x = -4 \pm \sqrt{5}$ satisfy the equation $x^2 + 8x + 11 = 0$?

82. What inference seems warranted as a result of Exercise 80? of Exercise 81?

95. Division of radicals. It is frequently necessary to find the approximate value of an expression which involves division by a radical expression. Thus $2 \div \sqrt{3}$, $(4 - \sqrt{3}) \div (2 - \sqrt{3})$, $\dfrac{\sqrt{3}}{\sqrt{5}}$, and $\dfrac{3\sqrt{2}}{\sqrt{5} - \sqrt{2}}$ are types which often occur.

To find the approximate value of $2 \div \sqrt{3}$, we may extract the square root of 3 to several decimal places and then divide 2 by the approximate root obtained. Both of these processes are long and one of them is unnecessary.

For, writing $2 \div \sqrt{3}$ in the form $\dfrac{2}{\sqrt{3}}$ and multiplying both terms of the fraction by $\sqrt{3}$ gives $\dfrac{2\sqrt{3}}{3}$. The process of finding the approximate value of $\dfrac{2\sqrt{3}}{3}$ involves but one long operation.

Similarly the process of finding the approximate value of $\sqrt{7} \div (\sqrt{7} - \sqrt{2})$ involves three rather lengthy operations, — the extracting of two square roots, and one long division. The labor of two of these operations can be avoided.

Evidently $\sqrt{7} \div (\sqrt{7} - \sqrt{2}) = \dfrac{\sqrt{7}}{\sqrt{7} - \sqrt{2}}$. Multiplying both terms

of this fraction by $\sqrt{7} + \sqrt{2}$ gives $\dfrac{\sqrt{7}(\sqrt{7} + \sqrt{2})}{(\sqrt{7} - \sqrt{2})(\sqrt{7} + \sqrt{2})}$, or

$\dfrac{7 + \sqrt{14}}{7 - 2}$, or $\dfrac{7 + \sqrt{14}}{5}$. Finding the value of $\dfrac{7 + \sqrt{14}}{5}$ involves only

one long operation, extracting the square root of 14.

As in the two preceding illustrations, division of radicals is usually an indirect process performed by means of a **rationalizing** factor for the divisor.

One radical expression is the **rationalizing factor** for another if the *product* of the two is *rational*.

A rationalizing factor of $\sqrt{3}$ is $\sqrt{3}$, for $\sqrt{3} \cdot \sqrt{3} = 3$.

For $\sqrt[3]{2}$ a rationalizing factor is $\sqrt[3]{4}$, since $\sqrt[3]{2} \cdot \sqrt[3]{4} = \sqrt[3]{8} = 2$.

Similarly $\sqrt{7} - \sqrt{2}$ is a rationalizing factor of $\sqrt{7} + \sqrt{2}$, as their product $(\sqrt{7} - \sqrt{2})(\sqrt{7} + \sqrt{2}) = 7 - 2 = 5$.

In like manner $(3\sqrt{5} - 2\sqrt{3})(3\sqrt{5} + 2\sqrt{3}) = 45 - 12 = 33$. Therefore $3\sqrt{5} - 2\sqrt{3}$ is a rationalizing factor of $3\sqrt{5} + 2\sqrt{3}$.

The binomial radicals of the last two illustrations are of the general types $\sqrt{a} + \sqrt{b}$ and $\sqrt{a} - \sqrt{b}$. Such binomials are called **conjugate** radicals and *either* is the rationalizing factor of the other. If a and b are rational, the product $(\sqrt{a} + \sqrt{b})(\sqrt{a} - \sqrt{b})$, or $a - b$, is a *rational* number.

There are many other types of radical expressions which have rationalizing factors. They seldom arise, however, and are too difficult for treatment in elementary algebra.*

An irrational expression may have more than one rationalizing factor. Thus $\sqrt{18}$, $\sqrt{8}$, and $\sqrt{2}$ are rationalizing factors of $\sqrt{18}$. For $\sqrt{18} \cdot \sqrt{18} = 18$; and $\sqrt{18} \cdot \sqrt{8} = \sqrt{144} = 12$; and $\sqrt{18} \cdot \sqrt{2} = \sqrt{36} = 6$. Similarly, since $\sqrt[3]{4} \cdot \sqrt[3]{2} = \sqrt[3]{8} = 2$, and $\sqrt[3]{4} \cdot \sqrt[3]{16} = \sqrt[3]{64} = 4$, both $\sqrt[3]{2}$ and $\sqrt[3]{16}$ are rationalizing factors of $\sqrt[3]{4}$. In practice it is best to choose for monomials the rationalizing factor which has the least radicand.

---

* See Hawkes's "Advanced Algebra," p. 62.

EXERCISES

Determine a rationalizing factor for each of the following expressions and find the product of the expression and the factor:

1. $\sqrt{5}$.

4. $\sqrt{8}$.

7. $\sqrt[3]{2}$.

10. $\sqrt[3]{16}$.

2. $3\sqrt{6}$.

5. $\sqrt{32}$.

8. $\sqrt[3]{3}$.

11. $\sqrt[3]{25}$.

3. $2\sqrt{7}$.

6. $\sqrt{27}$.

9. $2\sqrt[3]{5}$.

12. $\sqrt[3]{36}$.

13. $\sqrt[3]{49}$.

17. $3\sqrt{2} - 5$.

21. $\sqrt{3a} + \sqrt{x}$.

14. $\sqrt{2} + 3$.

18. $4\sqrt{3} - \sqrt{2}$.

22. $3\sqrt{x} - a\sqrt{2}$.

15. $\sqrt{3} - \sqrt{2}$.

19. $2\sqrt{5} + 7\sqrt{6}$.

23. $\sqrt{x+a} + \sqrt{x}$.

16. $3 + \sqrt{7}$.

20. $\sqrt{x} - \sqrt{a}$.

24. $\sqrt{x} - \sqrt{a-x}$.

25. $\sqrt{2ax - x^2} - \sqrt{ax}$.

The usefulness of rationalizing factors is illustrated in Examples 4–8 which follow.

The student should now study Examples 1–6, pp. 251–252, and the rule on pp. 252–253, and then solve Exercises 1–32, pp. 253–254.

EXAMPLES

1. Divide $\sqrt{6}$ by $\sqrt{2}$.

Solution: By direct division, $\sqrt{6} \div \sqrt{2} = \dfrac{\sqrt{6}}{\sqrt{2}} = \sqrt{\dfrac{6}{2}} = \sqrt{3}$.

2. Divide $6\sqrt{5}$ by $3\sqrt{3}$.

Solution: By direct division, coefficient by coefficient and radicand by radicand, $6\sqrt{5} \div 3\sqrt{3} = \dfrac{6\sqrt{5}}{3\sqrt{3}} = 2\sqrt{\dfrac{5}{3}}$, which becomes $\dfrac{2}{3}\sqrt{15}$.

3. Divide $8\sqrt{12}$ by $2\sqrt[3]{6}$.

Solution: Reducing the surds of the same order, and then proceeding as in direct division,

$$8\sqrt{12} \div 2\sqrt[3]{6} = \frac{8(12)^{\frac{1}{2}}}{2(6)^{\frac{1}{3}}} = \frac{4(12)^{\frac{3}{6}}}{(6)^{\frac{2}{6}}} = 4\sqrt[6]{\frac{12 \cdot 12 \cdot 12}{6 \cdot 6}}$$

$$= 4\sqrt[6]{2 \cdot 2 \cdot 12} = 4\sqrt[6]{48}.$$

If the monomial divisor is a surd, it is always possible and often far more convenient to divide by means of a rationalizing factor of the divisor.

4. Divide 4 by $\sqrt{3}$.

Solution: $4 \div \sqrt{3} = \dfrac{4}{\sqrt{3}} = \dfrac{4\sqrt{3}}{\sqrt{3}\sqrt{3}} = \dfrac{4\sqrt{3}}{3}$.

5. Divide 6 by $\sqrt[3]{3}$.

Solution: $6 \div \sqrt[3]{3} = \dfrac{6}{\sqrt[3]{3}} = \dfrac{6\sqrt[3]{9}}{\sqrt[3]{3} \cdot \sqrt[3]{9}} = \dfrac{6\sqrt[3]{9}}{\sqrt[3]{27}} = \dfrac{6\sqrt[3]{9}}{3} = 2\sqrt[3]{9}$.

6. Divide $\sqrt{3}$ by $\sqrt[3]{2}$.

Solution: $\sqrt{3} \div \sqrt[3]{2} = \dfrac{\sqrt{3}}{\sqrt[3]{2}} = \dfrac{\sqrt{3} \cdot \sqrt[3]{4}}{\sqrt[3]{2} \cdot \sqrt[3]{4}} = \dfrac{3^{\frac{1}{2}} \cdot 4^{\frac{1}{3}}}{2} = \dfrac{3^{\frac{3}{6}} \cdot 4^{\frac{2}{6}}}{2}$

$$= \tfrac{1}{2}\sqrt[6]{3^3 \cdot 4^2} = \tfrac{1}{2}\sqrt[6]{432}.$$

When the divisor is a binomial (or polynomial) radical, the practical method of division is an indirect method by means of a rationalizing factor.

7. Divide 8 by $3 + \sqrt{7}$.

Solution: $8 \div (3 + \sqrt{7}) = \dfrac{8}{3 + \sqrt{7}} = \dfrac{8(3 - \sqrt{7})}{(3 + \sqrt{7})(3 - \sqrt{7})}$

$$= \dfrac{24 - 8\sqrt{7}}{9 - 7} = 12 - 4\sqrt{7}.$$

8. Divide $\sqrt{5} + \sqrt{3}$ by $2\sqrt{5} - \sqrt{3}$.

Solution: $(\sqrt{5} + \sqrt{3}) \div (2\sqrt{5} - \sqrt{3})$

$$= \dfrac{\sqrt{5} + \sqrt{3}}{2\sqrt{5} - \sqrt{3}} = \dfrac{(\sqrt{5} + \sqrt{3})(2\sqrt{5} + \sqrt{3})}{(2\sqrt{5} - \sqrt{3})(2\sqrt{5} + \sqrt{3})}$$

$$= \dfrac{10 + 3\sqrt{15} + 3}{20 - 3} = \dfrac{13}{17} + \dfrac{3}{17}\sqrt{15}.$$

For division of radicals we may use the

RULE. *Write the dividend over the divisor in the form of a fraction.*

Then multiply the numerator and denominator of the fraction by the rationalizing factor of the denominator and simplify the resulting fraction.

Every irrational algebraic expression containing nothing more complicated than rational numbers and radicals has a rationalizing factor. To find this factor for any given irrational expression is a problem which requires considerable algebraic training. At the present time it is wholly beyond the student to find the rationalizing factor of even so simple an expression as the denominator of the fraction

$\dfrac{\sqrt{2} + \sqrt{3}}{\sqrt{2} + \sqrt[3]{2} + \sqrt[4]{2}}$. The approximate value of such a fraction can be

obtained, however, by dividing the sum of the approximate values of the roots in the numerator by the sum of the approximate values of the roots in the denominator.

EXERCISES

Perform the indicated division:

1. $\sqrt{10} \div \sqrt{2}$.

2. $(18)^{\frac{1}{2}} \div (3)^{\frac{1}{2}}$.

3. $\dfrac{\sqrt{6}}{\sqrt{18}}$.

4. $6 \div 2\sqrt{2}$.

5. $\dfrac{3\sqrt{12}}{\sqrt{6}}$.

6. $8\sqrt{15} \div 4\sqrt{5}$.

7. $\dfrac{10}{2\sqrt{5}}$.

8. $\dfrac{4\sqrt{10}}{8\sqrt{5}}$.

9. $8 \div 4\sqrt{3}$.

10. $\dfrac{3\sqrt{2}}{15\sqrt{8}}$.

11. $(\sqrt{6} + \sqrt{18}) \div 3\sqrt{2}$.

12. $(\sqrt{12} - \sqrt{24}) \div 2\sqrt{3}$.

13. $\dfrac{6\sqrt{10} + 4\sqrt{15} - \sqrt{20}}{2\sqrt{5}}$.

14. $(12 + \sqrt{3} + \sqrt{5}) \div \sqrt{6}$.

15. $\dfrac{\sqrt{6} - \sqrt{9} + 18}{2\sqrt{2}}$.

16. $(\sqrt{5} + 2) \div \sqrt{125}$.

17. $\sqrt{\frac{32}{10}} \div \sqrt{\frac{4}{5}}$.

18. $(xy)^{\frac{1}{2}} \div x^{\frac{1}{2}}$.

19. $a\sqrt{bc} \div d\sqrt{c}$.

20. $\dfrac{a^2\sqrt{c}}{a\sqrt{bc}}$.

21. $\sqrt[3]{16} \div \sqrt[3]{4}$.

22. $8\sqrt[3]{125} \div 4\sqrt[3]{25}$.

23. $\dfrac{2\sqrt[3]{5}}{3\sqrt[3]{4}}$.

24. $a\,9^{\frac{1}{3}} \div b\,8^{\frac{1}{3}}$.

25. $\sqrt[3]{\frac{1}{3}} \div \sqrt[3]{\frac{1}{4}}$.

26. $\sqrt[3]{4} \div \sqrt[2]{2}$.

27. $\sqrt{2} \div \sqrt[3]{4}$.

28. $4^{\frac{1}{3}} \div 6^{\frac{1}{2}}$.

29. $6^{\frac{1}{2}} \div 4^{\frac{1}{3}}$.

30. $\sqrt[5]{27} \div \sqrt{27}$.

31. $\sqrt[4]{\frac{1}{8}} \div \sqrt[3]{\frac{1}{2}}$.

32. $\sqrt[6]{\frac{a^2}{72\,a}} \div \sqrt[3]{\frac{a}{81}}$.

33. $5 \div (\sqrt{5} + 2)$.

HINT. Study Examples 7 and 8, p. 252.

34. $\dfrac{2}{2 - \sqrt{3}}$.

35. $4 \div (\sqrt{3} - \sqrt{2})$.

36. $\sqrt{5} \div (3\sqrt{2} - \sqrt{5})$.

37. $(\sqrt{5} - \sqrt{3}) \div (\sqrt{5} + \sqrt{3})$.

38. $\dfrac{4\sqrt{3} + 2\sqrt{2}}{4\sqrt{3} - 2\sqrt{2}}$.

39. $\dfrac{(2\sqrt{5} - 3\sqrt{3})}{5\sqrt{5} - 5}$.

Find to three decimals the approximate values of the following:

40. $3 + \sqrt{2}$.

41. $14 - 5\sqrt{7}$.

42. $6 \pm 2\sqrt{5}$.

43. $\dfrac{7 \pm \sqrt{6}}{3}$.

44. $3\sqrt{6} \div 2\sqrt{5}$.

45. $\dfrac{2\sqrt{5} + 1}{3\sqrt{5} - \sqrt{3}}$.

46. $\sqrt{2 - \sqrt{3}}$.

47. $\dfrac{\sqrt{3}}{\sqrt{3} + \sqrt[3]{4} + \sqrt[4]{5}}$, given $\sqrt[3]{4} = 1.5874$.

Change the following fractions to equivalent fractions having rational denominators:

48. $\dfrac{(\sqrt{a} + \sqrt{b})}{(\sqrt{a} - \sqrt{b})}$.

49. $\dfrac{2\sqrt{x} - \sqrt{a}}{\sqrt{x} + 3\sqrt{a}}$.

50. $\dfrac{(r\sqrt{3} + \sqrt{r})}{\sqrt{3} - \sqrt{r}}$.

51. $\dfrac{m\sqrt{n} + a\sqrt{b}}{m\sqrt{n} - a\sqrt{b}}$.

52. $\dfrac{\sqrt{a-2} - 2}{\sqrt{a-2} + 2}$.

53. $\dfrac{2}{\sqrt[4]{2} + \sqrt{2}}$.

Perform the indicated division:

54. $(x - \sqrt{a+b}) \div (x + \sqrt{a+b})$.

55. $(\sqrt{a} + \sqrt{b}) \div (\sqrt{c} + \sqrt{d})$.

56. Is there any real distinction between the direction which precedes Exercise 48 and that which precedes Exercise 54?

PROBLEMS

(Obtain answers in *simplest radical form*.)

1. One leg of a right triangle is 10 and the other is 5. Find the hypotenuse.

2. The hypotenuse of a right triangle is 10 and one leg is 5. Find the other leg and the area.

3. The hypotenuse of a right triangle is R and one leg is $\dfrac{R}{2}$. Find the other leg and the area.

4. Find the diagonal of a square whose side is 10.

5. Find the sides and the area of a square whose diagonal is 10.

6. Find the sides and the area of a square whose diagonal is $2R$.

7. The side of an equilateral triangle is 12. Find the altitude and the area.

8. The side of an equilateral triangle is S. Find the altitude and the area.

9. The altitude of an equilateral triangle is 10. Find the side and the area.

10. The legs of a right triangle are equal. Its hypotenuse is 20. Find the legs and the area of the triangle.

11. The legs of a right triangle are equal and its area is 32. Find the hypotenuse.

12. The legs of a right triangle are $\dfrac{R}{2}$ and $\dfrac{3R}{2}$. Find the hypotenuse.

13. One leg of a right triangle is $\dfrac{R}{5}$. The hypotenuse is R. Find the other leg.

14. The legs of a right triangle are R and $\dfrac{R}{2}\left(\sqrt{5}-1\right)$. Find the hypotenuse.

15. The legs of a right triangle are $\dfrac{R}{2}$ and $R - \dfrac{R}{2}\sqrt{3}$. Find the hypotenuse.

16. The base of a certain rectangle is $\dfrac{2R}{3}\sqrt{4-\sqrt{3}}$ and the altitude is $9R\dfrac{\sqrt{4+\sqrt{3}}}{10}$. Find the area of a second rectangle five times as long and three times as wide as the first.

96. Factors involving radicals. In the chapter on factoring it was definitely stated that factors involving radicals would not then be considered. This limitation on the character of a factor is no longer necessary. Consequently many expressions which previously have been regarded as prime may now be thought of as factorable. Thus $3x^2-1=(\sqrt{3}x+1)(\sqrt{3}x-1)$ and $4x^2-5=(2x+\sqrt{5})(2x-\sqrt{5})$.

It is not usual to allow the variable in an expression to occur under a radical sign in the factors. Hence, if x is a variable, the trinomial x^2+x+1 is not regarded as factorable into $(x+\sqrt{x}+1)(x-\sqrt{x}+1)$, though the student can easily show that $(x+\sqrt{x}+1)(x-\sqrt{x}+1)=x^2+x+1$.

Therefore in this extension of our notion of a factor it must be clearly understood that the use of radicals is limited to the coefficients in the terms of the factors. Such a conception of a factor is a necessity for certain work in advanced algebra and geometry, and is very desirable in solving equations by factoring.

To restrict the use of radicals in the way just indicated is necessary for the sake of definiteness. Otherwise it would be impossible to obey a direction to factor even so simple an expression as x^2-y^2; for if the variable is allowed under a radical sign in a factor, x^2-y^2 has an infinite number of factors.

Thus
$$x^2-y^2=(x+y)(x-y)$$
$$=(x+y)(\sqrt{x}+\sqrt{y})(\sqrt{x}-\sqrt{y})$$
$$=(x+y)(\sqrt{x}+\sqrt{y})(\sqrt[4]{x}+\sqrt[4]{y})(\sqrt[4]{x}-\sqrt[4]{y})$$
$$=\text{etc.}$$

The extension of factoring explained above can be applied to the solution of equations as follows :

EXAMPLE

Solve $x^2 - 7 = 0$ by factoring.

Solution: $\qquad\qquad\qquad x^2 - 7 = 0.$ $\qquad\qquad$ (1)

Then $\qquad (x + \sqrt{7})(x - \sqrt{7}) = 0.$ $\qquad\qquad$ (2)

Therefore $\qquad\qquad x + \sqrt{7} = 0,$ or $x = -\sqrt{7},$

and $\qquad\qquad\qquad x - \sqrt{7} = 0,$ or $x = \sqrt{7}.$

It is apparent at once that these values check in $x^2 - 7 = 0$.

In (2) it is obvious that if a root be substituted for the variable, one of the factors must become zero.

EXERCISES

Factor:

1. $x^2 - 6.$ 5. $4x^4 - 1.$ 9. $x^3 + 4.$

2. $3x^2 - 4.$ 6. $x^3 - 2.$ 10. $2x^3 + 8.$

3. $5x^2 - 1.$ 7. $x^3 + 6.$ 11. $2x^3 - 8.$

4. $x^4 - 4.$ 8. $3x^3 - 1.$ 12. $6x^3 + 24.$

Solve by factoring and check:

13. $x^2 - 2 = 0.$ 18. $3x^4 + 8 = 14x^2.$

14. $x^2 - 6 = 0.$ 19. $5x^4 - 16x^2 + 3 = 0.$

15. $2x^2 - 1 = 0.$ 20. $x^4 + 8a = 4x^2 + 2ax^2.$

16. $x^4 + 6 = 5x^2.$ 21. $ax^4 - x^2 + 3a = 3a^2x^2.$

17. $4x^4 + 5 = 12x^2.$ 22. $4x^4 + a = x^2 + 4ax^2.$

Biographical note. FRANÇOIS VIETA. The reason that algebra is a universal language which does not depend entirely on the nationality of the writer lies in the fact that the symbols used to indicate the various operations and relations are widely understood and adopted. This has not always been the case, and for a long time during the early history of the subject there was no accepted notation in algebra, but each man used any symbol that suited him. One of the men who did most to establish a fixed notation was François Vieta (1540–1603), a French lawyer who studied and wrote on mathematics as a pastime. He was in public life during his whole career, and was well known for his ability to decipher the hidden meaning of dispatches captured from the enemy.

It was he who established the use of the signs + and − for addition and subtraction, which, to be sure, had been used before his time, but were not generally accepted. He also denoted the known numbers in an equation by the consonants, B, C, D, etc., and the unknowns by the vowels A, E, I, etc. He also recognized the existence of negative roots of equations, but rejected them as absurd.

To denote the second and third powers of the unknown, he used the letters Q (*quadratus*) and C (*cubus*) respectively. Instead of using the sign =, he wrote aeq. (*aequalis* or *aequatur*). Thus Vieta would have written the equation $x^3 - 8x^2 + 16 = 40$ in the form

$$1\,C - 8\,Q + 16\,N \text{ aeq. } 40.$$

Before the time of Vieta this equation would have been written in a much more primitive notation. For instance, with writers only a little earlier it would appear as

$$\text{Cubus } \overline{m} \text{ 8Census } \overline{p} \text{ 16 rebus aequatur 40.}$$

It is easily seen that operations on equations in this form would be very hard to perform.

Vieta is further distinguished as being the first man to obtain an exact numerical expression for the number π, which occurs in geometry. His form of expression calls for an infinite number of operations which, of course, could never be performed, but the further one proceeded, the closer would be the approximation obtained. In a certain sense the familiar sign $\sqrt{}$ implies an infinite number of operations, for one can never go through the process of extracting the square root of 2, for instance, and come out even. Vieta's method of denoting π was, however, more involved than this, and made use of complicated irrational fractions.

FRANÇOIS VIETA

CHAPTER XXII

GRAPHICAL SOLUTION OF EQUATIONS IN ONE UNKNOWN

97. Graph of a linear function. An algebraic expression involving one or more letters is a **function** of the letter or letters involved.

Thus $2x + 3$ and $x^2 + 5x - 6$ are functions of one letter, x; $x^2 - 2xy + y^2$ and $x^3 + y^3$ are functions of two letters, x and y.

The letters of a function are usually referred to as **variables.**

A function is called **linear, quadratic,** or **cubic** according as its degree with respect to the variable (or variables) is first, second, or third respectively.

After a function of any variable, say x, has once been given, it is convenient and usual to refer to it later in the same discussion by the symbol $f(x)$, which is read *the function of x*, or, more briefly, *f of x.*

The numerical value of a linear function of x changes with every change in the variable.

Thus if $x = 1$, the linear function of x, $2x + 3$, equals $2 + 3$, or 5; if $x = 2$, $2x + 3$ equals $4 + 3$, or 7. The following table illustrates this change further.

When $x =$	-3	-2	-1	0	1	2	3
$f(x)$, $2x + 3 =$	-3	-1	1	3	5	7	9

The relation between x and the function $2x + 3$ may be represented graphically if OX continue to be the x-axis and OF (or the function axis) replace the y-axis of our previous graphical work. Beginning with $(-3, -3)$ and plotting the points corresponding to the numbers in the table, we locate

259

points *A*, *B*, *C*, *D*, *E*, *G*, and *H* respectively. The *graph* of the function $f(x) = 2x + 3$ is evidently the *straight line AH*.

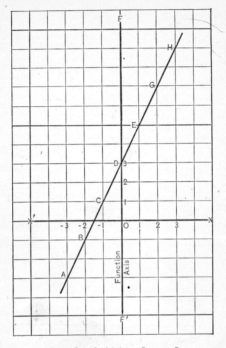

Graph of $f(x) = 2x + 3$

This process of plotting the relation between a function and the variable contained in the function is called *graphing the function*.

Care should always be taken in graphing to join the plotted points by a *smooth* curve or by a *straight* line, as the case may be. If the graph is not regular and graceful, it is almost certain that an error has been made in plotting the points. No equations in this book have graphs that are part straight line and part curve, or that present erratic changes in curvature. Although such curves have equations, they are usually very complicated.

EXERCISES

(Exercises 1–8 refer to the preceding graph.)

1. Read from the graph the value of x when $f(x)$ is zero.

2. Set $2x + 3$ equal to zero, and solve.

3. Compare the results of Exercises 1 and 2.

4. Read from the graph the value of x when $f(x)$ is 4.

5. Set $2x + 3$ equal to 4, and solve.

6. Compare the results of Exercises 4 and 5.

7. Can the value of x in $2x + 3 = 6$ be read from the graph? If so, read it.

8. Read from the graph the root of $2x + 3 = -2$.

9. Graph the function $f(x) = 5 - 2x$.

10. Can the root of $5 - 2x = 0$ be read from the graph just obtained? If so, read it.

11. From the graph of Exercise 9 read the roots of:

(a) $5 - 2x = 9$;   (c) $5 - 2x = -3$;
(b) $5 - 2x = 5$;   (d) $5 - 2x = -7$.

12. Check by substitution the roots obtained in Exercise 11.

13. What kind of a line do you expect the graph of any *linear function* of x to give?

98. Graph of a quadratic function. The quadratic function $f(x) = 4x^2 - 4x - 15$ may be graphed as follows:

When $x = 1$, $4x^2 - 4x - 15 = 4 - 4 - 15 = -15$, or $f(x) = -15$.

In like manner, the other numbers in the following table can be obtained.

When $x =$	-3	-2	-1	0	1	2	3	4
$f(x), 4x^2 - 4x - 15 =$	33	9	-7	-15	-15	-7	9	33

To represent the numbers in the preceding table conveniently, it is necessary to use *different scales* for x and $f(x)$.

The difference can be seen from the numbers along the axes in the following figure.

If we begin with $(-3, 33)$ and plot the points corresponding to the numbers in the table, we get the points A, B, C, D, E, G, H, and I respectively.

Drawing a smooth curve through these points gives the graph of the following figure. This curve is called a **parabola**.

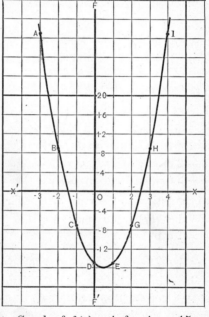

Graph of $f(x) = 4x^2 - 4x - 15$

The student should note that it is often best to represent values of $f(x)$ on a different scale from values of x. He should always inspect his table of values and decide what scale to use before plotting a single point. The scale should be as large as possible and yet show enough of the curve to indicate its shape clearly.

It will often be found convenient not to put the intersection of the axes in the center of the page.

EXERCISES

(Exercises 1, 4, 7, and 9 refer to the preceding graph.)

1. Read from the graph the values of x for which $4x^2 - 4x - 15$ equals zero.

2. Set $4x^2 - 4x - 15$ equal to zero, and solve by factoring.

3. Compare the answers to Exercises 1 and 2.

4. Read from the graph the value of x for which $f(x)$ equals 20.

5. What, then, are the roots of $4x^2 - 4x - 15 = 20$?

6. Solve $4x^2 - 4x - 15 = 20$ by factoring, and check your answers to Exercise 5.

7. Read from the graph the roots of:

(a) $4x^2 - 4x - 15 = 9$.　　(b) $4x^2 - 4x - 15 = -7$.

8. Check your answers to Exercise 7 by solving the equations (a) and (b) by factoring.

9. Can you read from the graph the value of x which makes $f(x)$ equal -25? equal -20? Explain.

10. Graph the function $x^2 - 2x - 4$.

First fill out the table:

When $x =$	-4	-3	-2	-1	0	1	2	3	4	5	6
$f(x)$, $x^2 - 2x - 4 =$				-1	-4	-5					

Then plot the eleven points and draw through them as smooth a curve as possible.

11. Is the curve obtained in Exercise 10 similar in shape to that of the preceding figure?

12. Read from the graph of Exercise 10 the approximate values of x which make the function $x^2 - 2x - 4$ equal zero.

13. What are the roots of the equation $x^2 - 2x - 4 = 0$?

14. Can you solve the equation $x^2 - 2x - 4 = 0$ by factoring? graphically?

15. If the terms of a quadratic equation be transposed so that the second member is zero, and then the function in the first member be graphed, can the roots of the original equation be read from the curve thus obtained? Explain.

Solve Exercises 16 and 17 graphically and check each by substituting in the original equation; or solve the equation by factoring, and compare results with those obtained graphically.

16. $x^2 - 3x = 4.$ **17.** $x^2 - 4x + 4 = 0.$

18. What peculiarity has the curve obtained in Exercise 17? How many roots has $x^2 - 4x + 4 = 0$? What values of x make $x^2 - 4x + 4$ equal zero? equal to $+4$? to -1? to -10?

Exercises 19 and 20 cannot be solved by the factoring previously explained. They have irrational roots, but the approximate values of the roots can be obtained graphically.

Solve Exercises 19 and 20 graphically.

19. $x^2 - 2x = 2.$ **20.** $x^2 + 2x = 5.$

21. Graph the linear function $3x + 4$, using the same scale for x and $f(x)$; then graph the function, using different scales. Compare the two lines obtained and the values of x and $f(x)$ where each graph crosses the x-axis and the F-axis respectively.

22. Proceed as in Exercise 21 with the quadratic function $x^2 + 3x + 1.$

99. Graphical illustration of imaginary roots. The solution of $x^2 + 1 = 0$ gives $x = \pm \sqrt{-1}$. These roots are *imaginary* numbers. Just now it is desirable to know that many quadratic equations have imaginary roots. It will be instructive also to see the result of an attempt at a graphical solution of a quadratic equation whose roots are imaginary. For this purpose we shall consider the three equations:

$$\text{I. } x^2 - 4x - 5 = 0.$$
$$\text{II. } x^2 - 4x + 4 = 0.$$
$$\text{III. } x^2 - 4x + 13 = 0.$$

The graphs of the functions in the left members of I, II, and III are given in the adjacent figure. The three functions differ only in their constant terms; for 9 added to the constant term of I gives the constant term of II, and 9 added to the constant term of II gives the constant term of III. Apparently, as the constant term is increased, the graph rises. It does not change its shape, nor does it move to the left nor to the right.

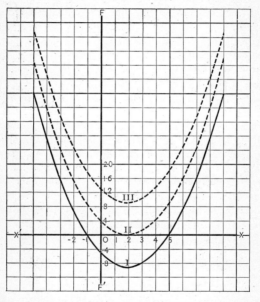

From the graph the roots of $x^2 - 4x - 5 = 0$ are seen to be 5 and -1. These results are easily obtained by factoring: $x^2 - 4x - 5 = 0$, or $(x - 5)(x + 1) = 0$. Therefore $x = 5$ or -1.

If we imagine curve I to move upward, the two roots change in value and become the single root of curve II, which touches the x-axis at a point where x equals 2. Solving $x^2 - 4x + 4 = 0$ by factoring gives $(x - 2)(x - 2) = 0$. Therefore $x = 2$.

If we now imagine curve I to move still farther upward from its position II, it will no longer cut the x-axis. Further, we do not expect that the graph when it reaches the position of III will show the roots of the equation $x^2 - 4x + 13 = 0$, as in fact it does not. The graph does show, however, that the value of $x^2 - 4x + 13$ at the lowest point of the curve is 9. This means that for *every real value* of x, positive or negative, $x^2 - 4x + 13$ is *never less than* 9. The graph of III, then, makes clear that no real number, if substituted for x, will make $x^2 - 4x + 13$ equal to zero.

In the next chapter an algebraic method of solving any quadratic is given. That method will later be used to show the roots of $x^2 - 4x + 13 = 0$ to be the imaginary expressions $2 + 3\sqrt{-1}$ and $2 - 3\sqrt{-1}$.

The preceding explanations show that the *real* roots of a quadratic equation can be obtained by the following steps.

1. Transpose the terms so that the second member is zero.

2. Graph the function in the first member.

3. Note the x-distance of each point at which the curve crosses (or touches) the x-axis. *The values of these x-distances are the roots of the quadratic.*

If the graph obtained in 2 does not cross the x-axis, the student knows that the roots are not real. He may still regard such equations as having roots and refer to them as *imaginary*. Later he will learn precisely what an imaginary number is, and how to solve any quadratic whose roots are imaginary.

EXERCISES

If possible, solve graphically :

1. $x^2 - 6x + 7 = 0.$ 3. $2x^2 + x + 1 = 0.$

2. $x^2 - 6x + 11 = 0.$ 4. $2x^2 + x - 1 = 0.$

CHAPTER XXIII

QUADRATIC EQUATIONS

100. Solution by completing the square. Before taking up the work which follows, the student should review the exercises in forming trinomial squares, p. 108.

EXAMPLES

1. Solve $\qquad x^2 + 6x - 16 = 0.$ $\hfill (1)$

Solution: Transposing, $\;x^2 + 6x = 16.$ $\hfill (2)$

Adding 9 to each member of (2),
$$x^2 + 6x + 9 = 25. \hfill (3)$$
Then $\qquad\qquad\qquad (x + 3)^2 = 5^2. \hfill (4)$

Extracting the square root of each member of (4),
$$x + 3 = \pm 5. \hfill (5)$$
Whence $\qquad\qquad\qquad x = -3 + 5, \text{ or } 2,$

and $\qquad\qquad\qquad\quad x = -3 - 5, \text{ or } -8.$

Check: Substituting 2 for x in (1),
$$4 + 12 - 16 = 0,$$
or $\qquad\qquad\qquad\qquad 0 = 0.$

Substituting -8 for x in (1),
$$64 - 48 - 16 = 0,$$
or $\qquad\qquad\qquad\qquad 0 = 0.$

The 9 added to each member of (2) is the square of half the coefficient of x; that is, $9 = (\frac{6}{2})^2$, or 3^2. If the coefficient of x^2 is 1, the trinomial square can always be completed by **adding the square of half the coefficient of x**. If the coefficient of x^2 is -1 or any number other than $+1$, the equation is solved as in the next example.

The sign $\pm$ properly belongs to each member of (5). Thus $\pm (x + 3) = \pm 5$. This, however, gives precisely the same roots as $x + 3 = \pm 5$, a fact which the student can easily verify. For this reason the sign $\pm$ is put before one member only in equations obtained as was equation (5).

2. Solve $\qquad 3\,x^2 - 7\,x - 20 = 0.$ (1)

Solution: Transposing, $\quad 3\,x^2 - 7\,x = 20.$ (2)

Dividing (2) by the coefficient of x^2,

$$x^2 - \frac{7\,x}{5} = \frac{20}{3}.$$ (3)

Adding $(-\frac{7}{6})^2$ to each member of (3),

$$x^2 - \frac{7}{3}\,x + (\tfrac{7}{6})^2 = \tfrac{20}{3} + \tfrac{49}{36} = \tfrac{289}{36}.$$ (4)

Then $\qquad\qquad (x - \tfrac{7}{6})^2 = (\tfrac{17}{6})^2.$ (5)

Extracting the square root of each member of (5),

$$x - \tfrac{7}{6} = \pm\,\tfrac{17}{6}.$$

Whence $\qquad\qquad x = \tfrac{7}{6} \pm \tfrac{17}{6}.$

$$= 4 \text{ or } -\tfrac{5}{3}.$$

Check: Substituting 4 for x in (1),

$$3 \cdot 4^2 - 7 \cdot 4 - 20 = 0.$$
$$48 - 28 - 20 = 0, \text{ or } 0 = 0.$$

Substituting $-\tfrac{5}{3}$ for x in (1),

$$3(-\tfrac{5}{3})^2 - 7(-\tfrac{5}{3}) - 20 = 0.$$
$$\tfrac{25}{3} + \tfrac{35}{3} - 20 = 0.$$
$$\tfrac{60}{3} - 20 = 0, \text{ or } 0 = 0.$$

3. Solve $\qquad 4\,x^2 - 4\,x - 79 = 0.$ (1)

Solution: Transposing, $\quad 4\,x^2 - 4\,x = 79.$ (2)

Dividing each member of (2) by 4,

$$x^2 - x = \tfrac{79}{4}.$$ (3)

Adding $(-\tfrac{1}{2})^2$ to each member of (3),

$$x^2 - x + (-\tfrac{1}{2})^2 = \tfrac{79}{4} + \tfrac{1}{4} = \tfrac{80}{4}.$$ (4)

Then $\qquad\qquad (x - \tfrac{1}{2})^2 = 20.$ (5)

Extracting the square root of each member of (5),

$$x - \tfrac{1}{2} = \pm\,\sqrt{20}.$$ (6)

Whence $\qquad\qquad x = \tfrac{1}{2} \pm 2\,\sqrt{5}.$ (7)

Now $\qquad\qquad \sqrt{5} = 2.2360 +.$

Then $\quad \tfrac{1}{2} + 2\,\sqrt{5} = .5 + 4.472 + = 4.972 +.$ (8)

Also $\quad \tfrac{1}{2} - 2\,\sqrt{5} = .5 - 4.472 + = -3.972 +.$ (9)

Check: Since (8) and (9) are not the *exact* values of x, they will, if substituted for x in (1), make its first member *nearly* but *not quite* zero. An exact check can be obtained by substituting the radical forms of the roots from equation (7) in equation (1).

The check may be shortened by substituting both roots at the same time as follows:

Substituting $\frac{1}{2} \pm 2\sqrt{5}$ for x in $4x^2 - 4x - 79 = 0$.

$$4\left(\tfrac{1}{2} \pm 2\sqrt{5}\right)^2 - 4\left(\tfrac{1}{2} \pm 2\sqrt{5}\right) - 79 = 0,$$
$$4\left(\tfrac{1}{4} \pm 2\sqrt{5} + 20\right) - 2 \mp 8\sqrt{5} - 79 = 0,$$
$$1 \pm 8\sqrt{5} + 80 - 2 \mp 8\sqrt{5} - 79 = 0.$$

The radical terms vanish because the two upper signs before them must first be taken together and then the two lower signs.

Therefore $1 + 80 - 2 - 79 = 0$, or $81 - 81 = 0$.

In quadratic equations like the preceding the radical forms of the roots are often sufficient; at other times values to two or three decimal places are necessary. Unless otherwise directed, obtain only the radical forms of irrational roots.

The student should note that the equations like $4x^2 - 4x - 79 = 0$ can be solved either graphically or by completing the square, but that their solution by factoring, though not impossible, is beyond him.

The method of solving a quadratic equation in x illustrated in the three examples preceding may be stated in the

RULE. *Transpose so that the terms containing x are in the first member and those which do not contain x are in the second.*

Divide both members of the equation by the coefficient of x^2 (unless the coefficient of x^2 is $+1$).

Then add to both members the square of one half the coefficient of x (in the equation just obtained), thus making the first member a perfect trinomial square.

Rewrite the equation, expressing the first member as the square of a binomial and the second member in its simplest form.

Extract the square root of both members of the equation and write the sign $\pm$ before the square root of the second member, thus obtaining two linear equations.

Solve for x the equation in which the second member is taken with the sign $+$ and then solve the equation in which the second member is taken with the sign $-$. The results are the roots of the quadratic.

CHECK. Substitute each result separately in place of x in the *original* equation. If the resulting equations are not obvious identities, simplify them until each becomes one.

EXERCISES

(Obtain the values of the radical answers in Exercises 10, 13, and 21 correct to three decimal places.)

Solve by completing the square, and check results:

1. $x^2 - 8x - 48 = 0.$

2. $x^2 - 5x - 14 = 0.$

3. $x(x + 2) - 5(x + 2) = 0.$

4. $\frac{3}{4} - y = y^2.$

5. $2y^2 - 9y + 4 = 0.$

6. $2y^2 + 5y = 0.$

7. $t^2 - 2t - 15 = 0.$

8. $3t^2 - 7t = 6.$

9. $9v = 5v^2 - 2.$

10. $x^2 - 2x - 4 = 0.$

11. $v^2 - \frac{7}{12}v - 1 = 0.$

12. $s^2 - 2s - 3\frac{1}{2} = 0.$

13. $h^2 + 10h + 13 = 0.$

14. $12t^2 - 25t + 12 = 0.$

15. $42 + 2z^2 = -19z.$

16. $15x^2 + 4x = 4.$

17. $1 - 6v^2 = 2v.$

18. $20s^2 + s = 1.$

19. $9x + 4 = 9x^2.$

20. $25x^2 - 20x - 12 = 0.$

21. $4x^2 = 1 - 4x.$

22. $x^2 + 4\sqrt{5}x = 25.$

23. $x^2 - 3\sqrt{2}x + 4 = 0.$

24. $1 - \frac{3\sqrt{3}}{2R} + \frac{3}{2R^2} = 0.$

25. $\frac{2x}{9} + \frac{2}{3} = \frac{7}{18x}.$

26. $\frac{1}{3} + \frac{x}{9} - \frac{2}{x} = 0.$

27. $\frac{2}{5v^2} + \frac{1}{4} - \frac{11}{10v} = 0.$

28. $\frac{3a}{2} + \frac{1}{2} - \frac{1}{3a} = 0.$

29. $\frac{25c}{2} - \frac{40}{c} - 40 = 0.$

30. $(x - 4)^2 - 3(x - 9) = 15.$

31. $(x - 2)(x + 3) = x(5x - 9) - 2.$

32. $x - \frac{3}{x + 2} = 0.$

33. $\frac{v^2}{v - 5} + \frac{5}{2} = 0.$

34. $\frac{3}{t - 7} + \frac{t}{4} = 0.$

35. $\frac{s}{s - 2} + \frac{s - 2}{s} = \frac{5}{2}.$

36. $\frac{7}{2y - 3} - \frac{5}{1 - y} = 12.$

37. $\frac{3 + x}{4 + x} - \frac{x - 5}{x - 6} = \frac{1}{12}.$

38. If $y = 2$, solve for x the equation $x^2 - xy - 3y^2 = -12.$

39. If $x = -3$, solve $x^2 - 4xy + x^3 + y^2 + 5 = 0$ for y.

40. $x^4 - 5\,x^2 + 4 = 0.$

This is not a quadratic equation, but many equations of this form can be solved by completing the square.

Solution:
$$x^4 - 5\,x^2 + 4 = 0.$$
$$x^4 - 5\,x^2 = -4.$$
$$x^4 - 5\,x^2 + \tfrac{25}{4} = -4 + \tfrac{25}{4} = \tfrac{9}{4}.$$
$$x^2 - \tfrac{5}{2} = \pm\,\tfrac{3}{2}.$$
$$x^2 = 4 \text{ or } 1.$$

Whence $\qquad\qquad x = \pm\,2 \text{ or } \pm\,1.$

Check as usual.

41. $x^4 - 13\,x^2 + 36 = 0.$

42. $4\,x^4 - 5\,x^2 + 1 = 0.$

43. $9\,x^4 - 37\,x^2 + 4 = 0.$

44. $4\,k^4 = 9\,k^2 - 2.$

45. $9\,s^4 + 12 = 31\,s^2.$

46. $4\,v^4 + 5 = 21\,v^2.$

47. Point out the error in the following:
$$9 - 30 = 49 - 70.$$
$$9 - 30 + 25 = 49 - 70 + 25.$$
$$(3 - 5)^2 = (7 - 5)^2.$$
$$3 - 5 = 7 - 5.$$
$$3 = 7.$$

101. Quadratic equations with literal coefficients. Such equations are solved as in Exercises 1 and 15 which follow.

EXERCISES

Solve for x by completing the square, and check:

1. $2\,a^2x^2 - ax - 1 = 0.$

Solution: Transposing, $\qquad 2\,a^2x^2 - ax = 1.$

Dividing by $2\,a^2,$ $\qquad\qquad x^2 - \dfrac{x}{2\,a} = \dfrac{1}{2\,a^2}.$

Completing the square, $\quad x^2 - \dfrac{x}{2\,a} + \left(-\dfrac{1}{4\,a}\right)^2 = \dfrac{1}{2\,a^2} + \dfrac{1}{16\,a^2}.$

Then $\qquad\qquad\qquad \left(x - \dfrac{1}{4\,a}\right)^2 = \dfrac{9}{16\,a^2}.$

Extracting the square root, $\qquad x - \dfrac{1}{4\,a} = \pm\,\dfrac{3}{4\,a}.$

Whence $\qquad\qquad x = \dfrac{1}{a}$ or $-\dfrac{1}{2\,a}$.

Check: Substituting $\dfrac{1}{a}$ for x in the original equation,

$$2\,a^2\left(\frac{1}{a}\right)^2 - a\left(\frac{1}{a}\right) - 1 = 0, \text{ or } 2 - 1 - 1 = 0.$$

Substituting $-\dfrac{1}{2\,a}$ for x in the original equation,

$$2\,a^2\left(-\frac{1}{2\,a}\right)^2 - a\left(-\frac{1}{2\,a}\right) - 1 = 0, \text{ or } \frac{1}{2} + \frac{1}{2} - 1 = 0.$$

2. $x^2 - ax - 2\,a^2 = 0.$ **9.** $x^2 + 4\,\sqrt{a}\,x - 5\,a = 0.$

3. $x^2 + 2\,ax + a^2 - 4 = 0.$ **10.** $2\,x^2 + 9\,x\,\sqrt{h} = 5\,h.$

4. $x^2 + 1 = a + 2\,x.$ **11.** $a^2x^2 + 2\,ab = a^2 + b^2.$

5. $3\,x^2 - ax = 10\,a^2.$ **12.** $5\,x^2 + ax = x.$

6. $3\,mx + 2\,m^2 = 2\,x^2.$ **13.** $x\,(x - b) = a\,(a + b).$

7. $a^2x^2 - 7\,ax + 10 = 0.$

8. $4\,x^2 + 4\,ax - 3\,a^2 = 0.$ **14.** $1 - \dfrac{4}{x} + \dfrac{4}{x^2} = \dfrac{b}{4\,x^2}.$

15. $x^2 + 2\,x = ax + 2\,a.$

HINT. $\qquad x^2 + (2 - a)\,x = 2\,a.$

$$x^2 + (2 - a)\,x + \left(\frac{2-a}{2}\right)^2 = 2\,a + \frac{4 - 4\,a + a^2}{4}.$$

$$\left(x + \frac{2-a}{2}\right)^2 = \frac{4 + 4\,a + a^2}{4}, \text{ etc.}$$

16. $x^2 - (a + 1)\,x + a = 0.$

17. $x^2 + bx + cx + bc = 0.$ **20.** $\dfrac{1}{a} - \dfrac{1}{5\,x} = 1 - \dfrac{5\,x}{a}.$

18. $x^2 - ax + 4\,x - 4\,a = 0.$ **21.** $x^2 + bx + c = 0.$

19. $x^2 + 2\,a^2b^2 = a^2x + 2\,b^2x.$ **22.** $ax^2 + bx + c = 0.$

102. Solution by formula. The equation

$$ax^2 + bx + c = 0$$

is the *general quadratic equation* in standard form. The student solved this equation in the preceding exercise and found

$$x = \frac{-\,b \pm \sqrt{b^2 - 4\,ac}}{2\,a}. \qquad (F)$$

The value (F) is a general result and may be used as a formula to solve any quadratic equation. The solution of a quadratic by formula requires less labor than any other method, except for such equations as can be solved by factoring at sight. Those with considerable experience in algebra seldom solve a quadratic by any other method than by formula.

EXAMPLES

Solve by formula and check:

1. $3x^2 - 5x = 8.$

Solution: Writing in standard form, $3x^2 - 5x - 8 = 0.$

Then 3 corresponds to a, -5 to b, and -8 to c in the general quadratic $ax^2 + bx + c = 0$. Substituting these values in (F), where

$$x = \frac{-b \pm \sqrt{b^2 - 4ac}}{2a},$$

gives

$$x = \frac{-(-5) \pm \sqrt{25 - 4 \cdot 3 (-8)}}{2 \cdot 3}$$

$$= \frac{5 \pm \sqrt{25 + 96}}{6} = \frac{5 \pm 11}{6} = \frac{8}{3} \text{ or } -1.$$

Check as usual.

2. $2k^2x^2 = kx + 1.$

Solution: Writing in standard form, $2k^2x^2 - kx - 1 = 0.$
Then $a = 2k^2$, $b = -k$, and $c = -1$.
Substituting these values in the formula (F),

$$x = \frac{-(-k) \pm \sqrt{(-k)^2 - 4 \cdot 2k^2(-1)}}{2 \cdot 2k^2}.$$

$$x = \frac{k \pm \sqrt{k^2 + 8k^2}}{4k^2} = \frac{k \pm 3k}{4k^2} = \frac{1}{k} \text{ or } -\frac{1}{2k}.$$

Check: Substituting $\dfrac{1}{k}$ for x in the original equation,

$$2k^2\left(\frac{1}{k}\right)^2 = k\left(\frac{1}{k}\right) + 1, \text{ or } 2 = 1 + 1.$$

Substituting $-\dfrac{1}{2k}$ for x in the original equation,

$$2k^2\left(-\frac{1}{2k}\right)^2 = k\left(-\frac{1}{2k}\right) + 1, \text{ or } \frac{1}{2} = -\frac{1}{2} + 1.$$

EXERCISES

Solve for x by formula and check:

1. $2x^2 + 5x + 2 = 0.$

2. $3x^2 + 5x = 2.$

3. $x^2 - 3x - 10 = 0.$

4. $2x + 2 = x^2.$

5. $x^2 - x = 1.$

6. $2x^2 - \dfrac{11x}{2} - \dfrac{15}{2} = 0.$

7. $2x^2 - 3x = 1.$

8. $4x + 5 = x^2.$

9. $x^2 + x\sqrt{5} = 10.$

10. $12x = 1 - 72x^2.$

11. $x^2 + 2hx - 3h^2 = 0.$

12. $2m^2 = 9mx + 5x^2.$

13. $2x^2 + kx - 3k^2 = 0.$

14. $x^2 + 2x\sqrt{a} - 3a = 0.$

15. $mx = -m^2 + 6x^2.$

16. $x^2 + \dfrac{Kx}{2}\sqrt{2} - K^2 = 0.$

17. $n^2x^2 - 3knx - 10k^2 = 0.$

18. $6m^2x^2 + 19mnx = 7n^2.$

19. $x^2 + 2x = hx + 2h.$

HINT. $x^2 + (2-h)x - 2h = 0.$ Then $a = 1$, $b = 2 - h$, and $c = -2h$. Substituting these values in (F),

$$x = \frac{-(2-h) \pm \sqrt{(2-h)^2 - 4 \cdot 1 \cdot (-2h)}}{2}, \text{ etc.}$$

20. $x^2 + rx - sx - rs = 0.$

21. $2x^2 + rs = rx + 2sx.$

22. $mnx^2 + nx = 3mx + 3.$

23. $mhx^2 + 4hx = 3mx + 12.$

PROBLEMS

(Reject all answers which do not satisfy the conditions of the problems.)

1. The sum of the square of a certain number and twice the number itself is 15. Find the number.

2. Find two numbers whose difference is 11 and whose product is 42.

3. If from twice the square of a certain number the number itself be taken away, the remainder is 45. Find the number.

4. Find two consecutive numbers whose product is 462.

5. Find two consecutive odd numbers whose product is 255.

6. Find three consecutive even numbers whose sum is $\frac{1}{6}$ of the product of the first two.

7. A rectangular field is 16 rods longer than it is wide. Its area is 32 acres (1 acre = 160 square rods). Find the dimensions of the field.

8. The sum of a certain number and its reciprocal is $4\frac{1}{20}$. Find the number.

9. The area of a triangular field is $5\frac{5}{8}$ acres. The base is 51 rods longer than the altitude. Find the base and the altitude.

10. Two square fields together contain 62.5 acres. A side of one is 20 rods longer than a side of the other. Find the side of each.

11. The area of a rectangle is 18 square inches less than twice the area of a square. The rectangle is 7 inches longer than the square, and a side of the latter equals the breadth of the rectangle. Find the side of the square.

12. The hypotenuse of a right triangle is 41 feet. One leg is 31 feet shorter than the other. Find the legs.

13. The legs of a right triangle are in the ratio of $3:4$. The hypotenuse is 20. Find the legs.

Fact from Geometry. If one angle of a right triangle is 30 degrees, the hypotenuse is twice the shorter leg. Conversely, if the hypotenuse of a right triangle is double one leg, one angle of the triangle is 30 degrees.

14. One angle of a right triangle is 30 degrees and its longer leg is 9. Find, correct to two decimal places, the other two sides.

15. The hypotenuse of a right triangle is 10 and one leg is $5\sqrt{3}$. Show that one angle of the triangle is 30 degrees and find the number of degrees in each angle of the triangle.

16. The area of a square in square feet and its perimeter in linear feet are expressed by the same number. Find the side.

17. The area of a square in square feet and its perimeter in inches are expressed by the same number. Find the side.

18. The area of a square in square inches and its perimeter in feet are expressed by the same number. Find the side of the square.

19. The dimensions of a certain rectangle and the longest straight line which can be drawn on its surface are represented in inches by three consecutive even numbers. Find its dimensions.

20. The dimensions of a rectangular box are in the ratio of $1:2:3$. Find the edges, if the entire outer surface is 792 square inches.

21. The edges of two cubical bins differ by one yard. Their volumes differ by 61 cubic yards. Find the edge of each bin.

22. The rates of two trains differ by 5 miles per hour. The faster requires 1 hour less time to run 280 miles. Find the rate of each train.

23. An automobile made a round trip of 160 miles in 9 hours. Returning, the rate was increased 4 miles per hour. Find the rate each way.

24. A page of a certain book is 2 inches longer than it is wide. The printed portion covers half the area of the page and the margin is 1 inch wide. Find the length and width of the page.

25. A man paid $16,000 for a farm. Later he sold all but 40 acres of it for the same sum, thereby gaining $20 on each acre sold. Find the number of acres in the farm.

26. The price of oranges being raised 10 cents per dozen, one gets 5 fewer oranges for 50 cents. Find the original price.

27. Two pumps together can fill a standpipe in 45 minutes. One pump alone requires 2 hours less time than the other. Find the time each requires alone.

28. Each of two trains ran 200 miles. One ran 7 miles per hour faster than the other and required 1 hour and 45 minutes less time. Find the rate of each train.

29. A and B leave point P at the same time, A going north and B east. Five hours later A has traveled 17 miles more than B and the distance between them is 53 miles. Find the rate of each.

30. A and B leave point P at the same time, A going northwest and B southwest. Five hours later A has traveled 9 miles less and B has traveled 8 miles less than the distance between them. Find the rate of each.

31. A stone, dropped from a balloon which was passing over a river, struck the water 15 seconds later. How high was the balloon at the time the stone was dropped?

HINT. The distance, S, through which a body falls from rest in t seconds is given by the equation $S = \dfrac{gt^2}{2}$, g being 32 feet.

32. A man drops a stone over a cliff and hears it strike the ground below $6\frac{1}{2}$ seconds later. If sound travels 1152 feet per second, find the height of the cliff.

GEOMETRICAL PROBLEMS

(The circumference of a circle is $2\pi R$, R being the radius. In the following problems use $\frac{22}{7}$ for π.)

1. The circumference of a carriage wheel is 11 feet. How many revolutions will it make while the carriage goes 55 yards?

2. The radius of a carriage wheel is 2 feet. How many revolutions does the wheel make while the carriage goes 132 yards?

3. The circumference of a fore wheel of a carriage is 2 feet less than that of a rear wheel. In going 140 yards the smaller wheel makes 5 revolutions more than the larger. Find the circumference of each wheel.

4. In going 100 yards a fore wheel of a carriage makes 5 revolutions more than one of the rear wheels. The circumference of one wheel is 2 feet less than that of the other. Find the circumference and the radius of each wheel.

5. The circumferences of two wheels of a wagon differ by 2 feet. Together the two wheels make 11 revolutions while the wagon goes a distance of 20 yards. Find the diameter of each wheel.

6. The radii of two circles differ by 7 inches, and their areas differ by 770 square inches. Find their radii.

If any two chords of a circle, AC and DE, cross at B, then
$$AB \times BC = DB \times BE.$$

7. In the adjacent figure $AC = 18$, $DB = 4$, and $BE = 20$. Find AB.

8. In the adjacent figure $AC = 5$ feet, $DB = 18$ inches, and $BE = 48$ inches. Find AB and BC.

If AB is a line drawn from a point on the circumference perpendicular to the diameter, CD, of the circle, then $AB \cdot AB = CB \cdot BD$.

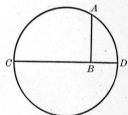

9. In the adjacent figure $AB = 9$ and $CD = 30$. Find CB and BD.

10. In the adjacent figure $AB = 20$ and $CB = 2 BD$. Find BD.

11. A line AB is 12 inches long. A point P is located on AB so that $AB : AP = AP : PB$. Find the length of AP. (Can a meaning be given to both answers?)

History of the quadratic equation. Though the development of the method of solving quadratic equations is closely connected with the general growth of algebra, yet it is possible to indicate the most important steps in the process rather briefly.

The first writer on formal algebra was Diophantos, who lived at Alexandria, in Egypt, about 300 A.D. Most of his work that is preserved is devoted to the solution of problems that lead to equations. So far as we know he was the first to indicate the unknown number by a single letter, in this respect being far in advance of many mathematicians who lived much later. It is a little remarkable, in fact, that as able and original a man as Diophantos should have exerted so little influence on his successors. He solved his quadratic equations by a method not unlike that of completing the square, but his imperfect knowledge of the nature of numbers made it impossible for him to understand the entire significance of the process. Though he made every effort not to consider equations whose roots were not positive integers, sometimes they would creep in, and under such circumstances, when his method led him to a negative or irrational root, he rejected the whole equation as absurd or impossible. Even when both of the roots were positive he took only the one afforded by the positive sign in the formula for solving a quadratic.

The difficulties of Diophantos are typical of those encountered by mathematicians for the next fifteen hundred years. The difficulty lay, not in finding a formal method of solving the equation, but in understanding the result after it was obtained. The meanings of negative and of imaginary numbers have been two of the most difficult of all mathematical ideas for men to grasp.

Five or six hundred years later the Hindus devised a general solution of the quadratic, but their chief advance over Diophantos lay in the fact that they did not regard an equation whose roots were negative as necessarily absurd, but merely rejected the negative result of solving such an equation with the remark, "It is inadequate; people do not approve of negative roots." The Hindus, however, did realize that a quadratic equation sometimes has two roots, a fact that Diophantos never comprehended. They even went so far as to illustrate the difference between positive and negative numbers by assets and debts.

No material gain in the understanding of the solutions of the quadratic can be found until the seventeenth century. The keenest mathematicians of the sixteenth century, like Cardan and Vieta, rejected negative solutions regularly, though by this time irrational solutions were admitted. In fact, in 1544 Stifel, a German, published an algebra in which irrational numbers are included among the numbers proper. But he affirms that except in the case where a quadratic equation has two positive roots, no equation has more than one root. It was not until the work of Descartes and Gauss became widely known that the nature of the roots of all kinds of quadratic equations was completely understood.

CHAPTER XXIV

GRAPHS OF QUADRATIC EQUATIONS IN TWO VARIABLES

103. Graph of a single equation. Before solving graphically a quadratic system, the method of graphing a single quadratic equation in two variables must be clearly understood.

EXAMPLES

1. Construct the graph of $y^2 = 4x$.

Solution: Solving the equation for y in terms of x, $y = \pm 2\sqrt{x}$.

We now assign values to x and then compute the approximate corresponding values of y. Tabulating the results gives:

$x =$	9	4	3	2	1	0	-1	Any negative value of x
$y =$	± 6	± 4	± 3.4	± 2.8	± 2	0	$2 \pm \sqrt{-1}$	Imaginary

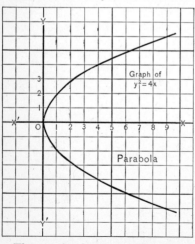

Graph of $y^2 = 4x$

Parabola

Using an x-axis and a y-axis as in graphing linear equations, plotting the points corresponding to the real numbers in the table, and drawing the curve determined by these points, we obtain the graph of the adjacent figure. Obviously y is a function of x; hence the y-axis corresponds to *the function* axis. The curve is a **parabola**. A similar curve was always obtained in Chapter XXII for the graph of a quadratic function of one variable.

The graph of any equation of the form $y^2 = ax$ is a *parabola*.

280

2. Graph the equation $xy = 6$.

Solution : Solving for y in terms of x, $y = \dfrac{6}{x}$.

Assigning values to x as indicated in the following table, we then compute the corresponding values of y.

$x =$	-6	-5	-4	-3	-2	-1	$-\frac{3}{4}$	$\frac{3}{4}$	1	2	3	4	5	6	8
$y =$	-1	$-\frac{6}{5}$	$-\frac{3}{2}$	-2	-3	-6	-8	8	6	3	2	$\frac{3}{2}$	$\frac{6}{5}$	1	$\frac{3}{4}$

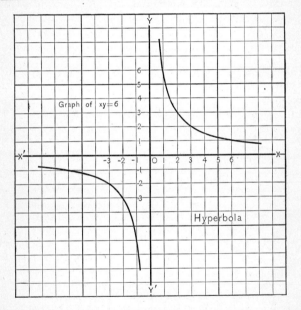

Proceeding as before with the numbers in the table, we obtain the two-branched curve of the above figure. The curve does not touch either axis. When x increases numerically y decreases. As x decreases from 1 toward 0, y becomes indefinitely great. Similarly, when x has a numerically great negative value, y has a numerically small negative value, and vice versa. The curve is called an **hyperbola.**

The graph of any equation of the form $\boldsymbol{xy = K}$ is an *hyperbola.* The curve for $xy = K$ ($K =$ any constant) is always in the same general position. That is, if K is positive, one branch of the curve lies in the first quadrant and the other branch in the third. If K is negative, one branch lies in the second quadrant and the other in the fourth.

3. Graph the equation $x^2 + y^2 = 25$.

Solution: Solving for y in terms of x, $y = \pm \sqrt{25 - x^2}$.

Assigning values to x as indicated in the following table, we compute the approximate corresponding values of y.

$x =$	-6	-5	-4	-3	-2	-1	0	1	2	3	4	5	6
$y =$	$\pm\sqrt{-11}$	0	± 3	± 4	± 4.58	± 4.89	± 5	± 4.89	± 4.58	± 4	± 3	0	$\pm\sqrt{-11}$

For values of x numerically greater than 5, y is *imaginary*. The points corresponding to the real numbers in the table lie on the **circle**

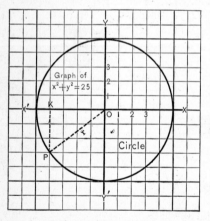

Graph of $x^2 + y^2 = 25$

Circle

in the adjacent figure. The center of the circle is at the origin and the radius is 5.

Further, the graph of any equation of the form $x^2 + y^2 = r^2$ is a *circle* whose radius is r. This can be proved from the right triangle PKO. If P represents *any* point on the circle, OK equals the x-distance of P, PK equals the y-distance, and OP equals the radius.

Now $\overline{OK}^2 + \overline{PK}^2 = \overline{OP}^2$; that is, $x^2 + y^2 = r^2$. It follows, then, that the graphs of $x^2 + y^2 = 9$ and $x^2 + y^2 = 8$ are circles whose centers are at the origin and whose radii are 3 and $\sqrt{8}$ respectively. Hereafter, when it is required to graph an equation of the form $x^2 + y^2 = r^2$, the student may use compasses, and, with the origin as the center and the proper radius, describe the circle at once.

4. Graph the equation $4x^2 + 9y^2 = 36$.

Solution : Solving for y in terms of x, $y = \pm\frac{2}{3}\sqrt{9 - x^2}$.

Assigning values to x as indicated in the following table, we compute the approximate corresponding values of y.

$x =$	-4	-3	-2	-1	0	$+1$	$+2$	$+3$	$+4$
$y =$	$\pm\frac{2}{3}\sqrt{-7}$	0	± 1.49	± 1.88	± 2	± 1.88	± 1.49	0	$\pm\frac{2}{3}\sqrt{-7}$

For values of x numerically greater than 3, y is *imaginary*. The points corresponding to the real numbers in the table lie on the graph of the following figure. The curve is called an **ellipse**.

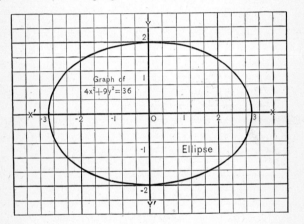

The graph of any equation of the form of $\boldsymbol{ax^2 + by^2 = c}$, in which a and b are unequal, is an *ellipse*.

EXERCISES

Construct the graphs of the following equations and state the name of the curve obtained :

1. $x^2 = 4y$.

2. $y^2 + 4x = 0$.

3. $x^2 + y^2 = 16$.

5. $x^2 - y^2 = 16$.

7. $xy = 12$.

4. $x^2 + y^2 = 10$.

6. $9x^2 + 4y^2 = 36$.

8. $xy = -6$.

9. $4x^2 - 9y^2 = 36$.

10. $25x^2 + 16y^2 = 400$.

Note. These three curves, the ellipse, the hyperbola, and the parabola, were first studied by the Greeks, who proved that they are the sections which one obtains by cutting a cone by a plane. Not for hundreds of years afterwards did any one imagine that these curves actually appeared in nature, for the Greeks regarded them merely as geometrical figures, and not at all as curves that had anything to do with our everyday life. One of the most important discoveries of astronomy was made by Kepler (1571–1630), who showed that the earth revolves around the sun in an ellipse, and stated the laws that govern the motion. Those comets that return to our field of vision periodically also have elliptic orbits, while those that appear once, never to be seen again, describe parabolic or hyperbolic paths. The path of a ball thrown in the air is also a parabola.

104. Graphical solution of a quadratic system in two variables. That we may solve a system of two quadratic equations by a method similar to that employed in § 81 for linear equations appears from the following

EXAMPLES

1. Solve graphically $\begin{cases} x^2 + y^2 = 34, & (1) \\ x + 2y + 7 = 0. & (2) \end{cases}$

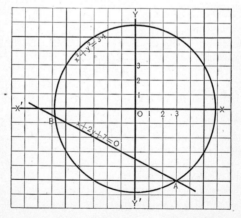

Solution: Constructing the graphs of (1) and (2) on the same scale and on the same axes, we obtain the circle and the straight

line of the figure on page 284. Each point of intersection of the two graphs determines one set of roots. For A, $x = 3$ and $y = -5$; for B, $x = -5\frac{4}{5}$ and $y = -\frac{3}{5}$.

2. Solve graphically $\begin{cases} 3x - 4y = 8, & (1) \\ x^2 = 4y + 18. & (2) \end{cases}$

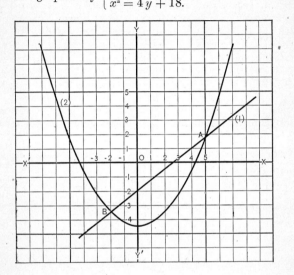

Solution: Constructing the graphs of (1) and (2), we obtain the straight line and the parabola of the adjacent figure. There are two sets of roots corresponding to the two points of intersection, which are:

$$A \begin{cases} x = 5, \\ y = 1\frac{3}{4}. \end{cases} \qquad\qquad B \begin{cases} x = -2, \\ y = -\frac{7}{2}. \end{cases}$$

Note. If the straight line in the preceding figure were moved downward in such a way that it always remained parallel to its present position, the points A and B would approach each other and finally coincide. When this happened the line would be tangent to the parabola at the point $x = \frac{3}{2}$, $y = -3\frac{15}{16}$.

Were the straight line moved still farther, it would neither touch nor intersect the parabola and there would be no graphical solution.

An illustration of these two conditions is given by the graphical solution of Exercises 8 and 9, p. 287.

3. Solve graphically $\begin{cases} x^2 - xy + y^2 = 25, & (1) \\ x^2 - y^2 = 8. & (2) \end{cases}$

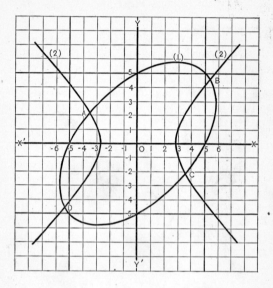

Solution: Constructing the graphs of (1) and (2), we obtain the ellipse and hyperbola of the adjacent figure. There are four sets of roots corresponding to the four points of intersection, which are approximately:

$$A \begin{cases} x = -3.6, \\ y = +2.2. \end{cases} \qquad C \begin{cases} x = +3.6, \\ y = -2.2. \end{cases}$$

$$B \begin{cases} x = +5.4, \\ y = +4.7. \end{cases} \qquad D \begin{cases} x = -5.4, \\ y = -4.7. \end{cases}$$

Examples 1, 2, and 3 partially illustrate the truth of the following statement:

If in a system of two equations in two variables one equation is of the mth degree and one of the nth, there are *usually* mn sets of roots (real or imaginary) *and never more than* mn *such sets*.

It is worth noting that the student can solve graphically a system like that given on page 286, though he will scarcely be able to solve such systems algebraically even after he has mastered this text.

Note. In equation (1), p. 286, a smaller number in place of 25 would give a smaller ellipse than the one in the figure, and it would be easy to find a number to replace 25 such that the resulting ellipse would just touch the hyperbola. Were a still smaller number used, the resulting ellipse would neither touch nor intersect the other curve. These varying conditions would result in (*a*) four sets of real roots, (*b*) two sets of real roots, (*c*) no set of real roots respectively.

EXERCISES

If possible, solve graphically each of the following systems:

1. $x^2 = 4y,$
$x + 2y = 4.$

2. $x^2 + y^2 = 25,$
$x - y = 7.$

3. $x^2 + y^2 = 16,$
$x^2 + y^2 = 25.$

4. $x^2 + y^2 = 9,$
$x - y = 8.$

5. $x^2 + y^2 = 16,$
$x^2 - y^2 = 9.$

6. $x^2 + y^2 = 9,$
$x^2 - y^2 = 16.$

7. $y^2 = 4x,$
$x^2 + 16y^2 = 16.$

8. $x^2 = 4y + 18,$
$3x - 4y = 20\frac{1}{4}.$

9. $x^2 = 4y + 18,$
$3x - 4y = 24.$

CHAPTER XXV

SYSTEMS SOLVABLE BY QUADRATICS

105. Introduction. The general equation of the second degree in two variables is $ax^2 + by^2 + cxy + dx + ey + f = 0$. To solve a pair of such equations requires the solution of an equation of the fourth degree. Also the solution of even the far more simple system $x^2 + y = 5$ and $y^2 + x = 3$ requires the solution of a biquadratic equation. In fact, only a *limited number* of systems of equations of the second degree in two variables are solvable by quadratics. The student should note that he can solve graphically for real roots any system of quadratic equations, provided the terms have numerical coefficients. The algebraic solution of such systems will be possible for him only after further study of algebra.

106. Linear and quadratic. Every system of equations in two variables in which one equation is **linear** and the other **quadratic** *can be solved by the method of substitution.*

EXAMPLE

Solve the system
$$\begin{cases} x^2 + y^2 = 5, & (1) \\ x - y = 1. & (2) \end{cases}$$

Solution: Solving (2) for x, $\qquad\qquad x = 1 + y.$ $\qquad$ (3)

Substituting $1 + y$ for x in (1), $(1 + y)^2 + y^2 = 5.$ $\qquad$ (4)

From (4), $\qquad\qquad\qquad\qquad y^2 + y - 2 = 0.$ $\qquad$ (5)

Solving (5) by formula,

$$y = \frac{-1 \pm \sqrt{1 + 8}}{2} = \frac{-1 \pm 3}{2} = 1 \text{ or } -2.$$

Substituting 1 for y in (3), $\qquad x = 1 + 1 = 2.$

Substituting -2 for y in (3), $\qquad x = 1 - 2 = -1.$

Therefore $\begin{cases} x = 2 \\ y = 1 \end{cases}$ and $\begin{cases} x = -1 \\ y = -2 \end{cases}$ are the two sets of roots.

Check: Substituting 2 for x and 1 for y in $\begin{cases} (1), & 4 + 1 = 5, \\ (2), & 2 - 1 = 1. \end{cases}$

Substituting -1 for x and -2 for y in $\begin{cases} (1), & 1 + 4 = 5, \\ (2), & -1 + 2 = 1. \end{cases}$

EXERCISES

Solve the following systems, pair results, and check each set of roots:

1. $x + y = 8,$
   $x^2 + y^2 = 34.$

2. $2m + n = 14,$
   $m^2 + 3mn = 49.$

3. $2m^2 + n^2 = 22,$
   $m - n\sqrt{5} = 0.$

4. $4s + 5t = 6,$
   $st = -2.$

5. $xy + 12 = 0,$
   $4x - 3y = 30.$

6. $x\sqrt{3} + 5y\sqrt{3} = -72,$
   $xy = -15.$

7. $3R_1 + 2R_2 = 5,$
   $R_1R_2 - 6R_1 = -3.$

8. $xy + y^2 - 5 = 0,$
   $xy + 20 = 0.$

9. $h^2 + k^2 + k = 10,$
   $h + k + 1 = 0.$

10. $m^2 + 3mn + n^2 = 22,$
    $2m = n.$

11. $x^2 + y^2 + 2x + 3y = 10,$
    $x - 5 = y.$

12. $y - x\sqrt{8} = 0,$
    $y^2 + x^3 = 9x.$

107. Special devices. Systems of equations are often met which can be solved by substitution, but which are more conveniently solved as in the following examples. It should be observed that in every case the aim of the device is to replace the given system by one or more equivalent systems of linear equations.

Note. Euclid (300 B.C.) solved systems of quadratic equations by means of geometry. But any solution that we would recognize as algebraic did not exist until the Arabs and the Hindus studied the subject. Although Diophantos solved many problems that lead to quadratic equations, he always expressed all of his unknowns in terms of one symbol, and so avoided systems of quadratics. We have seen how this may be done on page 51.

EXAMPLES

1. Solve the system
$$\begin{cases} x + y = 5, & (1) \\ xy = 6. & (2) \end{cases}$$

Solution: Squaring (1), $x^2 + 2xy + y^2 = 25.$ (3)

(2) · 4, $4xy = 24.$ (4)

(3) − (4), $x^2 - 2xy + y^2 = 1.$ '(5)

From (5), $x - y = \pm 1.$ (6)

From (6) and (1), $A \begin{cases} x + y = 5, & (1) \\ x - y = 1; & (7) \end{cases}$

                    $B \begin{cases} x + y = 5, & (1) \\ x - y = -1. & (8) \end{cases}$

Solving A and B, $\begin{cases} x = 3, \\ y = 2; \end{cases}$ and $\begin{cases} x = 2, \\ y = 3. \end{cases}$

2. Solve
$$\begin{cases} x^2 + y^2 = 13, & (1) \\ xy = 6. & (2) \end{cases}$$

Solution: (2) · 2, $2xy = 12.$ (3)

(1) + (3), $x^2 + 2xy + y^2 = 25.$ (4)

From (4), $x + y = \pm 5.$ (5)

(1) − (3), $x^2 - 2xy + y^2 = 1.$ (6)

From (6), $x - y = \pm 1.$ (7)

(5) and (7) combined give four pairs of equations:

$A \begin{cases} x + y = 5, & (8) \\ x - y = 1; & (9) \end{cases}$ $C \begin{cases} x + y = -5, & (11) \\ x - y = 1; & (9) \end{cases}$

$B \begin{cases} x + y = 5, & (8) \\ x - y = -1; & (10) \end{cases}$ $D \begin{cases} x + y = -5, & (11) \\ x - y = -1. & (10) \end{cases}$

The solution of A, B, C, and D is left to the student.

EXERCISES

Solve in a manner similar to that of the two preceding examples, pair results, and check each rational set of roots:

1. $\begin{aligned} x - y &= 1, \\ xy &= 12. \end{aligned}$ **4.** $\begin{aligned} 3x - y &= 12, \\ 9x^2 + y^2 &= 72. \end{aligned}$

2. $\begin{aligned} x + 2y &= 4, \\ xy + 6 &= 0. \end{aligned}$ **5.** $\begin{aligned} x^2 - 3xy + 4y^2 &= 11, \\ xy &= 10. \end{aligned}$

3. $\begin{aligned} x^2 + 4y^2 &= 41, \\ xy + 10 &= 0. \end{aligned}$ **6.** $\begin{aligned} x^2 + y^2 &= 25, \\ x^2 + 2xy + y^2 &= 49. \end{aligned}$

7. $x^2 + y^2 = 25,$
$x^2 - 2xy + y^2 = 49.$

9. $x^2 - xy = 4,$
$y^2 - xy = -3.$

8. $x^2 + y^2 = 15,$
$x + y = 3\sqrt{3}.$

10. $x^2 = y^2 + 5,$
$y^2 + xy = 10.$

Sometimes an equation simpler than either of those given can be derived from a system by dividing one equation by the other, *member by member*.

EXAMPLE

Solve
$$\begin{cases} x^2 - y^2 = 9, & (1) \\ x - y = 1. & (2) \end{cases}$$

HINT. Dividing (1) by (2), $x + y = 9.$ (3)

The system (2) and (3) is equivalent to the system (1) and (2) and is more easily solved than the latter.

EXERCISES

Solve (using division where possible), pair results, and check:

1. $x^2 - y^2 = 16,$
$x + y = 8.$

7. $x^2 y^2 + 6 = 5xy,$
$xy + 4 = 6.$

2. $\dfrac{1}{x^2} - \dfrac{1}{y^2} = 5,$
$\dfrac{1}{x} - \dfrac{1}{y} = 1.$

8. $x^4 = y^4 + 175,$
$x^2 = y^2 + 7.$

3. $R^2 h - 50 = 0,$
$Rh = 10.$

9. $x^2 - xy - 6y^2 = 16,$
$x - 3y = 1.$

4. $h^2 k - 100 = 0,$
$k^2 h + 80 = 0.$

10. $x^2 + 7 = 4xy + 5y^2,$
$x^2 = 1 + y^2.$

5. $P(1 + r)^2 = 112.36,$
$P + Pr = 106.$

11. $x^3 + y^3 = 12,$
$x + y = 2.$

12. $x^2 - xy + y^2 = 6,$
$x^3 + y^3 = 12.$

6. $\dfrac{gt^2}{2} = .0256,$
$gt = 1.28.$

13. $x + y = 2,$
$x^2 - xy + y^2 = 6.$

PROBLEMS

(Reject all results which do not satisfy the conditions of the problems.)

1. Find two numbers whose difference is 3, and the difference of whose squares is 45.

2. The sum of two numbers is 18 and the sum of their squares is 170. Find the numbers.

3. Find two numbers whose product is 108 and whose quotient is $\frac{3}{4}$.

4. The area of a right triangle is 84 square feet and its hypotenuse is 25 feet. Find the legs.

Note. In the tenth century there lived at least one man of remarkable mathematical talents, Gerbert, by name, who wrote on both algebra and geometry. One of the most difficult problems that he set himself to solve was that of finding the legs of a right triangle whose area and hypotenuse were known, and that he obtained the correct result is very remarkable when we consider the crude notation in which he did his work. One may compare the development of algebra at that time with that of the present time by observing that the problem, the solution of which was a brilliant achievement for one of the keenest mathematicians of the Middle Ages, is now solved with ease during the first year of algebra.

Gerbert was prominent in the church, and in 999 was elected pope and assumed the title of Sylvester II.

5. A rectangular field is 39 rods longer than it is wide, and its area is 10 acres. Find the length and the width.

6. The difference of the areas of two squares is 208 square feet and the difference of their perimeters is 32 feet. Find a side of each square.

7. The area of a rectangular field is $2\frac{1}{4}$ acres and one diagonal is 41 rods. Find the perimeter of the field.

8. The perimeter of a rectangle is 92 feet and its area is 504 square feet. Find the length and the width.

9. A mean proportional between two numbers is $\sqrt{40}$. The sum of their squares is 89. Find the numbers.

10. The value of a certain fraction is $\frac{2}{3}$. The fraction is squared and 50 is subtracted from the numerator and from the denominator of this result. The value of the fraction thus formed is $\frac{2}{7}$. Find the original fraction.

11. The base of a triangle is 5 inches longer than its altitude. Its area is $1\frac{1}{24}$ square feet. Find the base and the altitude of the triangle.

12. The volumes of two cubes differ by 1647 cubic inches. Their edges differ by 3 inches. Find the edge of each.

13. The sum of the radii of two circles is 27 inches and the difference of their areas is 81π square inches. Find the radii.

14. The perimeter of a rectangle is $3c$ and its area is $\dfrac{c^2}{2}$. Find its dimensions.

15. The area of a right triangle is $2a^2 - 2b^2$ and its hypotenuse is $2\sqrt{2a^2 + 2b^2}$. Find the legs.

16. The perimeter of a right triangle is 40 feet and its area is 60 square feet. Find the legs and the hypotenuse.

17. Do positive integers differing by 3 exist such that the sum of their squares is 115?

18. If a 2-digit number be multiplied by the sum of its digits, the product is 576. And if three times the sum of its digits be added to the number, the result is expressed by the digits in reverse order. Find the number.

19. The annual income from a certain investment is $48. If the principal were $200 more and the rate of interest 1% less, the annual income would be $2 more. Find the principal and the rate.

20. A wheelman leaves A and travels north. At the same time a second wheelman leaves a point 3 miles east of A and travels east. An hour after starting the shortest distance between them is 17 miles, and $2\frac{1}{2}$ hours later the distance is 53 miles. Find the rate of each.

GEOMETRICAL PROBLEMS

1. The sides of a triangle are 6, 8, and 10. Find the altitude on the side 10.

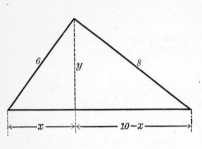

HINT. From the adjacent figure we easily obtain the system :
$$\begin{cases} x^2 + y^2 = 36, \\ (10 - x)^2 + y^2 = 64. \end{cases}$$

2. The sides of a triangle are 5, 12, and 13. Find the altitude on the side 13 and the area of the triangle.

3. The sides of a triangle are 13, 14, and 15. Find the altitude on the side 14 and the area of the triangle.

4. The sides of a triangle are 9, 10, and 17. Find the altitude on the side 9 and the area of the triangle.

5. The sides of a triangle are 11, 13, and 20. Find the altitude on the side 11 and the area of the triangle.

6. The parallel sides of a trapezoid are 14 and 26 respectively, and the two nonparallel sides are 10 each. Find the altitude of the trapezoid.

HINT. Let $ABCD$ be the trapezoid. Draw CE parallel to DA and CF perpendicular to AB. Then $EC = 10$, $AE = 14$, and $EB = 26 - 14$, or 12. If we let $EF = x$, FB must $= 12 - x$; then we can obtain the system of equations :
$$\begin{cases} x^2 + y^2 = 100, \\ (12 - x)^2 + y^2 = 100. \end{cases}$$

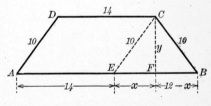

7. The two nonparallel sides of a trapezoid are 6 and 8 respectively, and the two bases are 4 and 14 respectively. Find the altitude of the trapezoid.

8. The bases of a trapezoid are 10 and 16 respectively, and the two nonparallel sides are 25 and 29. Find the altitude of the trapezoid and the area.

9. The sides of a trapezoid are 10, 20, 17, and 41. The sides 20 and 41 are the bases. Find the altitude and the area.

10. The sides of a trapezoid are 12, 25, 24, and 17. The sides 12 and 24 are parallel. Find the altitude and the area of the trapezoid.

11. The sides of a trapezoid are 9, 29, 30, and x. The sides 9 and 30 are the bases, and each is perpendicular to x. Find x and the area of the trapezoid.

12. The parallel sides of a trapezoid are 15 and 80; the other sides are 72 and 97. Find the altitude and the area of the trapezoid.

CHAPTER XXVI

EXPONENTS

108. Fundamental laws of exponents. The four laws of exponents used in the preceding chapters are:

I. Law of Multiplication,

$$x^a \cdot x^b = x^{a+b}.$$

II. Law of Division,

$$x^a \div x^b = x^{a-b}.$$

III. Law of Involution, or raising to a power,

$$(x^a)^b = x^{ab}.$$

IV. Law of Evolution, or extraction of roots,

$$\sqrt[b]{x^a} = x^{\frac{a}{b}}.$$

Law I may be stated more completely thus:

$$x^a \cdot x^b \cdot x^c \cdots = x^{a+b+c\cdots}.$$

Law III includes the more general forms:

(1) $$(x^a y^b)^c = x^{ac} y^{bc}.$$

(2) $$(((x^a)^b)^c) \cdots = x^{abc\cdots}.$$

When Laws I, II, and III were used in our previous work in multiplication and division, a and b were understood to be positive integers, and in Law II, a was greater than b. In the work on radicals the meaning of an exponent was extended so as to include fractional exponents, as defined by Law IV. Though the Laws I–IV in their previous applications have thus been restricted to positive integers and fractions, they hold, nevertheless, for any rational values of a and b. This fact will be assumed without proof. We shall fully explain, however, the meaning which, according to these laws, must be attached to a zero exponent and to negative exponents.

109. Meaning of a zero exponent. From Law II,

$$x^4 \div x^4 = x^{4-4} = x^0.$$

But $$x^4 \div x^4 = \frac{x^4}{x^4} = 1.$$

Therefore $$x^0 = 1.$$

More generally, $$x^a \div x^a = x^{a-a} = x^0,$$

and $$x^a \div x^a = \frac{x^a}{x^a} = 1.$$

As before, $$\boldsymbol{x^0 = 1.}$$

That is, any number (except zero) whose exponent is zero is equal to 1. Hence, if x is not zero, $4^0 = (\tfrac{2}{3})^0 = (-6)^0 = (5x)^0 = (x^2 - 2x + 1)^0$, for each equals 1.

110. Meaning of a negative exponent. From Law II,

$$a^3 \div a^5 = a^{3-5} = a^{-2}.$$

Obviously $$a^3 \div a^5 = \frac{a^3}{a^5} = \frac{1}{a^2}.$$

Therefore a^{-2} is another way of writing $\dfrac{1}{a^2}.$

Then $$4^{-3} = \frac{1}{4^3} = \frac{1}{64}.$$

Also $$a^{-\frac{2}{3}} = \frac{1}{a^{\frac{2}{3}}} = \frac{1}{\sqrt[3]{a^2}}.$$

In like manner, $$16^{-\frac{3}{4}} = \frac{1}{16^{\frac{3}{4}}} = \frac{1}{\sqrt[4]{16^3}} = \frac{1}{8}.$$

In general terms, $$\boldsymbol{x^{-a} = \frac{1}{x^a}.}$$

Consequently $$\frac{1}{x^{-a}} = \frac{1}{\dfrac{1}{x^a}} = x^a.$$

Similarly we obtain the more general results

$$\boldsymbol{bx^{-a} = \frac{b}{x^a}} \text{ and } \boldsymbol{\frac{b}{x^{-a}} = bx^a.}$$

Therefore: *Any **factor** of the numerator of a fraction may be omitted from the numerator and written as a **factor** of the denominator, and vice versa, if the sign of the exponent of the factor be changed.*

It follows that any expression involving negative exponents may be written as an expression involving only positive exponents. That is to say, negative exponents are not a mathematical necessity, but merely a convenience. The extension of the laws of exponents which brings with it the zero and the negative exponent is another illustration of the Law of Permanence of Form mentioned on page 61.

EXERCISES

Write with positive exponents and then simplify results:

1. 3^{-2}.

2. 4^{-3}.

3. $2^{-4} \cdot 3^0$.

4. $2^{-2} \cdot 3^{-4}$.

5. $7 \cdot 7^0 \cdot 0$.

6. $(\frac{1}{2})^{-3}$.

7. $(\frac{2}{3})^{-2} \cdot 4^0$.

8. $(\frac{4}{5})^{-3} \cdot (\frac{10}{3})^{-2}$.

9. $\dfrac{2}{3^{-2}}$.

10. $\dfrac{3}{3^0}$.

11. $\dfrac{12}{4^{-1}}$.

12. $5 \cdot 2^0 - (5 \cdot 2)^0$.

13. $\dfrac{4^{-2} \cdot 3^{-2}}{6^{-2}}$.

14. $(m - n)^0$,
     if $m \neq n$.

15. $32^{-\frac{2}{5}}$.

16. $0^5 \cdot 5^0$.

17. $4^{-\frac{1}{2}}$.

18. $8^{-\frac{1}{3}}$.

19. $16^{-\frac{1}{4}}$.

20. $8^{-\frac{2}{3}}$.

21. $16^{-\frac{3}{2}}$.

22. $25^{1.5}$.

23. $0^3 \cdot 0^{\frac{3}{4}}$.

24. $(-8)^{-\frac{2}{3}}$.

25. $(-64)^{-\frac{2}{3}}$.

26. $(-32)^{\frac{1}{5}}$.

27. $(32)^{-.4}$.

28. $(-125)^{-\frac{2}{3}}$.

29. $\sqrt[3]{27^{-2}}$.

30. $\sqrt[3]{8^{-2}}$.

31. $(\sqrt[3]{-8})^2$.

32. $(\frac{1}{2})^{-4} \cdot (\frac{1}{3})^{-3} \cdot (\frac{1}{2})^0$.

33. $(\frac{1}{6})^{-2}$.

34. $(.04)^{\frac{3}{2}}$.

35. $(.027)^{-\frac{2}{3}}$.

36. $(.064)^{-\frac{1}{3}}$.

37. $(.00032)^{\frac{2}{5}}$.

38. $\dfrac{\sqrt[3]{9^{-3}} \cdot \sqrt[2]{9^{-2}}}{3^{-4}}$.

39. $\dfrac{2^{-1}}{2^{-2} - 2^{-3}}$.   Hint. $\dfrac{2^{-1}}{2^{-2} - 2^{-3}} = \dfrac{\frac{1}{2}}{\frac{1}{2^2} - \frac{1}{2^3}}$, etc.

40. $\dfrac{3^{-2} - 2^{-2}}{3^{-1} - 2^{-1}}$.

41. $\dfrac{2^{-1} + 3^{-1}}{2^{-3} + 3^{-3}}$.

42. $\dfrac{3^{-3} - 2^{-3}}{3^{-1} - 2^{-1}}$.

In this chapter it must be remembered that the letters in a fraction may not take on such values as would make any denominator zero or any expression zero to the zero power.

Write with positive exponents and simplify results:

43. m^{-3}.

44. $2\,a^{-3}$.

45. $3\,ab^{-2}$.

46. $7\,x^2y^{-2}$.

47. $x^{-1}y^{-2}z$.

48. $4\,a^3b^{-2}c^2$.

49. $\dfrac{3}{a^{-2}}$.

50. $\dfrac{4\,x}{y^{-3}}$.

51. $\dfrac{4\,c^0}{xy^{-2}}$.

52. $\dfrac{4\,a^{-2}b^0}{y^{-5}}$.

53. $\dfrac{5^{-1}(ab)^0}{10^{-2}b^2}$.

54. $\dfrac{3\,a^3b^{-2}c}{4\,a^{-2}b^0}$.

55. $\dfrac{12\,x^2y^{-1}}{2\,yx^{-1}}$.

56. $\dfrac{10^{-1}a}{bc^3}$.

57. $\dfrac{4\,a^{-2}bc^{-3}}{6\,a^{-2}b^{-3}c^0}$.

58. $\dfrac{4^{-3}r^{-6}s^6}{s^{-2}r^{-2}t^3}$.

59. $\dfrac{2\,s^{-1}}{m^n a^{-b}}$.

60. $\dfrac{5\,x^2y^a}{x^{-m}y^{-4}}$.

61. $\dfrac{2}{a^{-2}-b^{-2}}$. **Hint.** $\dfrac{2}{a^{-2}-b^{-2}}=\dfrac{2}{\dfrac{1}{a^2}-\dfrac{1}{b^2}}$, etc.

62. $\dfrac{3}{a^{-1}+b^{-1}}$.

63. $\dfrac{a}{a^{-2}-b^{-2}}$.

64. $\dfrac{5\,se^2}{s^{-2}+e^{-2}}$.

65. $\dfrac{a^{-2}}{a^{-2}+b^{-2}}$.

66. $\dfrac{a^{-3}b^{-3}}{a^{-3}+b^{-3}}$.

67. $\dfrac{a^{-2}-b^{-2}}{a^{-1}+b^{-1}}$.

68. $\dfrac{a^{-4}-b^{-4}}{a^{-2}-b^{-2}}$.

69. $\dfrac{a^{-1}+b^{-1}}{a^{-3}+b^{-3}}$.

70. $\dfrac{a^{-3}-27^{-1}}{a^{-1}-3^{-1}}$.

Write without a denominator:

71. $\dfrac{2\,xy}{z^2}$.

72. $\dfrac{4\,a^3}{b^3}$.

73. $\dfrac{3\,x}{a^{-2}b^4}$.

74. $\dfrac{4\,sc^{-3}}{2^{-1}s^{-2}}$.

75. $\dfrac{12\,a^2b^3}{4\,xy^2}$.

76. $\dfrac{7\,x^{-1}y^2}{2^{-1}y^3}$.

77. $\dfrac{5\,ac^{-2}}{c\,(x-y)^2}$.

78. $\dfrac{7\,m^{-3}n^{\frac{1}{2}}}{m^{\frac{2}{3}}\,(m-n)^0}$.

79. $\dfrac{1}{5\,a^2(c+d)^{-3}}$.

80. $\dfrac{a\,(x-y)^{-2}}{bcx\,(x-y)}$.

81. $\dfrac{42\,m^{-n}n^{2m}}{56\,m^{-2n}n^{-3n}}$.

82. $\dfrac{r^{-1}s^2}{r^{-2}s^3\,(s-r)^3}$.

EXERCISES IN MULTIPLICATION

(Exercises 1–51 are oral.)

Perform the indicated multiplications:

1. $x^4 \cdot x^{-2}$.   **4.** $x^{\frac{2}{3}} \cdot x^{\frac{3}{2}}$.   **7.** $7 x^0 \cdot x^{\frac{2}{3}} \cdot x^{\frac{3}{2}}$.

2. $x^4 \cdot x^{\frac{1}{2}}$.   **5.** $x^{\frac{1}{2}} \cdot x^{\frac{1}{3}} \cdot x^0$.   **8.** $\sqrt{x} \cdot x^{\frac{1}{3}}$.

3. $x^{\frac{1}{3}} \cdot x^{\frac{1}{2}}$.   **6.** $x^{\frac{3}{4}} \cdot x^{\frac{4}{3}}$.   **9.** $\sqrt[3]{x} \cdot x^{\frac{1}{4}}$.

10. $(7 x)^0 \cdot 7 x^0 \cdot x^{\frac{1}{2}} x y$.   **17.** $e^{a-3} \cdot e^3$.

11. $\sqrt[3]{x} \cdot \sqrt[4]{x^3}$.   **18.** $e^{a-3} \cdot e^{2a+1}$.

12. $\sqrt[2]{x^{-4}} \cdot \sqrt[3]{x^{-6}}$.   **19.** $e^{3-2a} \cdot e^{2+3a}$.

13. $a \sqrt{ax} \cdot a^{\frac{1}{2}} \sqrt{ax^{-1}}$.   **20.** $e^0 \cdot e^{3a-1} \cdot e^{3-2a}$.

14. $c^2 \sqrt[3]{a^3 x^{-2}} \cdot c \sqrt[3]{a^3 x^{-2}}$.   **21.** $x \cdot x^a \cdot x^b \cdot x^0 \cdot x^{2b-3a}$.

15. $e^x \cdot e^{-x}$.

16. $e^x \cdot e^{2x}$.   **22.** $x^{a-b} \cdot y^a \cdot \dfrac{x^b}{y^{a-2}}$.

23. $(2^3)^3$.   **31.** $(x^{-3})^{-2}$.   **39.** $(a^2 b)^3 (a + b)$.

24. $(2^3)^{-2}$.   **32.** $(x^{-\frac{1}{2}})^{-\frac{1}{3}}$.   **40.** $(a^2)^{3x} \cdot a^{3x}$.

25. $(2^{-3})^{-2}$.   **33.** $(3 x^{-2})^3$.   **41.** $(a^3)^{2x} \cdot (a^2)^{3x}$.

26. $[(\frac{3}{2})^{-3}]^2$.   **34.** $(5 a^2)^{-3}$.   **42.** $(a^{x+1})^2 \cdot (a^{1-x})^2$.

27. $(x^2)^3$.   **35.** $(c^{-2} d)^2$.   **43.** $(a^3)^{x+y} \cdot (a^2)^{y-x}$.

28. $(x^{\frac{1}{2}})^4$.   **36.** $(5^0 \cdot 2^6 \cdot 3^3)^{\frac{1}{3}}$.   **44.** $(a^2 b)^x \cdot (b^2 a^3)^{2x}$.

29. $(x^{\frac{1}{3}})^{\frac{1}{2}}$.   **37.** $(25 a^4 b^6)^{-\frac{1}{2}}$.   **45.** $(x^2 - x^{-2}) x^3$.

30. $(x^2)^{-2}$.   **38.** $\left[(2 x^5)^0 \cdot 8 \cdot 4^{\frac{1}{2}} \right]^{\frac{2}{3}}$.   **46.** $(x^2 + x y^{-2}) x^{-2}$.

47. $(x^4 - a^4) x^{-2} a^{-2}$.   **50.** $(a^{\frac{1}{2}} - x^{\frac{1}{2}})(a^{\frac{1}{2}} + x^{\frac{1}{2}})$.

48. $(x^2 - 5 ax + 6 a^2) a^{\frac{2}{3}} x^{-\frac{2}{3}}$.   **51.** $(x^{\frac{1}{3}} + y^{\frac{1}{3}})(x^{\frac{1}{3}} - y^{\frac{1}{3}})$.

49. $(x^{\frac{1}{3}} + y^{\frac{1}{3}}) x^{\frac{2}{3}} y^{\frac{1}{3}}$.   **52.** $(a^{-2} + 3)(a^{-2} - 5)$.

Expand:

53. $(a^{-1} - a)^2$.

54. $(a^3 - 2 a^{-2})^3$.   **57.** $(a^{-1} + b^{-2})\left(\dfrac{1}{a} - \dfrac{1}{b^2} \right)$.

55. $(a^{-1} - 2 a + 3 a^{-2})^2$.   **58.** $(e^{2x} - 2 + e^{-2x})^2$.

56. $(e^x + e^{-x})^2$.   **59.** $\left(3 a^{-\frac{1}{2}} + 2 a^{\frac{2}{3}} \right)^2$.

60. $\left(a^{\frac{4}{5}} - 2\,a^{\frac{2}{5}}x + 4\,x^2\right)\left(a^{\frac{2}{5}} + 2\,x\right).$

61. $\left(x^{\frac{1}{3}} + 2\,y^{\frac{1}{3}}\right)\left(x^{\frac{2}{3}} - 2\,x^{\frac{1}{3}}y^{\frac{1}{3}} + 4\,y^{\frac{2}{3}}\right).$

62. $\left(a - a^{\frac{1}{2}}b^{\frac{1}{2}} + b\right)\left(a + a^{\frac{1}{2}}b^{\frac{1}{2}} + b\right).$

63. $\left(a^{\frac{1}{2}} + a^{\frac{1}{4}}b^{\frac{1}{4}} + b^{\frac{1}{2}}\right)\left(a^{\frac{1}{2}} - a^{\frac{1}{4}}b^{\frac{1}{4}} + b^{\frac{1}{2}}\right).$

64. $\left(x - x^{\frac{1}{2}}y^{-\frac{1}{2}} + y^{-1}\right)\left(x + x^{\frac{1}{2}}y^{-\frac{1}{2}} + y^{-1}\right).$

65. $\left(\sqrt[3]{a^5} - 3\,\sqrt[2]{a}\right)\left(\sqrt[3]{a^5} - 3\,\sqrt{a}\right).$

66. $\left(5\,\sqrt{c^{-5}}\ \sqrt[3]{d^{-3}} - a\,\sqrt[5]{c^{-2}}\right)^3.$

67. $\left(\sqrt{a} + \dfrac{\sqrt{b}}{c}\right)\left(\sqrt{a} + \dfrac{\sqrt{b}}{c}\right)^2.$

68. $\left(m^{n-1} - 5\,m^{n-2}a^n + 25\,a^{2n}\right)\left(m + 5\,a^n\right).$

69. $\left(r^{\frac{5}{2}} - r^2 + r^{\frac{3}{2}} - r + r^{\frac{1}{2}} - 1\right)\left(r^{\frac{1}{2}} + 1\right).$

70. $\left(16\,a^{\frac{4}{5}} + 8\,a^{\frac{3}{5}}b^{\frac{1}{2}} + 4\,a^{\frac{2}{5}}b + 2\,a^{\frac{1}{5}}b^{\frac{3}{2}} + b^2\right)\left(2\,a^{\frac{1}{5}} - b^{\frac{1}{2}}\right).$

71. $\left(25\,x^{-4} + 15\,x^{-2}y^{-8} + 9\,y^{-16}\right)\left(5\,x^{-2} - 3\,y^{-8}\right).$

EXERCISES IN DIVISION

Perform the indicated division:

1. $x^4 \div x^6.$

2. $x^3 \div x^{\frac{1}{3}}.$

3. $x^{\frac{1}{2}} \div x^2.$

4. $ax^{\frac{2}{3}} \div a^{\frac{1}{2}}x^2.$

5. $\dfrac{ax - a^2x^3}{a^2x^{\frac{1}{2}}}.$

6. $\left(x^a - 2\,x^{2a-1} + 3\,x^{3a-2}\right) \div x^{2a-1}.$

7. $\left(6\,a^{3+4n} - 9\,a^{n-2} + 5\,a^{2-n}\right) \div 3\,a^{n-2}.$

8. $(x - y) \div \left(x^{\frac{1}{2}} - y^{\frac{1}{2}}\right).$

9. $(x + y) \div \left(x^{\frac{1}{3}} + y^{\frac{1}{3}}\right).$

10. $(x - 8\,y) \div \left(x^{\frac{1}{3}} - 2\,y^{\frac{1}{3}}\right).$

11. $\left(16\,x^2 - 81\,y^2\right) \div \left(2\,x^{\frac{1}{2}} + 3\,y^{\frac{1}{2}}\right).$

12. $\left(a^3 - b^2\right) \div \left(\sqrt{a} + \sqrt[3]{b}\right).$

13. $\left(a^2 + ab^{-1} + b^{-2}\right) \div \left(a - a^{\frac{1}{2}}b^{-\frac{1}{2}} + b^{-1}\right).$

14. $\left(e^{2x} - 2 + e^{-2x}\right) \div \left(e^x - e^{-x}\right).$

15. $\left(e^{3x} + 3\,e^x + \dfrac{3}{e^x} + \dfrac{1}{e^{3x}}\right) \div \left(e^x + e^{-x}\right).$

16. $\left(e^{4x} - 4\,e^{2x} + 6 - 4\,e^{-2x} + e^{-4x}\right) \div \left(e^x - e^{-x}\right).$

17. $\left(a + a^{\frac{3}{5}}b^{\frac{2}{3}} + 2\,a^{\frac{2}{5}}b^{\frac{1}{3}} + 2\,b\right) \div \left(a^{\frac{3}{5}} + 2\,b^{\frac{1}{3}}\right).$

18. $(m^4 + 7\,m^2 + 8 - 7\,m^{-2} + m^{-4}) \div (m^2 + 5 - m^{-2}).$

19. $(2\,x^{2n-1} - x^{3n-2} + 9\,x^{5n-4}) \div (2\,x^{n-1} + 3\,x^{2n-2}).$

20. $\left(x^{-\frac{5}{2}}y - 2\,x^{-\frac{3}{2}}y^{\frac{1}{2}} - 8\,y^{\frac{1}{2}} + 16\,x\right) \div \left(x^{-\frac{1}{2}}y^{-\frac{1}{2}} - 8\,x^2y^{-1}\right).$

21. $\left(40\,ab - 16\,a^{\frac{19}{5}}b^{\frac{3}{4}} - 25\,a^{-\frac{9}{5}}b^{\frac{5}{4}}\right) \div \left(5\,a^{-\frac{2}{5}}b^{-\frac{3}{8}} - 4\,a^{\frac{12}{5}}b^{-\frac{5}{8}}\right).$

22. $(2\,x^{-2a} - 28\,x^{-a} + 33 + 38\,x^a + 11\,x^{2a} + x^{3a})$
$\qquad \div (x^a - 2\,x^{-a} + 4).$

23. $\left(25\,m^3 - 4\,mn^{\frac{4}{3}} + 4\,mn^2 - mn^{\frac{8}{3}}\right) \div \left(5\,m^{\frac{3}{2}} - 2\,n^{\frac{2}{3}}m^{\frac{1}{2}} + m^{\frac{1}{2}}n^{\frac{4}{3}}\right).$

Biographical note. JOHN WALLIS. To us, who use the notation of exponents every day, it seems so simple and natural a method of expressing the product of several equal factors, that it is difficult to understand why such a long time was necessary to develop it. But here, as in many other instances, it required a great man to discover what to us seems the most obvious relation. The man who brought the notation of exponents to its modern form was John Wallis (1616–1703), an Englishman. He was the son of a clergyman, and, like most scholars of his day, did not confine his interests to any one subject. Wallis became widely known by deciphering a military dispatch which contained a hidden meaning, and all his life was interested in such puzzling problems. He was at one time an instructor in Latin, Greek, and Hebrew, wrote books on theology and English grammar, and invented a method of teaching deaf mutes to talk. He was the most notable English mathematician before Sir Isaac Newton, who highly prized Wallis's work.

Though the idea of using negative and fractional exponents had occurred to writers before Wallis, it was he who showed their naturalness, and who introduced them permanently. He also was the first to use the ordinary sign ∞ to denote infinity.

JOHN WALLIS

CHAPTER XXVII

IRRATIONAL EQUATIONS

111. Definitions and typical solutions. An **irrational** or **radical equation** in one unknown is an equation in which the unknown letter occurs in a radicand.

Thus $3x + 2\sqrt{x} = 16$, $\sqrt{1-x} + \sqrt{x+3} = 2$, and $\sqrt[3]{x^2 - 8} = 0$ are irrational equations.

The following examples (1, 2, 4, and 5) illustrate the method of solution for some of the more simple irrational equations.

EXAMPLES

1. Solve $\sqrt{2x - 5} - 3 = 0$.

Solution: Transposing, $\sqrt{2x - 5} = 3$.
Squaring both members, $2x - 5 = 9$.
Solving, $x = 7$.

Check: Substituting 7 for x in the original equation,
$$\sqrt{14 - 5} - 3 = 0.$$
Whence $3 - 3 = 0$.

In irrational equations it is understood that each radical expression, not preceded by the sign $\pm$, is to have *one* sign and *only one;* therefore each radical will have *one* value and *only* one. That value is the *principal root* of the radical. This fact is of importance in checking.

2. Solve $2\sqrt[3]{8x^3 + \dfrac{19x^2}{2}} - 2x - 2 = 2x - 1$. $\qquad$ (1)

Solution: Transposing and collecting,

$$2\sqrt[3]{8x^3 + \frac{19x^2}{2}} = 4x + 1. \qquad (2)$$

Cubing each member of (2),
$$64x^3 + 76x^2 = 64x^3 + 48x^2 + 12x + 1. \qquad (3)$$

Transposing and collecting,
$$28\,x^2 - 12\,x - 1 = 0.$$
Factoring, $\qquad (2\,x - 1)(14\,x + 1) = 0.$
Therefore $\qquad\qquad\qquad x = \frac{1}{2}$ or $-\frac{1}{14}.$

Check: Substituting $\frac{1}{2}$ for x in (1),
$$2\sqrt[3]{1 + \frac{19}{8}} - 1 - 2 = 1 - 1.$$
$$2 \cdot \tfrac{3}{2} - 3 = 0.$$
$$3 - 3 = 0.$$

Substituting $-\frac{1}{14}$ for x in (1),
$$2\sqrt[3]{8(-\tfrac{1}{14})^3 + \tfrac{19}{2}(-\tfrac{1}{14})^2} + \tfrac{1}{7} - 2 = -\tfrac{1}{7} - 1.$$
$$2\left(+\frac{5}{14}\right) - \frac{13}{7} = -\frac{8}{7}, \text{ or } \frac{-8}{7} = \frac{-8}{7}.$$

It is easily possible to write a statement involving radical expressions which has the *form* of an equation but is not one. Thus $\sqrt{x+1} + \sqrt{x+3} + 1 = 0$ looks like an equation, but no value of x can satisfy it. A little closer inspection shows that the statement asserts that the sum of three positive numbers is zero, a condition clearly impossible. Statements like the one given are often called "impossible equations," though, strictly speaking, they are not equations at all. In the attempt to solve an apparent equation one may resort to the usual methods of solution and obtain a result which will not satisfy the original statement. Not until one tries to verify the result is the falsity of the original statement discovered.

3. Solve $1 + \sqrt{x+2} = \sqrt{x}.$ $\qquad\qquad\qquad\qquad$ (1)

Solution: Transposing, $\quad 1 - \sqrt{x} = -\sqrt{x+2}.$ $\qquad\qquad$ (2)

Squaring (2), $\qquad 1 - 2\sqrt{x} + x = x + 2.$ $\qquad\qquad$ (3)

Transposing and collecting,
$$-2\sqrt{x} = 1. \qquad\qquad\qquad\qquad (4)$$
Squaring (4), $\qquad\qquad 4\,x = 1.$ $\qquad\qquad\qquad\qquad$ (5)

(5) $\div$ 4, $\qquad\qquad\qquad x = \tfrac{1}{4}.$

Check: Substituting $\frac{1}{4}$ for x in (1),
$$1 + \sqrt{\tfrac{1}{4} + 2} = +\sqrt{\tfrac{1}{4}}.$$
$$1 + \tfrac{3}{2} = +\tfrac{1}{2}, \text{ or } \tfrac{5}{2} = \tfrac{1}{2}, \text{ which is false.}$$

It is fairly certain that the student did not see that the statement (1) was false until the attempt was made to verify the result. It appears, then, that the method of solution gives results which are not roots.

4. Solve $\sqrt{x-1} + \sqrt{3x+1} - 2 = 0$. $\qquad$ (1)

Solution: Transposing, $\sqrt{3x+1} = 2 - \sqrt{x-1}$. $\qquad$ (2)

Squaring both members of (2),
$$3x+1 = 4 - 4\sqrt{x-1} + x - 1. \qquad (3)$$

Transposing and collecting,
$$2x - 2 = -4\sqrt{x-1}. \qquad (4)$$

Dividing (4) by 2, $\qquad x - 1 = -2\sqrt{x-1}$. $\qquad$ (5)

Squaring both members of (5),
$$x^2 - 2x + 1 = 4x - 4. \qquad (6)$$

Transposing, $\qquad x^2 - 6x + 5 = 0$. $\qquad$ (7)

Factoring, $\qquad (x-1)(x-5) = 0$. $\qquad$ (8)

Therefore $\qquad x = 1 \text{ or } 5$.

Check: Substituting 1 for x in (1).
$$\sqrt{1-1} + \sqrt{3+1} - 2 = 0.$$
$$0 + 2 - 2 = 0.$$

Therefore 1 is a root of (1).

Substituting 5 for x in (1),
$$\sqrt{5-1} + \sqrt{15+1} - 2 = 0.$$
$$2 + 4 - 2 = 0,$$
or $\qquad\qquad\qquad\qquad 4 = 0 \text{ ; but } 4 \neq 0.$

Therefore 5 is not a root of (1). It was introduced by the process of squaring each member of equation (5). This process does not necessarily introduce a root. Thus 1 is a root of each of the equations (1) to (8), and, while 5 is a root of (6) and (7), it is not a root of (4), as may be verified by substitution. Further, (4) was obtained by squaring (2), yet neither the root 1 nor the root 5 was introduced at that point.

Values for the unknown introduced during the solution of an equation are called **extraneous** roots.

As we have seen, the solution of (1) leads to the quadratic $x^2 - 6x + 5 = 0$. Since (1) and (5) have the root 1 but not 5, it is obvious that with some radical equations one may resort to squaring once without introducing an *extraneous* root.

Equation (1) is typical of many radical equations which, when solved by rationalizing, give the roots not only of the original equation, but also of such equations as may be derived from it by giving each radical therein the sign $\pm$.

It will be seen from the next example, also, that the process of rationalization does not necessarily introduce extraneous roots.

5. Solve $\sqrt{x+2} + \sqrt{3-x} = 3$.   (1)

Solution: Transposing, $\sqrt{3-x} = 3 - \sqrt{x+2}$.   (2)

Squaring (2), $3 - x = 9 - 6\sqrt{x+2} + x + 2$. (3)

Transposing and collecting, $-2x - 8 = -6\sqrt{x+2}$.   (4)

(4) $\div -2$, $x + 4 = 3\sqrt{x+2}$.   (5)

Squaring (5), $x^2 + 8x + 16 = 9x + 18$.

Transposing and collecting, $x^2 - x - 2 = 0$.

Factoring, $(x-2)(x+1) = 0$.

Therefore $x = 2$ or -1.

Check: Substituting 2 for x in (1),

$$\sqrt{2+2} + \sqrt{3-2} = 3, \text{ or } 2 + 1 = 3.$$

Substituting -1 for x in (1),

$$\sqrt{-1+2} + \sqrt{3+1} = 3, \text{ or } 1 + 2 = 3.$$

Therefore equation (1) has two roots, 2 and -1.

It should be clear from the preceding examples that we cannot determine the number of roots of a given radical equation without solving it. Nor can we predict whether the given statement involving radicals is an equation. *Results obtained are roots if they satisfy the original statement, and not otherwise.*

The method of solving a radical equation may be stated in the

RULE. *Transpose the terms so that one radical expression (the least simple one) is the only term in the first member of the equation.*

Next raise both members of this equation to the same power as the index of the radical in the first member.

If radical expressions still remain, repeat the two preceding operations until an equation is obtained which is free from radicals. Then solve this equation.

CHECK. Substitute in the *original* equation and reduce the resulting radicals to their simplest form. Whenever the radicals are rational simplify by extracting the roots indicated. Never simplify by raising both members of the equation to any power, for extraneous roots introduced by that process would not then be detected.

Reject all extraneous roots.

EXERCISES

Solve, check results, and reject all extraneous roots:

1. $\sqrt{x-6} = 5$.

2. $\sqrt{x+5} + 3 = 6$.

3. $4\sqrt{x+9} + 5 = 17$.

4. $\sqrt[3]{2x+2} = 2$.

5. $\sqrt[3]{24x-19} + 4 = 1$.

6. $2\sqrt[3]{26x-5} + 13 = 3$.

7. $5x\sqrt{2x} = 15\sqrt{8x}$.

8. $\sqrt{4x} = \sqrt{x} + 3$.

9. $\sqrt{3x^2-2} + x = 8$.

10. $\sqrt[3]{2x+7} - \sqrt[3]{10+3x} = 0$.

11. $\sqrt[3]{x^2-x+2} + 3 = 5$.

12. $\sqrt[3]{85-5x} + \sqrt[3]{10x-45} = 0$.

13. $\sqrt{2x+3} = \sqrt[4]{15-x^2+2x-6}$.

14. $\sqrt{2+x} + \sqrt{10-3x} = 4$.

15. $\sqrt{x-2} + \sqrt{4x+1} = 3$.

16. $\sqrt{2x+7} = \sqrt{x} + 2$.

17. $\sqrt{x+2} = \sqrt{x} + 2$.

18. $\dfrac{\sqrt{x+9}}{\sqrt{x+2}} = \dfrac{4}{3}$.

19. $\dfrac{\sqrt{5x+2}}{\sqrt{2x-4}} = \sqrt{\dfrac{7x-2}{3x-8}}$.

20. $\dfrac{(x+4)^{\frac{1}{2}}}{3} = \dfrac{3}{(x+4)^{\frac{1}{2}}}$.

21. $\dfrac{2\sqrt{a}}{\sqrt{x-a}} - \dfrac{\sqrt{x+4a}}{3\sqrt{a}} = 0$.

22. $\dfrac{9x+8}{(8x+1)^{\frac{1}{2}}} = (10x+19)^{\frac{1}{2}}$.

23. $\dfrac{5}{\sqrt{2x}+1} = \dfrac{1}{9-\sqrt{8x}}$.

24. $(\tfrac{1}{2}+x)^{\frac{1}{2}} = \dfrac{1+2x}{(\tfrac{1}{2}+x)^{\frac{1}{2}}}$.

25. $(8x)^{\frac{1}{2}} - (8x-15)^{\frac{1}{2}} = \dfrac{7}{(8x-15)^{\frac{1}{2}}}$.

26. $(x-1)^{\frac{1}{2}} + (3x+1)^{\frac{1}{2}} = 6$.

27. $\sqrt{x+3} + \sqrt{x-4} = \sqrt{4x-3}$.

28. $\sqrt{2x-1} + \sqrt{x+3} - \sqrt{3x+2} = 0$.

29. $\sqrt{2x-1} + \sqrt{x+3} + \sqrt{3x+2} = 0$.

30. $\sqrt{3x+9} - \sqrt{8x^2+x+6} - 3 = 0$.

31. $\sqrt{9 - \sqrt{30 - \sqrt{20 + \sqrt{10x-25}}}} - 2 = 0$.

32. $x + 2\sqrt{x} - 8 = 0$.

32. $2x - 7x^{\frac{1}{2}} + 3 = 0$.

34. Solve for v, $E = \dfrac{mv^2}{2}$.

35. Solve for l and g, $t = \pi\sqrt{\dfrac{l}{g}}$.

36. Solve for R, $A = \pi R^2$.

37. Solve for R, $V = \dfrac{\pi R^2 H}{3}$

38. Solve for R, $\dfrac{R^2}{4} + S^2 = R^2$.

39. Solve for R, $\sqrt{R^2 - \left(\dfrac{R\sqrt{3}}{2}\right)^2} = A$.

40. Solve for R and a, $\left(\dfrac{R}{2}\sqrt{2 - \sqrt{2}}\right)^2 = R^2 - a^2$.

41. If a bullet is fired vertically, the least velocity, V, which it may have so that it will never return to the earth is given by the equation $V = \sqrt{2\,gR}$, ($g = 32$ feet per second, $R = 4000$ miles). Find the velocity in miles per second to the nearest whole number.

42. The greatest distance, x, that a ball can be thrown with velocity v (in feet per second) across a level field is given by one root of the equation $.976\,v^2x - gx^2 = 0$, ($g = 32$ feet). Under the conditions just stated a ball is thrown with a velocity of 100 feet per second. How far from the thrower did it strike the ground?

43. The greatest distance a baseball has been thrown is about 400 feet. With what velocity did it leave the thrower's hand?

CHAPTER XXVIII

VARIATION

112. Definitions. The word **quantity** denotes anything which is measureable. In this sense distance, rate, time, etc., are quantities.

Many operations and problems in mathematics deal with numerical measures of quantities, some of which are fixed and others constantly changing.

An abstract number, or the numerical measure of a fixed quantity, is called a **constant.**

Thus the abstract numbers 1, 3, and $-\frac{5}{7}$ are constants. Any definite quantities, as the area of a square whose side is 2, the circumference of a circle divided by its diameter (3.1416 nearly), the time of one revolution of the earth on its axis (23^h, 56^m, 4.09^s), and the velocity of light through space (186,330 miles per second), are constants.

The numerical measure of a changing quantity is called a **variable.**

For example, the distance (measured in any unit of length) between a passenger on a moving car and a point on the track either ahead of or behind him is a variable, decreasing in the first instance, increasing in the second. Other examples of variables are one's weight, the height of the mercury in the thermometer, and the distance to the sun.

The equation $x = 3\,y$ may refer to no physical quantities whatever, yet it is possible to imagine y as taking on in succession every possible numerical value, and the value of x as accompanying every change, and consequently always being three times as great as the corresponding value of y. In this sense, which is strictly mathematical, x and y are variables.

309

Problems in variation deal with at least two variables so related that any change in one is accompanied by a change in the other. Frequently one variable depends on several others.

For instance, the number of lines of printing on a page depends on the distance between the lines, the size of the type, and one dimension of the page.

The symbol for variation is $\propto$, and $x \propto y$ is read *x varies directly as y* or *x varies as y*.

113. Direct variation. One hundred feet of copper wire of a certain size weighs 32 pounds. Obviously a piece of the same kind 200 feet long would weigh 64 pounds; a piece 300 feet long would weigh 96 pounds, and so on.

Here we have two variables W (weight) and L (length) so related that the value of W depends on the value of L, and in such a way that W increases proportionately as L increases. That is, W is directly proportional or merely proportional to L. Hence, if W_1 and W_2 are *any* two weights corresponding to the lengths L_1 and L_2 respectively,

$$W_1 : W_2 = L_1 : L_2. \tag{1}$$

In the form of a variation (1) becomes

$$W \propto L.$$

In general, if $x \propto y$, and x and y denote *any* corresponding values of the variables, and x_1 and y_1 a *particular* pair of corresponding values,

$$\frac{x}{x_1} = \frac{y}{y_1}. \tag{2}$$

From (2),

$$x = \left(\frac{x_1}{y_1}\right)y. \tag{3}$$

But $\frac{x_1}{y_1}$ is a constant, being the quotient of two definite numbers.

Call this constant K and (3) may be written

$$x = Ky.$$

That is, if one variable varies as a second, the first equals the second multiplied by a constant.

Thus for the copper wire just mentioned, $W = \frac{32}{100} L$, or $\frac{8}{25} L$. Here, though W varies as L varies, W is always equal to L multiplied by the constant $\frac{8}{25}$.

The phrase **varies with** is often incorrectly used in place of **varies as**. The latter should be used to denote a *proportional* change in one variable with respect to a second; the former should not be so used. A boy's height varies *with* his age, but does not vary *as* his age. At 3 years the average boy is about 3 feet tall; at 12 years he is about 5 feet. At the latter time, if his height varied as his age from 3 years up to 12 years, he would be 12 feet tall.

114. Inverse variation. If a tank full of water is emptied in 24 minutes through a "smooth" outlet in which the area of the opening, A, is 1 square inch, an outlet in which A is 2 square inches would empty the tank twice as quickly, or in 12 minutes. And an outlet in which A is 3 square inches would empty the tank in 8 minutes.

Suppose it possible to increase or decrease A at will. We then have in t, the time required to empty the tank, and in A, the area of the opening, two related variables such that if A increases, t will decrease proportionally; while if A decreases, t will increase proportionally. That is, t and A are inversely proportional. This means that when A is doubled, t is halved; when A is trebled, t is divided by 3, and so on. The relation existing between the numerical values of A and t given in the preceding paragraph illustrates the truth of the last statement and of (1) which follows.

Now let t_1 and t_2 be *any* two times corresponding to the areas A_1 and A_2 respectively; then

$$t_1 : t_2 = A_2 : A_1. \tag{1}$$

The letters and the subscripts in (1) say: *The first time is to the second time as the second area is to the first area.*

The proportion (1) may be put in another form.

First, $$t_1 \cdot A_1 = t_2 \cdot A_2. \tag{2}$$

Dividing (2) by A_1A_2, $\quad \dfrac{t_1}{A_2} = \dfrac{t_2}{A_1}$, $\qquad\qquad$ (3)

or $\qquad\qquad t_1\left(\dfrac{1}{A_2}\right) = t_2\left(\dfrac{1}{A_1}\right)$. $\qquad\qquad$ (4)

Whence $\qquad\qquad t_1 : t_2 = \dfrac{1}{A_1} : \dfrac{1}{A_2}$. $\qquad\qquad$ (5)

Here the subscripts on the t's and those on the A's in (5) come in the same order.

In the form of a variation (5) becomes $t \propto \dfrac{1}{A}$.

In general x varies **inversely** as y when x varies as the **reciprocal** of y; that is,

$$x \propto \frac{1}{y}. \qquad\qquad (6)$$

And if x and y denote any corresponding values of the variable, and x_1 and y_1 a particular pair of corresponding values,

$$x : x_1 = \frac{1}{y} : \frac{1}{y_1}. \qquad\qquad (7)$$

Whence $\qquad\qquad \dfrac{x}{y_1} = \dfrac{x_1}{y}$, or $xy = x_1y_1$. $\qquad\qquad$ (8)

But x_1y_1 is a constant, being the product of two definite numbers. Call this constant K.

Then (8) becomes $\qquad xy = K.$

That is, if one variable varies inversely as another, the product of the two is a constant.

115. Joint variation. If the base of a triangle remains constant while the altitude varies, the area will vary as the altitude. Similarly, if the base varies while the altitude remains constant, the area will vary as the base. If *both* base and altitude vary, the area varies as the product of the two; that is, the area of the triangle varies **jointly** as the base and altitude. Further, if at *any* time A_1 denotes the area of a variable triangle, and h_1 and b_1 the corresponding altitude and base, and if A_2 denotes the area at *any other* time, and h_2 and b_2 the corresponding altitude and base, then $A_1 : A_2 = h_1b_1 : h_2b_2$.

In the form of a variation this last becomes

$$A \propto hb.$$

In general, any variable x varies jointly as two others, y and z, if

$$x \propto yz. \qquad (1)$$

If x varies jointly as y and z, and if x, y, and z denote *any* corresponding values of the variables, while x_1, y_1, and z_1 denote a *particular* set of such values, then

$$\frac{x}{x_1} = \frac{yz}{y_1 z_1}. \qquad (2)$$

From (2), $\qquad x = \left(\frac{x_1}{y_1 z_1}\right) yz.$

But the fraction $\dfrac{x_1}{y_1 z_1}$ is a constant, since x_1, y_1, and z_1 are particular values of the variables x, y, and z. Calling this constant K, we may write $x \propto yz$ as the equation

$$x = Kyz.$$

One variable may vary directly as one variable (or several variables) and inversely as another (or several others). Also one variable may vary as the square, or the cube, or the square root, or the reciprocal, or as any algebraic expression whatever involving the other variable (or variables).

The theory of variation is really involved in proportion, but this fact is not obvious to the beginner. Hence it is necessary to make clear the meaning of the terms used in variation, and to show how proportion is applied to the solution of problems in variation. It is doubly necessary that the student himself make this application in many cases, otherwise he will not readily grasp numerous relations in physics, in chemistry, and in astronomy; for many important laws of these sciences are often stated in the form of a variation. In connection with these laws many problems arise which require for their solution clear notions of the principles of variation. With a knowledge of proportion only, the student would often find the laws vague and the problems difficult.

PROBLEMS

1. If $x \propto y$, and $x = 4$ when $y = 6$, find x when $y = 8$.

Solution: The variation is direct. Therefore

$$\frac{x_1}{x_2} = \frac{y_1}{y_2}. \tag{1}$$

Substituting in (1), $\dfrac{4}{x_2} = \dfrac{6}{8}.$ (2)

Solving (2), $x_2 = 5\frac{1}{3}.$

2. If $x \propto y$, and $x = 6$ when $y = 10$, find y when $x = 15$.

3. If $x \propto y$, and $x = h$ when $y = k$, find y when $x = m$.

4. If x varies inversely as y, and $x = 6$ when $y = 7$, find x when $y = 21$.

Solution: The variation is inverse. Hence

$$x_1 : x_2 = \frac{1}{y_1} : \frac{1}{y_2}. \tag{1}$$

Substituting in (1), $6 : x_2 = \frac{1}{7} : \frac{1}{21}.$

Solving (2), $x_2 = 2.$

5. If $x \propto \dfrac{1}{y}$, and $x = 4$ when $y = 100$, find x when $y = 10$.

6. If $y \propto \dfrac{1}{z}$, and $y = h$ when $z = k$, find y when $z = m$.

7. If x varies jointly as y and z, and $x = 24$ when $y = 6$ and $z = 8$, find x when $y = 9$ and $z = 4$.

Solution: The variation is joint. Therefore

$$\frac{x_1}{x_2} = \frac{y_1 z_1}{y_2 z_2}. \tag{1}$$

Substituting in (1), $\dfrac{24}{x_2} = \dfrac{6 \cdot 8}{9 \cdot 4}.$ (2)

Solving (2), $x_2 = 18.$

8. If x varies jointly as y and z, and $x = 3$ when $y = 4$ and $z = 5$, find x when $y = 20$ and $z = 2$.

9. If x varies directly as y and inversely as z, and $x = 10$ when $y = 4$ and $z = 9$, find x when $y = 2$ and $z = 6$.

HINT. Here $x_1 : x_2 = \dfrac{y_1}{z_1} : \dfrac{y_2}{z_2}.$

10. If d varies directly as t^2, and $d = 64$ when $t = 2$, find d when $t = 4$.

HINT. Here
$$\frac{d_1}{d_2} = \frac{t_1^2}{t_2^2}.$$

11. If V varies directly as T and inversely as P, and $V = 80$ when $P = 15$ and $T = 400$, find P when $T = 450$ and $V = 45$.

12. The weight of any object below the surface of the earth varies directly as its distance from the center of the earth. An object weighs 100 pounds at the surface of the earth. What would be its weight (a) 1000 miles below the surface (radius of the earth = 4000 miles)? (b) 2000 miles below the surface? (c) at the center of the earth?

13. If a wagon wheel 4 feet 8 inches in diameter makes 360 revolutions in going a certain distance, how many revolutions will a wheel 5 feet in diameter make in going the same distance?

14. The distance which sound travels varies directly as the time. A man measures with a stop watch the time between the sight of the smoke from a hunter's gun and the sound of its report. When the hunter was one mile distant, the time was $4\frac{2}{5}$ seconds. How far off was the hunter when the observed time was 2 seconds?

15. When the volume of air in a bicycle pump is 24 cubic inches, the pressure on the handle is 30 pounds. Later, when the volume of air is 20 cubic inches, the pressure is 36 pounds. Assume that a proportion exists here, determine whether it is direct or inverse, and find the volume of the air when the pressure is 48 pounds.

16. The distance (in feet) through which a body falls from rest varies as the square of the time in seconds. If a body falls 16 feet in one second, how far will it fall in 6 seconds?

17. The intensity (brightness) of light varies inversely as the square of the distance from the source of the light. A reader holds his book 4 feet from a lamp, and later 6 feet distant. At which distance does the page appear brighter? How many times as bright?

18. A lamp shines on the page of a book 9 feet distant. Where must the book be held so that the page will receive four times as much light? twice as much light?

19. The weight of an object above the surface of the earth varies inversely as the square of its distance from the center of the earth. An object weighs 100 pounds at the surface of the earth. What would it weigh (*a*) 1000 miles above the surface? (*b*) 2000 miles above the surface? (*c*) 4000 miles?

20. The area of a circle varies as the square of its radius. The area of a certain circle is 154 square inches and its radius is 7 inches. Find the radius of a circle whose area is 594 square inches.

21. The weight of a sphere of given material varies directly as the cube of its radius. Two spheres of the same material have radii 2 inches and 6 inches respectively. The first weighs 6 pounds. Find the weight of the second.

22. The time required by a pendulum to make one vibration varies directly as the square root of its length. If a pendulum 100 centimeters long vibrates once in one second, find the time of one vibration of a pendulum 64 centimeters long.

23. Find the length of a pendulum which vibrates once in 2 seconds.

24. The pressure of wind on a flat (plane) surface varies jointly as the area of the surface and the square of the wind's velocity. The pressure on one square foot is .9 pounds when the wind is moving at the rate of 15 miles per hour. Find the velocity of the wind when the pressure on one square yard is 18 pounds.

25. Give concrete illustrations of direct, inverse, and joint variation different from those given in this book.

CHAPTER XXIX

IMAGINARIES

116. Definitions. When the square root of a negative number arose in our previous work, it was called an **imaginary,** and no attempt was then made to use it or to explain its meaning. The treatment of imaginaries was deferred because there were so many topics of more importance to the beginner. It must not be supposed, however, that imaginaries are not of great value in mathematics. They are also of much use in certain branches of applied science; and it is unfortunate that symbols which can be used in numerical computations to obtain practical results should ever have been called imaginary. By such a name something unreal and fanciful is suggested. To obviate this it has been proposed to call imaginary numbers *orthotomic* numbers, but this name has been little used.

The equation $x^2 + 1 = 0$, or $x^2 = -1$, asks the question, "What is the number whose square is -1?" By defining a new number, $\sqrt{-1}$, as a number whose square is -1, we obtain one root for the equation $x^2 + 1 = 0$. Similarly $\sqrt{-5}$ is a number whose square is -5. And, in general, $\sqrt{-n}$ is a number whose square is $-n$. Obviously $\sqrt{-5}$ means something very different from $\sqrt{5}$.

The positive numbers are all multiples of the unit $+1$, and the negative numbers are all multiples of the unit -1. Similarly **pure imaginary** numbers are real multiples of the imaginary unit $\sqrt{-1}$.

Thus $\sqrt{-1} + \sqrt{-1} = 2\sqrt{-1}$ and $\sqrt{-1} + 2\sqrt{-1} = 3\sqrt{-1}$, etc. Further, $\sqrt{-4} = 2\sqrt{-1}$; $\sqrt{-a^2} = a\sqrt{-1}$; $\sqrt{-5} = \sqrt{5}\sqrt{-1}$.

The imaginary unit $\sqrt{-1}$ is often denoted by the letter i; that is, $3\sqrt{-1} = 3\,i$.

If a real number be united to a pure imaginary by a plus sign or a minus sign, the expression is called a **complex number.**

Thus $-2 + \sqrt{-1}$ and $3 - 2\sqrt{-4}$ are *complex numbers.* The general form of a complex number is $a + bi$, in which a and b may be any real numbers.

Biographical note. KARL FRIEDRICH GAUSS. Standing in the very front rank of mathematicians, with Archimedes and Newton, is Karl Friedrich Gauss (1777–1855). He was the son of a bricklayer and was afforded an education, much against the will of his parents, by a nobleman who had noticed his remarkable talents.

Up to his time the imaginary numbers were not clearly understood, and were usually thought of as absurd and inadmissible. The situation reminds one of the time when negative numbers were similarly regarded, and the veil was removed from both in about the same way. It was found that negative numbers really had a significance; that they could be used in problems that involve debt, opposite directions, and many other everyday relations. The interpretation of imaginary numbers is not quite so obvious, but none the less actual and simple. As soon as it was seen that they could be represented with real numbers as points on a plane, the ice was broken, and it needed only the insight and authority of a man like Gauss to give them their proper place in mathematics. He also used the letter i for $\sqrt{-1}$.

Gauss was the first man to prove that every rational, integral equation in one unknown, whatever its degree, possesses a root. In fact, during his life he gave three distinct demonstrations of this theorem which had baffled all the attempts of mathematicians before his time.

In collaboration with another professor at the University of Göttingen he invented the telegraph independently of the American, S. F. B. Morse, and probably earlier.

117. Addition and subtraction of imaginaries. The fundamental operations of addition and subtraction are performed on imaginary and complex numbers as they are performed on real numbers and ordinary radicals of the same form.

Thus $2\sqrt{-1} + 4\sqrt{-1} = 6\sqrt{-1},$

and $5\sqrt{-1} - 3\sqrt{-1} = 2\sqrt{-1}.$

Also $3 + 5\sqrt{-1} + 4 - 2\sqrt{-1} = 7 + 3\sqrt{-1}.$

Similarly $a + bi + c + di = a + c + (b + d)i.$

KARL FRIEDRICH GAUSS

EXERCISES

Simplify :

1. $3\sqrt{-1} + 4\sqrt{-1} - 2\sqrt{-1}$.   **6.** $5\sqrt{-36x^2} - 2\sqrt{-49x^2}$.

2. $\sqrt{-4}$.   **7.** $\sqrt{-18} + \sqrt{-8}$.

3. $\sqrt{-25}$.   **8.** $(-12)^{\frac{1}{2}} + (-27)^{\frac{1}{2}}$.

4. $5\sqrt{-1} + \sqrt{-9}$.   **9.** $3 + 2\sqrt{-1} + 5 - 6\sqrt{-1}$.

5. $\sqrt{-4} + \sqrt{-16}$.   **10.** $5\sqrt{-x^2} - 7a - 3\sqrt{-x^2}$.

11. $4 - 8\sqrt{-1} + 16 - 3\sqrt{-4}$.

12. $6 - 2\sqrt{-64x^2} - 3\sqrt{-25x^2} + 8$.

13. $18 - 3(-1)^{\frac{1}{2}} + 6(-2)^{\frac{1}{2}} + (-100)^{\frac{1}{2}} + 4$.

14. $5\sqrt{-3} + 3\sqrt{-2} - \sqrt{-27} + 2\sqrt{-8}$.

15. $6\sqrt{-4a^4} - 7a^2\sqrt{-9} + 3\sqrt{-6} - 5\sqrt{-24}$.

16. $\left(12 - 6\sqrt{-9}\right) - \left(15 + 2\sqrt{-36}\right)$.

17. $3a - 2x - \left(2a\sqrt{-a^2} - 5ra^2\sqrt{-1}\right)$.

18. $(x - iy) - (n - iv)$.

Write as a multiple of $\sqrt{-1}$:

19. $\sqrt{-10}$.   **21.** $2\sqrt{-3}$.   **23.** $a\sqrt{-b}$.

20. $\sqrt{-6}$.   **22.** $\sqrt{-a}$.   **24.** $\sqrt{-a-b}$.

118. Multiplication of imaginaries. By the definition of square root, the square of $\sqrt{-n}$ is $-n$.

Therefore

$$\left(\sqrt{-1}\right)^2 = -1.$$
$$\left(\sqrt{-1}\right)^3 = \left(\sqrt{-1}\right)^2\sqrt{-1} = -1\sqrt{-1}.$$
$$\left(\sqrt{-1}\right)^4 = \left(\sqrt{-1}\right)^2\left(\sqrt{-1}\right)^2 = (-1)(-1) = 1.$$

To multiply $\sqrt{-2}$ by $\sqrt{-3}$ we write $\sqrt{-2}$ as $\sqrt{2}\cdot\sqrt{-1}$, and $\sqrt{-3}$ as $\sqrt{3}\cdot\sqrt{-1}$.

Then $\sqrt{-2}\cdot\sqrt{-3} = \left(\sqrt{2}\cdot\sqrt{-1}\right)\left(\sqrt{3}\cdot\sqrt{-1}\right)$
$$= \sqrt{6}\cdot\sqrt{-1}\cdot\sqrt{-1} = -\sqrt{6}.$$

Similarly

$$2\sqrt{-5}\left(-3\sqrt{-2}\right) = 2\sqrt{5}\cdot\sqrt{-1}\left(-3\sqrt{2}\cdot\sqrt{-1}\right) = 6\sqrt{10}.$$

In general, if $\sqrt{-a}$ and $\sqrt{-b}$ are two imaginaries whose product (or quotient) is desired, they should first be written in the form $\sqrt{a} \cdot \sqrt{-1}$ and $\sqrt{b} \cdot \sqrt{-1}$ and the multiplication (or division) should then be performed. This method will prevent many errors.

In this connection it must be clearly understood that one rule followed in multiplication of radicals (see p. 247) does not apply to imaginary numbers.

Thus $\sqrt{2} \cdot \sqrt{3} = \sqrt{2 \cdot 3} = \sqrt{6}$.

But $\sqrt{-2} \cdot \sqrt{-3}$ **does not equal** $\sqrt{(-2)(-3)}$, which equals $\sqrt{6}$.

In multiplying two complex numbers, first write each expression in the form $a + bi$, and then proceed as in the following

EXAMPLE

Multiply $2 + \sqrt{-3}$ by $3 - \sqrt{-7}$.

Solution: $2 + \sqrt{-3} = 2 + \sqrt{3} \cdot \sqrt{-1}$.

$\qquad\qquad 3 - \sqrt{-7} = 3 - \sqrt{7}\sqrt{-1}$.

Multiplying, $\qquad 6 + 3\sqrt{3}\sqrt{-1} - 2\sqrt{7}\sqrt{-1} + \sqrt{21}$

Rewriting, $\qquad 6 + 3\sqrt{-3} - 2\sqrt{-7} + \sqrt{21}$.

EXERCISES

Perform the indicated multiplications and simplify results:

1. $\left(\sqrt{-1}\right)^5$.   3. $\left(\sqrt{-1}\right)^7$.   5. $2\sqrt{-1} \cdot 3\sqrt{-1}$.

2. $\left(\sqrt{-1}\right)^6$.   4. $\left(\sqrt{-1}\right)^8$.   6. $\sqrt{-9} \cdot \sqrt{-16}$.

7. $\sqrt{-5}\left(-\sqrt{-6}\right)$.   15. $\left(4 - 2\sqrt{3}\,i\right)\left(4 + 2\sqrt{3}\,i\right)$.

8. $\sqrt{-25} \cdot \sqrt{3}$.   16. $\left(3 + \sqrt{-1}\right)\left(6 - \sqrt{-2}\right)$.

9. $2\sqrt{-3} \cdot 3\sqrt{-2}$.   17. $\left(4 - 2\,i\right)\left(3 - 2\sqrt{3}\,i\right)$.

10. $\sqrt{-m} \cdot \sqrt{-n}$.   18. $\left(a + ib\right)\left(c + id\right)$.

11. $4\sqrt{-5}\left(-3\sqrt{-6}\right)$.   19. $\left(a + ib\right)\left(a + ib\right)$.

12. $\sqrt{a+b} \cdot \sqrt{-a-b}$.   20. $\left(a + bi\right)\left(a - bi\right)$.

13. $\left(2 + \sqrt{-1}\right)\left(2 - \sqrt{-1}\right)$.   21. $\left(-\frac{1}{2} + \frac{1}{2}\sqrt{-3}\right)^2$.

14. $\left(3 + \sqrt{-2}\right)\left(3 - \sqrt{-2}\right)$.   22. $\left(-\frac{1}{2} - \frac{1}{2}\sqrt{-3}\right)^2$.

But to be in opposition the earth must in x days go round the sun once more than Mars does.

Therefore
$$\frac{x}{365} = \frac{x}{687} + 1.$$

Whence
$$x = 779 +.$$

Therefore the required date is November 11, 1911.

7. If a planet is between the earth and the sun and in a straight (nearly) line with them, the planet is said to be in *conjunction*. Venus was in (superior) conjunction April 28, 1909. If Venus revolves about the sun once in 225 days, find the approximate date of the next conjunction.

8. Jupiter revolves about the sun once in 4332 days. Jupiter was in opposition February 28, 1909. Find the approximate date of the next opposition.

9. Saturn revolves about the sun once in 10,759 days. It was in opposition April 3, 1909. Find the approximate date of the next opposition.

10. Two men travel in the same direction around an island, one making the circuit every $2\frac{1}{2}$ hours and the other every 3 hours. If they start together, after how many hours will they be together again?

11. Three automobiles travel in the same direction around a circular road. They make the circuit in $2\frac{3}{4}$ hours, $3\frac{1}{3}$ hours, and $4\frac{2}{5}$ hours respectively. If they start at the same time, after how many hours are the three together again?

12. Is the answer to Exercise 10 an integral multiple of $2\frac{1}{2}$ and 3? Is it the least integral multiple?

13. Is the answer to Exercise 11 an integral multiple of $2\frac{3}{4}$, $3\frac{1}{3}$, and $4\frac{2}{5}$? Is it the least integral multiple?

14. Reduce $2\frac{3}{4}$, $3\frac{1}{3}$, and $4\frac{2}{5}$ to improper fractions and divide the L.C.M. of the numerators by the G.C.D. of the denominators. Compare the result with the answer to Exercise 11.

15. The method of finding the L.C.M. of two or more fractions or mixed numbers is hinted at in Exercise 14. State a rule therefor. Find by the rule the L.C.M. of $1\frac{1}{6}$, $2\frac{1}{3}$, and $3\frac{1}{3}$.

16. Find by the same rule the L.C.M. of $\frac{a}{b}$ and $\frac{c}{d}$; of $\frac{a}{b}$, $\frac{c}{d}$, and $\frac{e}{f}$.

17. How many ounces of alloy must be added to 56 ounces of silver to make a composition 70% silver?

18. Gun metal of a certain grade is composed of 16% tin and 84% copper. How much tin must be added to 410 pounds of this gun metal to make a composition 18% tin?

HINT. Since the composition is 16% tin, then $\frac{16}{100} \cdot 410 =$ the number of pounds of tin in the first composition.

Let $x =$ the number of pounds of tin to be added.

Then $\frac{16 \cdot 410}{100} + x =$ the number of pounds of tin in the second composition, and $410 + x =$ the number of pounds of both metals in the second composition.

Therefore $\dfrac{\dfrac{16 \cdot 410}{100} + x}{410 + x} = \dfrac{18}{100}$.

19. A 30-gallon mixture of milk and water tests 16% cream. How much water has been added if the milk is known to test 20% cream?

20. How many gallons of alcohol 90% pure must be mixed with 10 gallons of alcohol 95% pure so as to make a mixture 92% pure?

21. It is desired to have a 10-gallon mixture of 45% alcohol. Two mixtures, one of 95% alcohol and another of 15% alcohol, are to be used. How many gallons of each will be required to make the desired mixture?

22. A chemist has the same acid in two strengths. Eight liters of one mixed with 12 liters of the other gives a mixture 84% pure, and 3 liters of the first mixed with 2 liters of the second gives a mixture 86% pure. Find the per cent of purity of each acid.

23. The diameter of the earth is $3\frac{2}{3}$ times that of the moon, and the difference of the two diameters is 5760 miles. Find each.

24. The diameter of the sun is 3220 miles greater than one hundred and nine times the diameter of the earth, and the sum of the two diameters is 874,420 miles. Find each.

25. The distance of the earth from the sun is $387\frac{1}{2}$ times the earth's distance from the moon. Light traveling 186,000 miles per second would require 8 minutes $18\frac{22}{31}$ seconds longer to go from the earth to the sun than from the earth to the moon. Find each distance.

26. The mean distance between Mars and the earth when they are on opposite sides of the sun is 234,500,000 miles. When the two planets are nearest each other on the same side of the sun, the mean distance between them is 48,500,000 miles. Find the distance of each from the sun.

27. The diameter of Jupiter is $10\frac{9}{11}$ times the diameter of the earth, and the sum of their diameters is 94,320 miles. Find each diameter.

28. The dimensions of a rectangular box in inches are expressed by three consecutive numbers. The surface of the box is 292 square inches. Find the dimensions.

29. A three-inch square is cut from each corner of a square piece of tin. The sides are then turned up and an open box is formed, the volume of which is 300 cubic inches. Find the size of the piece of tin.

30. A piece of tin is 8 inches by 12 inches. From each corner a square is cut whose side is x inches. The sides are turned up and an open box is formed. Show that its volume is $4x^3 - 40x^2 + 96x$.

31. Now a certain value of x gives for the box in Exercise 30 the greatest possible volume. That value is one root of the equation $12x^2 - 80x + 96 = 0$. Find the value of x.

32. A rectangular box is 8 inches long. Its volume is **192** cubic inches and the area of its six faces is 208 square inches. Find the three dimensions.

33. A messenger leaves the rear of an army 25 miles long as it begins its day's march. He goes to the front and at once returns, reaching the rear as the army camps for the night. How far did he travel if the army went 25 miles during the day?

Note on negative numbers. One who has a limited acquaintance with algebra is inclined to wonder over the reluctance with which the early masters of mathematics accepted the concept of negative numbers. If one has not really mastered the concept, however, he will have considerable difficulty in giving consistent answers to the following questions:

1. Is -20 greater than $+5$?

2. May a distance east of a certain point be considered positive and a distance west of that point negative?

3. Would a lazy man prefer to walk -20 miles from such a point rather than $+5$ miles from it, if he were convinced that -20 is less than $+5$?

Here the difficulty is due largely to the use of the terms *greater than* and *less than*. That 7 is greater than 3 is obvious from common-sense reasoning like this: The number 7 is greater than 3, because from a group of 7 objects 3 objects may be taken away and some objects will remain. Now algebra parts with this clear arithmetical notion of greater and less when it extends subtraction so as to include the taking away (subtraction) of a greater number from a less. Algebra states a definite rule for subtraction, — a rule which in its application contradicts no result obtained in arithmetic. The rule, however, does give new results. For instance, it determines the result when 7 is subtracted from 3, — an operation which arithmetic does not attempt. Upon this rule of subtraction, which in a certain sense is a definition, algebra bases its definition of the expressions *greater than* and *less than*, which follows:

The number $a >$, $=$, or $<$ the number b according as $a - b$ is positive, zero, or negative.

Therefore -20 is less than $+5$ in no concrete or arithmetical sense, but in the algebraic sense; that is, in the sense that it accords with the preceding definition.

A little closer inspection of the nature of a negative number may help to clear matters farther. The result of subtracting 7 from 3 may be viewed in two ways. The more abstract view is to regard − 4 as a mark of order in the scale of numbers :

$$\cdots, \, -5, \, -4, \, -3, \, -2, \, -1, \, 0, \, 1, \, 2, \, 3, \, 4, \, \cdots.$$

Then − 20 would be less than 5 in the sense that − 20 comes before 5 in the scale From this point of view, then, negative numbers have *ordinal* but not *cardinal* values. This is only another way of saying that *no group of objects exists whose number is negative*.

A different view of a negative number, − 4 for example, is to regard it as an operand (a symbol denoting both a number and an operation); that is, as a subtraction of 4 delayed only until there arises in the course of further operations a number from which to subtract it.

Those who desire a fuller discussion than the one which precedes, are referred to Fine's "College Algebra," or to Chrystal's "Text-Book of Algebra."

INDEX

FIRST COURSE IN ALGEBRA

By HERBERT E. HAWKES, Professor of Mathematics in Columbia University, WILLIAM A. LUBY and FRANK C. TOUTON, Instructors in Mathematics, Central High School, Kansas City, Mo.

12mo, cloth, vii + 334 pages, illustrated, list price, $1.00

SELDOM has a textbook met with such signal success at its first appearance as Hawkes, Luby, and Touton's "First Course in Algebra." Following are some of the features on which this success is founded:

1. **Sanity**
   It embodies a one year's course which is thorough, but not too difficult, with due attention to the really valuable recent developments in the teaching of algebra. No hobby is ridden.

2. **Careful Gradation**
   The topics, drill exercises, and problems were selected and arranged with the greatest care and with a constant regard for the ability of average pupils.

2. **Balance of Technic and Reasoning Power**
   Ample drill in the elementary technic of algebra is accompanied by a commensurate development of reasoning power.

4. **Wealth of Illustrative Material**
   In the explanation of points which experience has shown to be difficult for students to grasp, there is an abundance of illustrative material which assists the pupil to understand the subject.

5. **Abundance of Carefully Selected Problems**
   Great care is given the important question of problems. The large number included in the book will be found practical, interesting, — as they bear on the pupil's everyday life, — and unusually well graded.

6. **Reference to Arithmetic**
   In the explanation of algebraic processes the student's confidence is established by constant references to the already familiar subject of arithmetic.

7. **Correlation with Geometry and Physics**
   The choice of topics and their treatment was determined by the fact that many students now study geometry and physics after one year's work in algebra.

8. **Sensible Treatment of Factoring**
   Only the simpler types of factors are considered. Many examples give the student timely assistance with the numerous difficulties which necessarily arise. The frequent lists of review exercises in factoring should give a secure grasp of forms and methods in the shortest possible time.

119½

GINN AND COMPANY PUBLISHERS

SECOND COURSE IN ALGEBRA

By HERBERT E. HAWKES, Professor of Mathematics in Columbia University,
WILLIAM A. LUBY, Head of the Department of Mathematics, Central
High School, Kansas, Mo., and FRANK C. TOUTON, Principal
of Central High School, St. Joseph, Mo.

12mo, cloth, viii + 264 pages, illustrated, 75 cents

THIS book is designed to follow the authors' " First Course in Algebra " and continues the distinctive methods — liberal use of illustrative material, introduction of numerous interesting and " thinkable " problems, correlation with arithmetic, geometry, and physics, and extended work with graphs — which marked the earlier volume. As in the " First Course," prominence is given the equation ; the habit of checking results is constantly encouraged ; and frequent short reviews are a feature throughout.

The earlier chapters present a brief but thorough review of the first-year work, giving each topic a broader and more advanced treatment than is permissible in the " First Course." The new material and the many new applications make the entire review appeal to the student as fresh and inviting. The later chapters introduce such further topics as progressions, limits and infinity, ratio and proportion, logarithms, and the binomial theorem.

The aim throughout has been to select those topics considered necessary for the best secondary schools and to treat each in a clear, practical, and attractive manner. The authors have sought to prepare a text that will lead the student to think clearly as well as to acquire the necessary facility on the technical side of algebra.

119 b

GINN AND COMPANY PUBLISHERS

TEXTBOOKS ON MATHEMATICS
FOR HIGHER SCHOOLS AND COLLEGES

GINN AND COMPANY Publishers

$\sqrt{2} = 1.414+$

$\sqrt{3} = 1.732+$

$\sqrt{5} = 2.236+$

$\sqrt{7} = 2.645+$